Mersenne and the
Learning of the Schools

CORNELL HISTORY OF SCIENCE SERIES

Editor: L. Pearce Williams

The Scientific Reinterpretation of Form
    by Norma E. Emerton

Geology in the Nineteenth Century:
Changing Views of a Changing World
    by Mott T. Greene

Mersenne and the Learning of the Schools
    by Peter Dear

MERSENNE AND THE LEARNING OF THE SCHOOLS

Peter Dear

CORNELL UNIVERSITY PRESS

ITHACA AND LONDON

THIS BOOK HAS BEEN PUBLISHED WITH THE AID OF A GRANT FROM
THE HULL MEMORIAL PUBLICATION FUND OF CORNELL UNIVERSITY.

First published 1988 by Cornell University Press.

International Standard Book Number 0-8014-1875-5
Library of Congress Catalog Card Number 87–23935
Printed in the United States of America
Librarians: Library of Congress cataloging information
appears on the last page of the book.

The paper in this book is acid-free and meets the guidelines
for permanence and durability of the Committee on Production
Guidelines for Book Longevity of the Council on Library Resources.

To P.C.M.C.D.

Foreword

I⊤ is both fitting and proper that Cornell University Press
publish a work by a Cornell University professor challenging the thesis of Cornell's first president. Andrew Dickson White's *History of the
Warfare of Science with Theology in Christendom* (1896) was a Voltairean
attack on Christian theology and the barriers it had created to prevent
the growth of science. Finding antiscientific clerics or their supporters
almost everywhere, White deplored the generally nefarious influence
of churches on the progress of the human spirit. The paradigm was,
of course, the Galileo affair, as it has remained until this day.

In recent years, this view has come under increasing attack. Such
scholars as Richard Westfall, John Heilbron, Margaret Osler, and
Edward Davis have revealed the importance for science of the religious dimension and shown that the "conflict" was more imagined
than real. In particular, the Scientific Revolution of the seventeenth
century looks more and more like a movement in which the basic
ideas of science and theology were radically revised and the relations
between the two areas fundamentally redefined. The result was not
conflict but surprising harmony.

One of the major figures in this realignment, although not a giant
of science, was the Minim monk Marin Mersenne. Mersenne has long
been known to historians of science, of course, as one of the great
correspondents of the Scientific Revolution who, through his letters,
spread the good news of scientific discovery throughout the learned
world of Europe. What Professor Dear has done in this work is to
reveal a different dimension of Mersenne's activities. Here he appears
as a natural philosopher wrestling with some of the philosophical
problems raised by the New Learning and coming down quite sound-

ly on the side of modernity. If there is any warfare here, it is restricted to a few minor and barely detectable skirmishes. Instead, Mersenne, with the full approval of his clerical brethren, moved easily in the new world of ideas and devoted a good part of his energies to removing possible causes of conflict. Professor Dear's study is, therefore, a real contribution to the reevaluation of the relations between science and theology in the crucial period of the birth of modern science. It is no exaggeration to suggest that he has opened up a whole new world of the social history of science which he, and future historians, will no doubt eagerly explore to the edification of us all.

L. Pearce Williams

Ithaca, New York

Contents

Acknowledgments

I HAVE benefited from the advice and assistance of many people in the writing of this book. While I was a graduate student in Princeton University's Program in the History of Science, my adviser, Michael Mahoney, applied his sharp critical abilities to earlier formulations of ideas appearing here. Every member of the program's faculty, however, contributed through encouragement, example, and apparently genuine interest. Anthony Grafton acted as a valuable guide in my first explorations of the arcane intellectual world of the sixteenth and early seventeenth centuries. Versions of some chapters were read and commented upon by Hans Aarsleff, Edith Sylla, and the late Charles Schmitt, whose help and encouragement, during both my time at Princeton and my year at Imperial College, London, are particularly remembered.

Simon Schaffer read the original draft, and I trust he will forgive my disregard of his suggestion that I go further into Mersenne's controversy with Fludd. He was a continual source of stimulation while I worked on the book at Cambridge and indirectly influenced its final form to a considerable degree. Nicholas Jardine also provided a model of thoughtful and profound scholarship, and his approval of my efforts counted for a great deal.

On a more material level, I am indebted to John Elliott for taking me on as his research assistant at the Institute for Advanced Study during 1983–84, and to the Master and Fellows of Gonville and Caius College, Cambridge, who elected me to a Research Fellowship which allowed uninterrupted work on the book.

Chapters 2 and 3 are descended from, and supersede, an article, "Marin Mersenne and the Probabilistic Roots of 'Mitigated Scepticism,'" *Journal of the History of Philosophy* 22 (April 1984), 173–205. I am grateful to the journal's editor for permission to reproduce material. Chapter 7 derives from "Mersenne and the Language of Philosophy," in Klaus D. Dutz and Ludger Kaczmarek, eds., *Rekonstruktion und Interpretation: Problemgeschichtliche Studien zur Sprachtheorie von Ockham bis Humboldt* (Tübingen: Gunter Narr Verlag, 1985), pp. 197–241.

I wish to thank L. Pearce Williams for inviting me to contribute to the Cornell History of Science Series and for his comments and suggestions, and Cornell University Press for finding readers who challenged and stimulated my efforts in an exemplary way. The Press did not provide my best reader, however; that honor (though she may not agree with the description) belongs to my wife, Pauline. Not only did she reassure me when I had doubts, but she also performed the equally—I cannot honestly say "more"—important task of telling me when I'd written nonsense. This book is dedicated to her, because she deserves it, and may be pressed into service again.

PETER DEAR

Ithaca, New York

Author's Note on Translations

W<small>ITH ONLY</small> a few exceptions, indicated in notes to the text, the translations in this book are my own. I have preferred to risk erring on the side of literalness, and as a consequence some passages lack that general felicity of expression which might with justice be demanded of my own prose. Mersenne's French, in particular, is often long-winded, convoluted, and even ungrammatical; it would risk misrepresenting the nuances of his meaning, and would certainly misrepresent his literary talents, to strive for polished English renderings. These considerations do not, of course, absolve me of responsibility for such lapses in translation as I must undoubtedly have committed through my own ignorance or stylistic shortcomings.

P. R. D.

Mersenne and the
Learning of the Schools

CHAPTER ONE

Introduction

ALL THE industry devoted by historians in recent decades to the study of science in the seventeenth century has left intact the sense that the period should properly be characterized as the "Scientific Revolution." The difficulty in identifying a scholarly consensus as to the precise nature of that revolution, however, serves to emphasize its enormous complexity. It seems clear that no single account can hope to provide an integrated understanding of this crucial reconstitution of knowledge and the world: the Scientific Revolution cannot be treated as a historical "episode." Rather, like the Renaissance (though perhaps with fewer iconoclasts to doubt its existence), it encompasses a collection of diverse focuses for investigation. Nonetheless, the fact remains that the ways in which educated Europeans talked about the world in 1700 differed enormously from those of 1600.

Certain features of the new world view (if a unitary character may be ascribed to it) recur frequently in discussions of the period. An idiosyncratic listing of some of those features might include the attribution of importance to deliberate and recordable experimentation; the acceptance of mathematics as a privileged tool for disclosing nature; the reassignment of the causes of certain perceived attributes of things from the things themselves to the perceptual apprehensions of the observer (the "primary and secondary quality" distinction); the associated plausibility of seeing the world as a kind of machine; the idea of natural philosophy as a research enterprise rather than as a body of knowledge; and the reconstruction of the social basis of knowledge around a positive evaluation of cooperative research.

No individual in the first half of the seventeenth century, and few in the second, instantiates every one of those features. However, they

[1]

achieved some sort of definitive social embodiment in the second half of the century, forming the basis of commonality for a group that might be represented, for example, by those considered *persona grata* by the Académie Royale des Sciences in Paris or the Royal Society of London; or delineated by the international correspondence of Henry Oldenburg, the Royal Society's secretary and publisher of the *Philosophical Transactions,* the first scientific journal. A strong sense of novelty existed in these circles, witnessed by the frequent use of such terms as "the new philosophy" or "the experimental philosophy" or, most expressively, John Wilkins's phrase describing the brief of the early Royal Society, "physico-mathematicall experimentall learning." The derogation of the established learning of the universities and colleges that frequently attended such attempts at self-definition, together with similar rhetoric from notable figures earlier in the century, gives the Scientific Revolution the appearance of a revolt against scholasticism; indeed, it long received almost unquestioned characterization on that basis. The complexity of historical reality, however, suggests that such a view leaves out too much of the activity creating the appearance.

That activity, though not the continuing motivations for its maintenance and development, had become established between about 1610 and 1650. The names of Galileo, Descartes, and Gassendi assumed prominent places in the intellectual pantheon of later decades, and their writings were seen as foundational. The historian can only agree with such an evaluation, not merely because the ideas put forward by these people provided grist to the philosophical mills of those who followed, but because the creation of the community that first made the evaluation ipso facto relied on their endeavors and concerns. Thus much of the importance of individuals in this earlier part of the seventeenth century derives from the models they presented for the conduct of natural philosophy, models which subsequently formed the basis for the culmination of the Scientific Revolution—the establishment of a consolidated and self-sustaining community largely defined through reference to the checklist suggested above.

Those models perforce differed from one another. Galileo, for example, is the "Father of Modern Science" only if Descartes is not, given the deep-seated differences in their views. The sense in which either, or anyone else, might be so qualified relies solely on the degree to which various aspects of his work found adoption later on. Historical investigation must therefore focus on comprehending the shape of each model for conducting natural philosophy as the product of circumstance and purpose, integrated with a social foundation in order to explain how it could have become part of an enterprise having a reality transcending the fantasies of one person.

One such model, that of Marin Mersenne, not only correlates with features common to those of his more illustrious contemporaries and consonant with later developments, but embodies a view of natural philosophy as a particular sort of cooperative research which exhibits the social dimensions of the Scientific Revolution. Mersenne, the Minim monk whose Parisian cell was the center of a wide correspondence with whoever appeared to him philosophically like-minded,[1] saw knowledge of nature as a cumulative acquisition of experimentally or observationally ratified facts made into demonstrative science through the techniques of mathematics. Demonstrability implied the accessibility of knowledge to all, in the manner of geometrical truths; the acquisition of experimentally or observationally ratified facts, however, required the exchange of trustworthy and preferably testable information among those able to acquire them. Mersenne's agenda for natural philosophy thus contrasts with the arrogant independence of Descartes and the combativeness of Galileo; it more closely resembles the later endeavors of Henry Oldenburg. In the 1630s and 1640s Mersenne helped to develop and provide with a sense of identity the largely extra-academic community canvassed in Oldenburg's vast correspondence of the 1660s and 1670s. He is often described as a "one-man scientific journal," and the metaphor neatly expresses the social implications of his philosophical thought.

Robert Lenoble, in his classic work *Mersenne ou la naissance du mécanisme* (1943), integrated an account of Mersenne's thought with its immediate motivations—social, ideological, and religious—to produce a picture not seriously modified since. Lenoble showed Mersenne constructing an approach to natural philosophy that was tailored to support social stability and to combat religious division through apologetic defense of orthodox Catholic positions on the relationship of God to His Creation, defending in particular the authenticity of miracles by limiting the possibilities inherent in the ordinary course of nature (the operational, mathematical lawlikeness of the world constituting what Lenoble described as Mersenne's "mechanism"). Richard Popkin's more recent work on Mersenne's attempts to combat philosophical scepticism in the 1620s has complemented Lenoble by showing how the moral, and hence social, dangers of scepticism that Mersenne and his contemporaries perceived prompt-

1. On Mersenne's order, see P. J. S. Whitmore, *The Order of Minims in Seventeenth-Century France* (The Hague, 1967).

ed the monk's stress on a science of appearances as an alternative to the Aristotelianism of the schools; the latter, which pretended to a knowledge of the true natures of things, proved too vulnerable to sceptical attack.[2] However, the intended social functions of Mersenne's ideas and the actual social motivations prompting them do not exhaust their importance.

One of the most striking aspects of Mersenne's work is that, although centrally characteristic in many ways of the Scientific Revolution, it is also deliberately unrevolutionary. Descartes, Galileo, Bacon, and others of Mersenne's near-contemporaries incorporated claims of novelty into their rhetoric, stressing the departure of their natural philosophies from the Aristotelianism promulgated in one form or another in the schools. Mersenne actively promoted the work of such iconoclasts; among many other things, he arranged for the publication of some of Descartes's writings and produced his own versions of a number of Galileo's. Yet despite his sympathy with the aims of these innovators, he avoided casting himself in the role they preferred. Although he became increasingly dubious of the merits of Aristotelian physics, he never chose to range himself against it insofar as it was incorporated into an established institutional structure to the defense of which he was largely committed. The true character of his position therefore demands explanation.

Mersenne, who lived from 1588 to 1648, spent most of his adult life in Paris. Soon after his move to the Minim convent off the Place Royale in 1619, his literary career got under way with works of a religious and apologetic nature; he turned shortly thereafter to the publication of treatises that dealt primarily with mathematical sciences of the physical world. The sciences of music, mechanics, and optics engaged his attention above all others, but the religious significance of his work was never submerged, always remaining a central motivation. His correspondence expanded throughout the 1620s, and by the following decade his role as a philosophical intelligencer had become firmly established.[3] This study draws on books and let-

2. Richard H. Popkin, *The History of Scepticism from Erasmus to Spinoza* (Berkeley, 1979).

3. There are various accounts of Mersenne's life. The basic source is his fellow Minim Hilarion de Coste, *La vie du R. P. Marin Mersenne, théologien, philosophe et mathématicien, de l'Ordre des Pères Minimes* (Paris, 1649), reproduced in Philippe Tamizey de Larroque, ed., *Les correspondants de Peiresc* (1879–97; facsimile rpt., Geneva, 1972), 2:436–97. René Thuillier, *Diarium patrum, fratrum et sororum Ordinis Minimorum Provinciae Franciae* (Paris, 1709; facsimile rpt., Geneva, 1972), 2:90–113, relies heavily on De Coste. Modern accounts are Robert Lenoble, *Mersenne ou la naissance du mécanisme* (Paris, 1943), chap. 1; Cornélis de Waard, "Vie de Mersenne," in *Correspondance du P.*

ters written throughout his career, and the following list of his major publications provides a useful chronological framework.[4]

L'usage de la raison (1623), a devotional work, recently rediscovered, which discusses the religious functions of the understanding and the will and includes what amount to "spiritual exercises."[5]

L'analyse de la vie spirituelle (1623), now lost.

Quaestiones in Genesim (1623), a massive, incomplete commentary on Genesis, including attacks on heretical natural philosophies and "atheists," with many mathematical and physical digressions.

Observationes (1623), a kind of supplement to *Quaestiones*, which criticizes naturalistic doctrines that contain heretical implications regarding such matters as the nature of the soul and the dependence of the natural world on God.

L'impieté des deistes (1624), a two-volume defense of providence that includes a lengthy assault on Giordano Bruno and gives important place to the mathematical sciences. Its first volume was reissued under a different title in 1630.

La verité des sciences (1625), a defense of the possibility of knowing truths against the claims of Pyrrhonian scepticism, using mathematics as the main weapon.

Synopsis mathematica (1626), a compendium of sections devoted to presenting solid mathematical knowledge from the best authors in such areas as optics, statics, and branches of geometry.

Traité de l'harmonie universelle (1627), a work on aspects of the theory of music.

Questions inouyes (1634), a miscellany of discussions of mathematical and physical problems, akin to the pseudo-Aristotelian *Problemata*.

Questions harmoniques (1634), a discussion of various musical issues incorporating a sceptical work against music theory by La Mothe Le Vayer, with Mersenne's reply.

Marin Mersenne, ed. C. de Waard et al. (Paris, 1932–), 1:xix–lv (hereafter cited as Mersenne *Correspondance*); and a useful treatment in David Allen Duncan, "The Tyranny of Opinions Undermined" (diss., Vanderbilt University, 1981), chap. 1.

4. Publication details for these books may be found in the bibliography, which should be consulted in conjunction with that in Lenoble, *Mersenne*. (In quotations from and titles of French works by Mersenne and his contemporaries, I have reproduced the spelling and accent usage of the period rather than follow the conventions of modern French.)

5. For an account of its rediscovery, see Armand Beaulieu, "Découverte d'un livre de Mersenne," *Revue d'histoire des sciences* 35 (1982), 55–56. The only known copy is in the Vatican Library, to which I am grateful for a microfilm.

Questions theologiques (1634), a miscellany similar to *Questions inouyes.*

Les mechaniques de Galilée (1634), a French paraphrase of a manuscript on statics by Galileo, which had circulated since the beginning of the century.

Les preludes de l'harmonie universelle (1634), another miscellany focused loosely on musical questions.[6]

Harmonie universelle (1636–37), a large-scale work on all aspects of music, theoretical and practical, including sections on mechanics that deal with Galileo's ideas from the *Dialogue* of 1632.

Harmonicorum libri XII (1636; reissued with a few additions in 1648), a shorter Latin version of the *Harmonie universelle.*

Les nouvelles pensées de Galilée (1638/9), paraphrasing selected material from Galileo's *Two New Sciences* of 1638.

Universae geometriae . . . synopsis (1644), an augmented version of the *Synopsis mathematica* of 1626, including short optical treatises by William Warner and Thomas Hobbes.

Cogitata physico-mathematica (1644), a compendium of material on mathematical sciences such as ballistics, hydraulics, pneumatics, mechanics, and music.

Novarum observationum. . . tomus III (1647), a continuation of the *Cogitata* and on similar themes, including material on Torricelli's barometric experiments brought back by Mersenne to France after a visit to Italy, and republishing an astronomical work written by Roberval.

L'optique et la catoptrique (1651), a posthumous work on one of the major classical mathematical sciences.

This catalogue provides an excellent overview of Mersenne's central interests. In concentrating on mathematical sciences, he effectively rejected a natural philosophy not only of the kind advocated by Aristotle but also of the sort developed by Descartes; that is, a true physics speaking of the causes underlying natural processes. Mathematical sciences dealt with measurable appearances, not inner natures. At the same time, Mersenne's use of mathematical modes of demonstration in some ways mirrored Descartes's ideal and, even more, that of Galileo; hence his promotion of their ideas. The implications of his eclectic attitude should be contrasted with Galileo's lack of interest in Kepler's work and with Descartes's tendency to dismiss Galileo's work because of the differences between Galileo's procedures and his own. In order to emphasize its open-ended or

6. The five works of 1634 have recently been reprinted (Paris: Fayard, 1985), in the care of André Pessel. I have not used this volume.

dynamic quality, I shall frequently refer to Mersenne's model for the conduct of natural philosophy as an "agenda": it comprised lines along which he thought the study of nature should proceed, rather than simply a body of knowledge that he wished to present. Mersenne's agenda, combined with his efforts as an intelligencer, served to consolidate, if only partially, an emerging community of natural philosophers following new ways of construing the world.[7] His social role cannot be understood without it.

This book attempts, therefore, to investigate how Mersenne constructed his agenda. It builds upon Lenoble's and Popkin's accounts of his motivations and purposes to show the constraints and possibilities of the conceptual materials with which he pursued his goals and the crucial importance of arguments, concepts, and techniques drawn from orthodox school sources. The kinds of doctrines routinely promulgated by the Jesuits—Mersenne's early teachers and the dominant intellectual force in the Catholic world—provided him with tools by which even an apparently revolutionary break with existing, officially sanctioned views about nature and its study could appear compatible with established learning. Exploiting the orthodoxy that attached to the rich content of contemporary Catholic curricula, Mersenne created an agenda for natural philosophy capable of assimilating and even celebrating the new departures of his more illustrious contemporaries, and in effect displayed the reliance of the latter, despite their claims to the contrary, on philosophical idioms and achievements belonging to the learning of the schools. How he did so is the subject of the following pages.

A note on terminology: my use of the words "scholastic" and "scholasticism" in this book should not be taken as endorsing a picture of a monolithic, entrenched body of dogma surviving from the Middle Ages by dint of blind enforcement. The same applies to my use of "Aristotelianism." Many identifiable doctrinal variants of the latter existed in the sixteenth and seventeenth centuries, as Charles Schmitt in particular has emphasized,[8] and I shall generally mean by it no more than the uses and interpretations of Aristotle that informed the standard teaching texts of the Jesuits. Similarly, "scholasticism" here refers to a mode of scholarship—usually employing the genre of commentary and *quaestio*—inherited from the techniques developed in the thirteenth century to cope with the task of assimilating ancient, especially Aristotelian, writings, and structuring the pedagogical tech-

7. This point is made in Alistair C. Crombie, "Marin Mersenne and the Seventeenth-Century Problem of Scientific Acceptability," *Physis* 17 (1975), 188–89.
8. Charles B. Schmitt, *Aristotle and the Renaissance* (Cambridge, Mass., 1983), chap. 1, "Renaissance Aristotelianisms."

niques of medieval and Renaissance universities and colleges.[9] The "learning of the schools," furthermore, refers not simply to "scholastic Aristotelianism" but also to the results of the pedagogical innovations associated with humanism. The schools of the early seventeenth century, including the Jesuit colleges, had incorporated both.

9. The seventeenth century saw the rise of a scholastic textbook genre constructed around the material previously found in commentaries. This disruption of the literary and hence pedagogical structure of learning must surely be related to the demise of scholasticism: see Sister Mary Richard Reif, "Natural Philosophy in Some Early Seventeenth Century Scholastic Textbooks" (diss., St. Louis University, 1962). On the other hand, F. Edward Cranz, in his introduction to *A Bibliography of Aristotle Editions, 1501–1600* (Baden-Baden, 1984), p. xiii, notes that the Jesuit Coïmbra commentaries on Aristotle reinvigorated the commentary genre. Practically none of the school doctrines on which Mersenne drew was unique to the Jesuits, but the Jesuits' intellectual dominance in the Catholic world and their provision of Mersenne's early training make them the natural focus of this study.

CHAPTER TWO

Humanism and the Implications of Rhetoric

M ERSENNE'S heavy folio volume of 1623 is usually known by the abbreviated title *Quaestiones in Genesim*. The full title, like those of so many contemporary books (in the days before dust-jacket blurbs), runs to more than fifty words.[1] Five in particular signal the decidedly postmedieval flavor of this incomplete commentary on the first book of the Bible: "Graecorum, et Hebraeorum Musica instauratur" (the music of the Greeks and Hebrews is restored). Not only does this seem out of place in an apparently scholastic work, but it is sufficiently contrary to the image of Mersenne as a forward-looking philosophical innovator for Robert Lenoble to have labeled him as, in this regard, "farouchement conservateur," even "rétrograde."[2] Be that as it may, the attitude towards music expressed in Mersenne's writings of the early 1620s reflects basic assumptions underlying humanist pedagogy.

The humanist program of educational reform in the fifteenth and sixteenth centuries had involved a largely successful attempt at promoting a positive reevaluation of their subjects by teachers of grammar, rhetoric, and poetics. Centered on rhetoric, this program looked to classical antiquity, especially the republican Rome of Cicero, for its cultural model.[3] The humanist saw the pursuit of the eloquence man-

1. Marin Mersenne, *Quaestiones in Genesim* (Paris, 1623), bound together with *Observationes;* see Lenoble, *Mersenne,* pp. xii–xiii, for full bibliographical details and minor variants between copies; also William L. Hine, "Mersenne Variants," *Isis* 67 (1976), 98–103. The work is discussed briefly in Arnold Williams, *The Common Expositor* (Chapel Hill, N.C., 1948), chap. 9, esp. pp. 178–80.

2. Lenoble, *Mersenne,* p. 527.

3. I draw my basic use of the word "humanism" from the work of Paul Oskar Kristeller; see, e.g., his masterly essay "The Humanist Movement," in *Renaissance Thought: The Classic, Scholastic, and Humanist Strains* (New York, 1961), pp. 3–23.

ifested in ancient authors such as Cicero as being at the same time the pursuit of wisdom; indeed, the true value of all ancient texts lay in the wisdom prerequisite to their production.[4] The path of learning therefore led, through attempts at imitation, towards the goal of restoring that ancient wisdom, and what is known as "musical humanism" formed a part of the broader humanist project.[5]

The dream of the restoration of ancient music announced in the title of Mersenne's book was no mere historian's ambition; he castigated those who would attempt to introduce innovations that violated ancient musical canons.[6] Two years later, in *La verité des sciences*, he pursued the same goal: discussing the problem of finding the most beautiful melody possible on a given subject, he hoped "that with the help of God we will reach this perfection. . . or at least that we will approach it very closely, particularly if I can reestablish what the ancients practiced in their melodies."[7] Mersenne frequently used such terms as "latter-day Orpheus" to praise contemporary musicians, and although after the 1620s these expressions took on the character above all of classical ornamentation, they expressed a belief firmly held during his early career that ancient music had been capable of producing marvelous effects on its audience unparalleled among the moderns.[8] Many remarks of classical writers gave evidence of the therapeutic, even mystical, powers of the musicians of antiquity.[9] The same seemed true of Hebrew music, as the Bible recorded—and so Mersenne could condemn as "false and blasphe-

---

4. An excellent treatment of this subject is Hanna H. Gray, "Renaissance Humanism," *Journal of the History of Ideas* 24 (1963), 497–514; also Jerrold E. Siegel, *Rhetoric and Philosophy in Renaissance Humanism* (Princeton, N.J., 1968).

5. See, in general, Frances A. Yates, *The French Academies of the Sixteenth Century* (London, 1947), esp. pp. 64–68, 284–90; D. P. Walker, *Studies in Musical Science in the Late Renaissance* (London, 1978), and "Musical Humanism in the Sixteenth and Early Seventeenth Centuries," *Music Review* 2 (1941), 1–13, 111–21, 220–27, 288–308, and 3 (1942), 55–71. For an account along similar lines, concentrating especially on Mersenne, see Duncan, "The Tyranny of Opinions Undermined," chap. 3.

6. Lenoble, *Mersenne*, p. 527.

7. Marin Mersenne, *La verité des sciences* (Paris, 1625), pp. 558–59. Juan Luis Vives (*De tradendis disciplinis*, bk. 4, chap. 5) said that "in music we have deteriorated much from the older masters," and he recommended attempting to imitate them; see *Vives: On Education*, trans. Foster Watson (Cambridge, 1913), p. 205.

8. Another classical parallel that appealed to Mersenne was Amphion; Mauduit was the "Amphion of our century": Mersenne *Correspondance*, 1:575. For a discussion of Mersenne's relations with Jacques Mauduit and the latter's involvement with an academy designed to "renovate the ancient way of composing," see De Waard's long note in ibid., pp. 44–45. Even after having left full-blown musical humanism behind, Mersenne made such remarks as that priests should conduct themselves like "Christian Orpheuses" in the music of the Mass: Marin Mersenne, *Harmonie universelle* (Paris, 1636–37), "Premiere Preface Generale au Lecteur," [p. 11].

9. Lenoble, *Mersenne*, p. 526. For a modern discussion based on the sorts of texts that inspired these attitudes in the Renaissance, see Helmut and Hans Huchzermeyer, "Die

mous" the opinion of those who cast doubt on such claims.[10] Although Mersenne's faith in its extraordinary efficacy did not last, his interest in ancient music never abated. Always there remained the tantalizing vision of recovering the lost musical knowledge of antiquity.[11]

The project of "restoration" extended beyond music, however; it also encompassed mathematics. Mersenne devoted the final three of *La verité*'s four books to a refutation of Pyrrhonian scepticism taking the form of "proof by ostension."[12] The indubitable knowledge he parades before his reader is predominantly mathematical, both pure and applied, and in the course of exposition his spokesman in this dialogue, the Christian Philosopher, considers the prospects for the perfection of geometry. In order to achieve excellence, he says, "it would be necessary to reestablish the Analysis of the ancients, but I don't expect that anyone will complete this heroic work, if some excellent and bold geometer doesn't employ his time and trouble on it: for I hardly foresee its appearance, for the reason that we don't have all the books of the ancients necessary to this project, even if still more of them were recovered. Perhaps you [the Sceptic, the Christian Philosopher's antagonist] will be very glad if I list these books, so that if you come across any of those which we don't have, you can carefully conserve it."[13] There follows a listing of lost mathematical works by Euclid, Apollonius, Aristaeus, and Eratosthenes (all known from remarks in Pappus's *Mathematical Collections*), and a sketch of what has been done thus far by way of restoration. Ghetaldus, Viète (in his *Apollonius Gallus*), Hardy, and Anderson have all contributed, says the Christian Philosopher, either by restoring particular texts or by attempting, like Viète and Anderson, to reconstruct ancient analysis *in toto*.[14] But, he continues, Anderson and Viète are no longer with us: "Please God to cause to be reborn in this century some new Archimedes', who will conduct mathematics to its former perfection," silencing modern ignoramuses who think they can outdo Euclid.[15]

Bedeutung des Rythmus in der Musiktherapie der Griechen von der Frühzeit bis zum Beginn des Hellenismus," *Sudhoffs Archiv* 58 (1974), 113–48.

10. Lenoble, *Mersenne*, p. 527.

11. See ibid., pp. 522–31; Marin Mersenne, *Questions harmoniques* (Paris, 1634), Q. 5, pp. 252–76, "A sçavoir si les Grecs, & les autres Anciens ont esté plus sçavans que nous en la Theorie, & en la pratique de la Musique," where the answer is "no." *Harmonie universelle* contains recurring remarks on ancient music.

12. I borrow the term from John A. Schuster, "Descartes and the Scientific Revolution, 1618–1634" (diss., Princeton University, 1977), chap. 3. Lenoble (*Mersenne*, p. 192) compares the strategy to Diogenes' rhetorical perambulations.

13. Mersenne, *La verité*, p. 748.

14. Ibid., pp. 748–49.

15. Ibid., p. 750.

Descartes took pains in his *Geometry* to stress the improbability of the ancient mathematicians having possessed the form of analysis that he presented; he did so precisely in order to counter the belief, held by Viète and humanist mathematicians generally, that the theorems contained in the synthetic geometrical works of the Greeks had first been discovered through the use of an analytic method.[16] In effect, the humanist project, which Descartes's striving for originality made him reject, was to reconstruct the scaffolding from knowledge of the building.[17] In *La verité des sciences,* Mersenne appears to have taken the validity and worth of that project for granted; mathematics, like music, is to be conducted "to its former perfection," and only renovators, not innovators, are to be countenanced. Later, for Mersenne as for most contemporary mathematicians, the new directions taken by Descartes and Fermat must have rendered the vision of restoration entertained by Viète an irrelevancy.[18] But although this perspective may have played little functional role in his subsequent career, its presence in Mersenne's early writings betrays an attitude towards antiquity and towards the primacy of method over content that had been inculcated by the Jesuits' humanistic "course of letters," an attitude of which rhetoric was the cornerstone.[19]

The Jesuits' policy of admitting scholarship pupils into their colleges had enabled Mersenne, the son of a laborer, to receive one of the finest educations in Europe. On arrival at the college of La Flèche soon after its foundation in 1604, and having already undergone elementary grammar training at Le Mans, he straightaway started his studies of the humanities: that is, poetics and rhetoric.[20] Assuming

16. René Descartes, "Géometrie," in *Oeuvres de Descartes* (Paris: J. Vrin, 1964–1971), 6:376–79.

17. On the humanist project in mathematics, see Michael Sean Mahoney, *The Mathematical Career of Pierre de Fermat* (Princeton, N.J., 1973), pp. 2–4; Paul Lawrence Rose, *The Italian Renaissance of Mathematics* (Geneva, 1975); and esp. JoAnn S. Morse, "The Reception of Diophantus' Arithmetic in the Renaissance" (diss., Princeton University, 1981).

18. In point of fact, the new developments in algebra seem to have quite left Mersenne behind; he never addressed them in his own writings.

19. "Mathematical and rhetorical imitation shared the assumption that the ancients' authority lay not in their results—theorems or locutions—but in their skills. Just as a humanist read Cicero to discover not so much what he said as how he said it, so Regiomontanus read Archimedes to discover how he had proved what he proved": Morse, "Diophantus," p. 36.

20. De Coste, *Vie,* p. 442. Details of Mersenne's education at the college must remain conjectural, but studies of French Jesuit colleges in the seventeenth century indicate reasonably close consonance between curricular structure and such statements of pedagogical policy as the 1599 *Ratio studiorum,* to which La Flèche was one of the earliest subscribers: see, above all, François de Dainville, *La naissance de l'humanisme moderne* (Paris, 1940). Dainville's essays on Jesuit education have been collected in idem, *L'éducation des Jésuites, XVIᵉ–XVIIIᵉ siècles* (Paris, 1978). More recent discussions include

that the college then operated according to the typical pattern, this means that he entered the second class of the "course of letters," having skipped the preparatory classes—numbered sixth through third—which covered Latin and Greek grammar.[21] The Jesuits' course of letters was essentially humanistic in conception, with a strong emphasis on Latin authors; it aimed at teaching pupils both to read and to speak Latin but only to read Greek.[22] During his first two years at La Flèche, therefore, Mersenne would have undergone an intensive training in the appreciation and imitation of classical orators, historians, and poets. Properly cultivated, he then devoted three years to the philosophy course: the first year covered logic as well as ethics, structured chiefly around the appropriate Aristotelian texts; the second year, peripatetic physics and the mathematical disciplines; the third year, metaphysics, based on Aristotle's *Metaphysics* and *De anima*.[23]

According to his biographer and fellow-Minim, Hilarion de Coste, Mersenne also studied "several treatises of theology" at La Flèche,[24] although chronology indicates that he must have left the college in about 1609, after completing the three classes of the philosophy course, without proceeding to the course of theology. Formal theological training at the Sorbonne, "where resides the strength and support of faith," as De Coste put it, served him in its stead; together

---

Georges Snyders, *La pédagogie en France aux XVIIᵉ et XVIIIᵉ siècles* (Paris, 1965); Roger Chartier, Dominique Julia, and Marie-Madeleine Compère, *L'éducation en France du XVIᵉ au XVIIIᵉ siècle* (Paris, 1976), as well as subsequent references. On La Flèche, see Camille de Rochemonteix, *Un collège de Jésuites aux XVIIᵉ & XVIIIᵉ siècles* (Le Mans, 1889), 3:4, on *Ratio studiorum*. College records for La Flèche are sparse for the early period but provide some supplementary information; textbooks printed at La Flèche during its earliest years come closer to evidencing actual pedagogical content than do the lists of classical texts found in the curricula—see Rochemonteix, *Collège*, 3:29, 4:27, and below—although, once again, apparent uniformity between colleges allows quite firm inferences to be made about La Flèche simply from knowledge of what textbooks were usually employed. There are also various occasional sources of information about La Flèche during Mersenne's time there; in particular, De Coste names some of Mersenne's teachers and courses of study. J. Sirven, *Les années d'apprentissage de Descartes (1596–1628)* (Paris, 1928), chap. 1, gives an account of Descartes's education at La Flèche, drawing on Rochemonteix, Baillet's biography of Descartes, and notes in the Descartes *Oeuvres*.

21. De Coste, *Vie*, p. 442; see Rochemonteix, *Collège*, 3:4–12.

22. Dainville, *Naissance*, p. 106. On the establishment of the Jesuits' "course of letters," see R. R. Bolgar, *The Classical Heritage and Its Beneficiaries* (Cambridge, 1954), pp. 357–59.

23. See Rochemonteix, *College*, 4:27–49; and more generally, Dainville, *Naissance*, chap. 2, esp. pp. 85–90. See also De Waard's more or less reliable reconstruction of Mersenne's curriculum at La Flèche in his "Vie de Mersenne," Mersenne *Correspondance* 1:xx–xxi.

24. De Coste, *Vie*, p. 442.

with further classical studies at the Collège de France, this occupied Mersenne for the two years prior to his entry into the Order of Minims, in 1611.[25] The following eight years saw him proceed from the rank of novice to that of priest, and to the post of teacher at the Minim convent at Nevers, where he became Corrector. In 1619 he returned to Paris, to the Convent of the Annunciation and Saint Francis de Paule, just off the Place Royale.[26] By that time Mersenne had learned Hebrew[27] and had acquired, we must assume, much of the erudition displayed in his bulky publications of the early 1620s. Those works do more than bear witness to the scholarly labors of the previous decade, however; they also owe much to the five years spent at La Flèche, where the Jesuits' amalgam of humanism and scholastic Aristotelianism[28] had equipped Mersenne with an outlook characteristic of the best pedagogy of the period.

The second year of Mersenne's publishing career, 1624, saw the appearance of *L'impiété des deistes,* a dialogue that pits a Theologian, Mersenne's standard-bearer, against a tractable Deist.[29] The work begins with an encounter between its two protagonists as they travel the same road, and Mersenne handles the exchange as a simple rhetorical exercise, drawing on unremarkable commonplaces to achieve his ends. The Deist opens by explaining that he is journeying in search of places the farthest removed from the commerce of men, and he justifies his poor opinion of the latter with reference to the "malice and infidelity of their spirits, and the misery of their bodies."[30] In order to disabuse the Deist of such improper notions, the Theologian relates a sub-dialogue between Aesculapius, Vesta, and Urania. Aesculapius undertakes the task indicated by Mersenne's chapter heading, "In which the excellence of man is declared"; praising man's body, he compares it to a house, to a commonwealth, and finally to the whole world.[31] The next chapter elaborates the theme by showing "how man does everything, makes use of everything, and commands the world in everything."[32] It

25. Ibid., p. 443; see also Larroque's notes on Mersenne's teachers, pp. 443–44. L. W. B. Brockliss emphasizes the current lack of knowledge about education at the University of Paris in this period: see his "Philosophy Teaching in France, 1600–1740," *History of Universities* 1 (1981), 133.

26. Lenoble, *Mersenne,* pp. 19–23; De Coste, *Vie,* pp. 446–47.

27. De Coste, *Vie,* p. 446.

28. On this point, see Eugenio Garin, *L'éducation de l'homme moderne,* trans. (from Italian) Jacqueline Humbert ([Paris], 1968), pp. 183–89; Garin emphasizes Jesuit education as a training in the service of the Church.

29. Marin Mersenne, *L'impiété des deistes* (Paris, 1624); see C. J. Betts, *Early Deism in France* (The Hague, 1984), chap. 2.

30. Mersenne, *L'impiété,* 1:1–2.

31. Ibid., pp. 1, 5, 11, 15.

32. Ibid., p. 21.

commences stirringly: "The world is truly a great miracle, but man seems to me so much more marvelous in that he is smaller, and nonetheless he has so much subtlety that by natural magic he can represent in a diaphanous body, and very distinctly, all that appears on the horizon. He can, like a Vulcan and a Prometheus, draw fire from wherever he pleases, imitate thunder like Salmoneus, make a rainbow by the gushing of a fountain."[33] Indeed, "What cannot man do?" flourishes Mersenne. Anyone who has read Pico della Mirandola's *Oration* will recognize immediately the use here of familiar Renaissance topoi.[34] These are the sorts of material that would be jotted down in a student's rhetoric notebook, and one can imagine a column headed "production of natural wonders" containing reference to the classical exploits of Vulcan, Prometheus, and Salmoneus.[35] Mersenne deployed commonplaces to construct his argument in proper humanist fashion, just as he had learned to do from the Jesuits.

Mersenne's introduction to rhetoric at La Flèche almost certainly came through a work used there from the college's earliest years: Cyprian Soarez's *De arte rhetorica*.[36] Written as an elementary textbook for the schools of the Society of Jesus, it found wide favor there and, from its first appearance in 1562, saw many cheap reprintings.[37] The book's precepts are taken from the three standard authorities—Aristotle, Cicero, and Quintilian—and there is little to distinguish it from any number of other rhetoric texts of the sixteenth and seventeenth centuries.[38] Commending eloquence from the good example of the Greek and Latin Church Fathers, the Jesuit Soarez nonetheless in practice showed Mersenne how the Romans did it.[39]

Rhetorical techniques in fact formed part of a cultural resource

33. Ibid., p. 22.

34. For a discussion of such ideas, see Paul Oskar Kristeller, *Renaissance Concepts of Man and Other Essays* (New York, 1972), pp. 1–21, "The Dignity of Man"; for discussion and examples, see Giovanni Gentile, "Il concetto dell'uomo nel rinascimento," in *Opere complete* (Firenze, 1940), 11:47–113. Clearly, Mersenne does not mean to advocate neo-Platonism by these remarks: see (apart from Lenoble, *Mersenne*) Frances Yates, *Giordano Bruno and the Hermetic Tradition* (Chicago, 1964), pp. 434–37.

35. See Bolgar, *Classical Heritage*, pp. 269–75. A classic description of the "notebook method" occurs in Battista Guarino's *De ordine docendi et studendi*, trans. in William Harrison Woodward, ed., *Vittorino da Feltre and Other Humanist Educators* (New York, 1974), p. 173.

36. For its use at La Flèche, see Rochemonteix, *Collège*, 3:29. The edition I have used is Cyprian Soarez, *De arte rhetorica libri tres, ex Aristotele, Cicerone & Quintiliano praecipue deprompti* (Rouen, 1605).

37. Chartier, Julia, and Compère, *L'éducation*, p. 197; Peter France, *Rhetoric and Truth in France* (Oxford, 1972), p. 13. A particularly good examination of this book is in Peter Bayley, *French Pulpit Oratory, 1598–1650* (Cambridge, 1980), pp. 23–29.

38. For a clear account of the context and structure of such textbooks, see France, *Rhetoric*, chap. 1, esp. pp. 8–27; see also Bayley, *Pulpit Oratory*, chap. 2.

39. Soarez, *De arte*, preface.

common to all educated Europeans of the time, as a letter written to Mersenne in about 1626 reminds us. The correspondent, René Moreau, wrote concerning a discussion in *La verité des sciences*. Mersenne's problem, "to know whether it is possible to find or give a musical tune or melody that will be the most perfect and finished of all," elicited from Moreau the response that since one could not know whether any given melody was the most perfect possible simply from its own internal merits, one would have to compare it with every other possible melody. Alternatively, even if one wrote a tune conforming perfectly to all the appropriate rules, there would still be no guarantee of its being the most perfect in relation to any particular audience.[40] Moreau chose an analogy from rhetoric to clarify the point: "If I were asked whether a man could succeed in making a discourse or oration that had every part of eloquence at the peak of perfection, I would reply that it is completely impossible, since one cannot achieve all the diversity of orations that can be made. . . . [An oration made according to the rules of rhetoric of the greatest orators] ought to be held as the most perfect and artistic [*artificiel*] although with regard to its effect it would be neither the most agreeable to the ear, perhaps, nor the most persuasive."[41] Moreau could be certain of Mersenne's complete familiarity with the art of rhetoric, because everyone learned it at school; its teachings therefore provided a basic reference point for learned discourse.

Since for the humanist the value of oratorical techniques lay in their status as vehicles of wisdom, both civic and philosophical,[42] Mersenne's rhetoric notebook served as more than a repository of elegancies; it also acted as a model of rational structure. "Everything that is in the world is accompanied by a contrary," the Christian Philosopher observes in *La verité*, assembling under this standard heading such items as the Aristotelian qualities, light and shadow, and examples from Ecclesiasticus. "In this way the world is similar to a beautiful oration in rhetoric, in which one employs opposites and contraries to highlight more the subject being treated, for all the diversities which we see in this world are so many rhetorical periods and figures, to draw us to the praise of God and to the recognition of His marvels."[43]

40. René Moreau to Mersenne (c. 1625–26), Mersenne *Correspondance*, 1:633–34.
41. Ibid., p. 634. Mersenne took these remarks from Moreau's letter and included them, practically word for word and with no acknowledgment, in *Harmonie universelle*, "Des chants," p. 105. Marc Fumaroli has characterized this period in France as the "age of eloquence": *L'âge de l'éloquence* (Geneva, 1980).
42. Gray, "Renaissance Humanism."
43. Mersenne, *La verité*, p. 426. On contraries, see Soarez, *De arte*, pp. 40–42. The mapping of rhetorical categories onto the true constitution of the world had ample

This view of rhetoric stresses its importance as a practical tool of persuasion, "to draw us to the praise of God," and shows its relevance to our knowledge of nature insofar as nature is itself an ordered creation of God intended to produce a persuasive effect on those who experience it.

Mersenne did not wholeheartedly endorse all aspects of contemporary rhetoric, however. The Christian Philosopher in *La verité* had nothing against neologisms—of which, indeed, Soarez had approved—but he recognized that some people saw them as violations of linguistic propriety. He was perfectly content that

artisans, and those who make profession of some particular science, invent new terms, if they mean something, although they appear barbarous and very crude to these young writers, who wish very much to smooth [*frizer*], make effeminate, soften, and polish their language. That is why I disapprove of the fact that those who take pleasure in the beautiful language of Cicero rebuke the terms which we use in the philosophy schools, because we know as well as they that these ways of speaking are not Ciceronian, but we use them as far as they express better or more briefly what we want to say.[44]

A similar point is implied in the preface to his first publication, *L'usage de la raison* (1623), and in the preface to *L'impieté des deistes* Mersenne comments on his own "extremely simple and succinct" style, claiming that "the simplicity and candor of the Catholic faith doesn't need to be explained or defended by affected, inflated, elevated, or metaphorical words."[45] Those many places where Mersenne honors his stylistic rule only in the breach no doubt expose the irony of this rhetorical ploy, but it reflects a genuine and uncharacteristic bitterness—witness this passage from *La verité*: "We see that many poets and writers who have nothing but language are well received among the great and the lords of the kingdom, and that those who are truly learned [*sçavans*], and who could perform marvels in peace and war if they were employed and valued [*caressez*], are held in such scorn that they are regarded as of no account."[46] Mersenne's "sçavans" in this

precedent; see Kenneth J. Knoespel, "The Narrative Matter of Mathematics," *Philological Quarterly* (forthcoming).

44. Mersenne, *La verité*, p. 75. Bayley, *Pulpit Oratory*, p. 27, notes that Soarez approves of the invention of new words in *De arte*, bk.III, chaps. 6, 7.

45. Mersenne, *L'impieté*, vol. 1, preface [pp. 5–6]. Marin Mersenne, *L'usage de la raison* (Paris, 1623), pp. 13–16, labors this point heavily.

46. Mersenne, *La verité*, p. 751.

discussion are mathematicians, cast in the role of Plutarch's Archimedes.

In his early writings, then, Mersenne displayed apparently conflicting opinions about rhetoric: on the one hand he made ample use of rhetorical techniques and even compared the world to an oration; on the other hand he criticized sharply the emptiness and vanity of those "who have nothing but language." These two attitudes imply no real contradiction, however, because rhetoric was divided into distinct departments. Soarez listed the conventional five parts of rhetoric: *inventio*, the appraisal and choice of appropriate materials; *dispositio*, the proper arrangement of those materials; *elocutio*, style and the selection of suitable verbal ornamentation; *memoria*, memory of the relevant materials; and *pronunciatio*, delivery.[47] During the course of the sixteenth and seventeenth centuries humanist approaches to logic and rhetoric brought about an increased emphasis in rhetorical texts on the last three parts, especially *elocutio*, at the expense of the first two.[48] By the early seventeenth century this tendency had become sufficiently widespread to prompt Mersenne's complaints against a rhetoric dependent on ornamentation and empty eloquence. For Mersenne, that aspect of rhetoric which dealt with the formal construction of effective discourse, chiefly covered by *inventio* and *dispositio*, stood apart from and higher than the practice of those "who have nothing but language." Petrus Ramus had accentuated the distinction by co-opting *inventio* and *dispositio* (known to Ramists as *judicio*) for his own form of logic, leaving to rhetoric itself only those parts relating to the theatrical side of the art.[49] Soarez himself had implicitly divided rhetoric in a similar way by presenting dialectic and eloquence as the principal "materials of rhetoric."[50] "Dialectic" (invariably a synonym for "logic"), which Soarez meant to encompass *inventio* and *dispositio*, thus threatened to leave eloquence—as Ramus did—unattended. Paradoxically, Soarez actually placed much greater emphasis in his textbook on the first two parts of rhetoric, giving a comparatively sketchy treatment of the remaining three, and this may partly explain Mersenne's predilections.[51] Soarez's presentation of dialectic as a department of rhetoric reflects in its turn the more

47. Soarez, *De arte*, pp. 24–26.

48. Chartier, Julia, and Compère, *L'éducation*, pp. 197–98.

49. See France, *Rhetoric*, pp. 15–16, and below. Lee A. Sonnino, *A Handbook to Sixteenth-Century Rhetoric* (London, 1968), is a useful reference work explaining the meaning of technical terms.

50. Soarez, *De arte*, p. 21.

51. Bayley (*Pulpit Oratory*, p. 28) observes Soarez's concentration on *inventio* and *dispositio* and his "extremely cursory" treatment of memory, pronunciation, and gesture.

rhetorical approach to logic promoted by humanism. Humanist dialectic, in contrast to scholastic logic, emphasized not certain demonstration but forms of argument—dialectic as a "ratio disserendi," to use Cicero's term—and hence paid especial attention to persuasive or probable arguments of a kind familiar to rhetoricians. *Inventio*, as Soarez said, drew not just on "res verae" but also on "res verisimiles," requiring a logic that dealt with probabilities as well as certainties.[52]

The humanist approach to dialectic had initially been promulgated in Germany. Rudolf Agricola's *De inventione dialectica*, written around 1479, came into widespread use in German universities during the 1520s and 1530s and formed the prototype for subsequent textbooks by such influential educational reformers as Sturm and Melanchthon. The new dialectic soon took hold in England, as well as stimulating the even more radical innovations of Ramus in France.[53] It also became established in the teaching of the Jesuits as an integral part of humanist pedagogy: the "course of letters" preceding the philosophy course in the Jesuit colleges shows the extent to which they had adopted the humanist revaluation of grammar and rhetoric.[54] Soarez's book reflects their equal adoption of reforms in the third subject of the medieval trivium, logic, despite its assignment to philosophy in the Jesuit curriculum.

Thomas Spencer, the author of an early seventeenth-century English logic text, noted that according to the Jesuits *"the end of Logick, is a framing of the means of discoursing"*; and again, that *"the Jesuites . . . define Logick, to be no more, but an art of discoursing."*[55] His observations were prompted by an adherence to the humanist approach found, for example, in the textbook that Mersenne probably used at La Flèche: Pedro da Fonseca's *Institutiones dialecticae*.[56] As that work shows, the retention of the usual Aristotelian texts in the Jesuit logic

52. Soarez, *De arte*, p. 25. This issue, as well as the contemporary practical synonymity of "logic" and "dialectic," is discussed further in Chapter 3, below.

53. For a discussion of humanist dialectic, see Lisa Jardine, *Francis Bacon: Discovery and the Art of Discourse* (Cambridge, 1974), chap. 1, esp. pp. 31–58; Cesare Vasoli, *La dialettica e la retorica dell'Umanesimo* (Milan, 1968); Walter J. Ong, *Ramus: Method and the Decay of Dialogue* (New York, 1979), chap. 5 (on Agricola). For an illuminating discussion of humanist dialectic and its impact on grammar training and notions of language, see Terrence Heath, "Logical Grammar, Grammatical Logic, and Humanism in Three German Universities," *Studies in the Renaissance* 18 (1971), 9–64. See also Chapter 3, below.

54. On grammatical doctrines, see Heath, "Logical Grammar," and Chapter 7, below.

55. Tho. Spencer, *The Art of Logick, Delivered in the Precepts of* Aristotle *and* Ramus (London, 1638; preface "To the Reader" dated 1628), pp. 6, 8. Spencer appears to base his remarks on the Coïmbra commentators.

56. Rochemonteix, *Collège*, 4:27; I have used Fonseca, *Institutionum dialecticarum libri octo* (Venice, 1611).

curriculum disguises the shift away from the scholastic approach, much as Ramist pedagogy accomplished its innovations within a similarly traditional curriculum.[57] Dialectic had become a "ratio disserendi," a practical art of discourse which, although dealing with formal demonstration because it was useful, treated it as one tool among many. Book I of *Institutiones dialecticae* opens with a conventional oratorical tactic designed to justify the usual identification of logic and dialectic, at the same time showing that the latter term more clearly expressed the discipline's true nature. The tactic is to provide an etymology.

> When every subject [*doctrina*] that is examined by reason is committed to be discussed (that is, something unknown is to be disclosed from something known, in oration), in the discussion many errors occur, and some sort of art of inquiry is necessary which will show the appropriate forms of discussing and will not in any way hastily take false teaching for true. This art, which those who first invented it named "dialectic," the ancient peripatetics later called "logic." And, indeed, rightly on both sides. For dialectic is, in Latin, called the way, or doctrine, of discoursing [*disserendi ratio, sive doctrina*]. For that which is in Greek διαλέγεσθαι, whence this name derives, is, in Latin, "to discourse" [*disserere*]. The same interpretation of the name, on Cicero's authority, agrees with the word "logic."[58]

The appeal to Cicero in this opening passage clearly signals the tenor of the work.

While not a textbook modeled on Ramus's dichotomous *Dialectica*, as many were in this period, Fonseca's manual differs sharply from the old scholastic stalwart, Peter of Spain's *Summulae logicales*.[59] Fonseca's Book I, like Peter's, defines the scope of dialectic; unlike Peter's, it places the discipline within the context of a Ciceronian *ratio disserendi*.[60] Analysis of terms in the scholastic text has given way to consideration of the proper construction of discourse, and so the balance of themes is quite altered.[61] Apart from the syllogism, Fonseca considers

57. Charles B. Schmitt, *Cicero Scepticus: A Study of the Influence of the* Academica *in the Renaissance* (The Hague, 1972), p. 91.

58. Fonseca, *Institutiones*, p. 9. On the use of etymologies, see Nicholas Jardine, *The Birth of History and Philosophy of Science: Kepler's* A Defence of Tycho against Ursus *with Essays on Its Provenance and Significance* (Cambridge, 1984), pp. 211–12, 213–14.

59. Peter of Spain, *Tractatus, called afterwards Summule Logicales* (Assen, 1972). Examples of Ramist texts that I have consulted are Antony Wotton, ed., *The Art of Logick . . . by Peter Ramus* (London, 1626); Dudley Fenner, *The Artes of Logike and Rethorike* (1584), facsimile rpt. in Robert D. Pepper, ed., *Four Tudor Books on Education* (Gainesville, Fl., 1966), pp. 143–80.

60. And see, e.g., Fonseca's discussion of the roles of invention and judgment in forming arguments: *Institutiones*, pp. 176–78.

61. Gabriel Codina Mir (*Aux sources de la pédagogie des Jésuites* [Rome, 1968], p. 86) asserts, on the basis of the fact that rhetoric and dialectic formed separate parts of the

enthymeme (a form of argument resembling a syllogism but lacking either the major or the minor premise, which is therefore taken as understood), induction by enumeration (the procedure criticized by Francis Bacon), and the use of topics or commonplaces as an instrument of persuasion (sanctioned by Aristotle's *Topics*). All these appear in Peter of Spain, but their relative weighting and their purpose in Fonseca's text serve a different conception of the nature of dialectic. Commonplaces, for example, become much more central to Fonseca's treatment, where for Peter they could only be peripheral to a discipline concerned with the legitimacy of forms of inference. When Fonseca cites Cicero on the indifference of translating the Greek word ιδὲα as "forma" or "species," he remarks that "truly, dialecticians are not much hampered by a religion of words," and his target can only be the terminology-conscious medieval scholastic logicians.[62] Fonseca might have been less sanguine about the matter, however, had he lacked a good classical precedent for the translation.

Regular public disputations formed part of the standard curriculum in Jesuit colleges, and Mersenne, we are told, acquitted himself well in such exercises.[63] They provided a forum for putting rhetorical and dialectical training into practice; unlike the scholastic disputation, in which the participants aimed at displaying their ability at the incisive employment of logical rigor in support of a proposition, that of the Jesuits would have been conducted "in utramque partem," as Cicero put it: that is, on either side of the question. They did not intend simply to provide a *sic et non*, however; the participants attempted to show their virtuosity by rendering their position more probable, by persuading the audience towards a judgment in their favor. In the 1550s, the Jesuit Hieronymus Nadal condemned the scholastic style of disputation in confessing that "we too have formerly croaked and haggled at the top of our voice by means of syllogisms

---

Jesuit curriculum, that Jesuit teaching "would never mix the study of rhetoric with that of dialectic"; this inference seems to be quite misleading. A sense of the changes involved is given by Lisa Jardine's observation (*Bacon*, p. 31) that Agricola changed the sense of the term *probabiliter* from Peter of Spain's "plausible," "believed by the majority," "holding for the most part," to something like "apt" or "appropriate" in a literary sense, sanctioning the use of fables and the like in persuasive discourse.

62. Fonseca, *Institutiones*, p. 54. L. Jardine (*Bacon*, p. 20) describes Peter of Spain's textbook as "a technical training in the analysis and classification of terms"; "dialectic is a study of language and its usage, rather than of concepts and thought processes." For a more extended discussion of dialectic by Fonseca, bringing out his humanist perspective even more strongly, see his *Commentariorum in Metaphysicorum Aristotelis Stagiritae libros tomi quatuor* (1615; facsimile rpt., Hildesheim, 1964), esp. 1:525–26.

63. Lenoble, *Mersenne*, p. 19; no reference given, presumably drawn from Thuillier, *Diarium*, 2:93.

and barbarisms in the disputations of the Faculty of Theology," and the lingering presence of scholastic overtones to the whole notion of formal disputation seems sometimes to have encouraged resentment from Jesuit teachers.[64] Oratory provided a more congenial model.

The humanist approach to dialectic probably suited the Jesuits for two main reasons. First of all, its adoption accorded with their constant efforts to maintain the forefront in matters of learning and scholarship. The mathematician Christopher Clavius argued for an increased emphasis on his subject in the colleges in part by observing that Jesuits were being disgraced by their mathematical ignorance at "convocations of the most illustrious men"; Émile Durkheim has summed up their motivations by remarking that "in order to direct the century better, it was necessary for [the Jesuit] to speak its language, to assimilate its spirit."[65] A second and more specific reason was that the Society of Jesus, as an order dedicated to a propagandist mission, had a pressing practical interest in techniques of persuasion. The imperative to match or surpass their Protestant rivals in all the argumentative arenas chosen by the latter required a mastery of rhetoric and a dialectic suited to the achievement, not of logical subtleties or demonstration for its own sake, but of an effective case. For Jesuits, dialectic was no academic luxury.[66]

The humanistic aspect of the academic orthodoxy on which Mersenne drew for his own work had a significance beyond the commonplace assumptions about antiquity found in his earlier writings: it proved to be of great significance in the development of his mature approach to natural philosophy. This stemmed from the nature of humanist dialectic. As an art of reasoning, dialectic determined and delimited the legitimacy of knowledge claims. The probabilistic character of the humanist approach to the discipline therefore affected Mersenne's evaluation of natural philosophical knowledge. The following chapter shows how he used it to justify a new agenda for the study of nature, intended to supplant the physics of the schools.

64. Nadal quoted in Codina Mir, Sources, p. 288; Dainville, Naissance, p. 136. The Ratio studiorum of 1586 depicts teachers of humanities in the Jesuit colleges having to struggle for status against the philosophers and theologians: see Bolgar, Classical Heritage, pp. 449–50.

65. Christoph Clavius, "Modus quo disciplinae mathematicae in scholis Societatis possent promoveri," in Monumenta Paedagogica Societatis Iesu quae primam Rationem Studiorum anno 1586 praecessere (Madrid, 1901), pp. 471–72; Émile Durkheim, L'évolution pédagogique en France, 2 vols. (Paris, 1938), 2:76.

66. Fumaroli, L'âge de l'éloquence, pp. 179–202, considers the practical use of rhetoric by Jesuits in France in the seventeenth century.

CHAPTER THREE

Dialectic, Probabilism, and "Mitigated Scepticism"

I

For Robert Lenoble, Mersenne appeared as the prototypical modern scientist, rejecting essentialism and establishing a science based upon the mathematical coordination of sense perceptions and on operational, quantitative predictions. This new vision of science, said Lenoble, involved a radical regrounding of knowledge, statements of which—above all in works of 1634—constituted Mersenne's own "discourse on method."[1] He argued that Mersenne was primarily concerned, especially during the early part of his career, with refuting naturalistic and magical doctrines that appeared to threaten the concept of a regular or law-governed nature, and thus to defend miracles as genuine cases of divine intervention. Since Mersenne (for whatever reasons) rejected scholastic Aristotelianism, with its own version of a law-governed nature, he needed a replacement possessing an equally strong emphasis on that notion and found it in a form of "mechanism".[2]

This account can in large part be accepted. *Quaestiones in Genesim* (1623) and *L'impieté des deistes* (1624) both involve apologetic defenses of orthodox Catholicism directed against just the targets singled out by Lenoble,[3] and considerations drawn from the mathematical sci-

---

1. Lenoble, *Mersenne*, pp. 337–65.
2. Ibid., pp. 157–67, and chap. 3 passim. "Mechanism," in Lenoble's usage, does not necessarily refer to corpuscular mechanism.
3. For a recent elaboration of this view of Mersenne's early apologetic targets, see William L. Hine, "Marin Mersenne: Renaissance Naturalism and Renaissance Magic," in Brian Vickers, ed., *Occult and Scientific Mentalities in the Renaissance* (Cambridge, 1984), pp. 165–76.

ences provided Mersenne with a major source of arguments. In *Quaestiones,* to take a notable example, Mersenne opposes the position of the sixteenth-century Paduan philosopher Pomponazzi and his follower Vanini (notorious in France at this time), who both espoused naturalism. This doctrine presented nature as a self-motivating, self-sufficient system not requiring divine or supernatural agency to sustain it or to produce any of its particular effects. It thus implied the heretical notion that the physical world was independent of God. In order to avoid direct conflict between his philosophy and orthodox theology, Pomponazzi had invoked the principle of "double-truth" already condemned in the thirteenth century. Mersenne's fundamentally Thomistic belief in the intimate connection between philosophy and theology, however, led him to view Pomponazzi and his followers as nothing more than promulgators of heresy.[4] Naturalistic attempts to explain angelic apparitions in the Bible as purely natural optical illusions gave Mersenne an opportunity to strike back, and he did so by deploying theorems from geometrical optics to demonstrate the catoptrical impossibility of such an explanation.[5] For Lenoble, this maneuver typified Mersenne's move towards a mathematical and operational paradigm of natural philosophy as a means of responding to the challenge of philosophical unorthodoxy.[6] Lenoble's assessment of Mersenne's apologetic purposes and their crucial importance in shaping his natural philosophical program is certainly correct; however, it must not be assumed that Mersenne's aims in any strong sense determined the means he adopted to pursue them. Although he took every opportunity to turn his discussions of such mathematical sciences as optics to the support of the theological and moral doctrines he favored and the detraction of those he disliked, his mathematical digressions frequently occur with no appreciable argumentative purpose at all.

In *L'impieté des deistes* there is much material on optics and mathematical astronomy, some of which does have a clear connection to the announced theme of the book: namely, the confutation of deists and libertines (including, in the second volume, Giordano Bruno). Thus Mersenne turns parabolic mirrors to theological account through an analogy between the union of a multiplicity of parallel rays at the focus of such a mirror and the relationship of God's perfect simplicity

---

4. See Lenoble, *Mersenne,* esp. pp. 112–21; Schuster, "Descartes," chap. 3; William L. Hine, "Mersenne and Vanini," *Renaissance Quarterly* 29 (1976), 52–65. Gianni Paganini, "L'anthropologie naturaliste d'un esprit fort," *XVIIᵉ siècle,* no. 149 (1985), 349–77, discusses an underground work of this kind from the early seventeenth century.

5. Mersenne, *Quaestiones in Genesim,* cols. 470, 506–37.

6. Lenoble, *Mersenne,* p. 235.

to the multiplicity of His creatures.[7] Most mathematical material in the work has no such connection, however; there are, for example, many chapters on the determination of astronomical distances and proportions and on the size of the earth, appropriate to a treatise on cosmography but with no real relevance to apologetics. The heading of Volume II, Chapter 26, conveys much of the work's flavor: "To know if the transubstantiation of bread into the body of Jesus Christ, death, and the resurrection can subsist with the universal soul of the world: and what is the distance, the size, and the motion of the planet called Venus and Lucifer."[8] Presumably something inadvertently left out of the astronomical discussions several chapters earlier, the treatment of Venus is pure digression, without even the pretence of any connection to the weighty issues (relating to Bruno's ideas) that accompany it.[9]

Quaestiones and *L'impieté* both exhibit this mixture of arguments from the mathematical sciences deployed in support of orthodoxy, and mathematical material presented apparently for its own sake. Each also contains large amounts of properly theological and scholastic-metaphysical discussion, as well as some more or less peripatetic natural philosophy. Mersenne's strong predilection for mathematical topics considerably overshadows the latter, however, and it dominates his subsequent work *La verité des sciences* (1625). This is in large measure due to the new apologetic target Mersenne had chosen, one only briefly touched on in his previous writings. Richard H. Popkin sees that target, Pyrrhonian scepticism, as the principal philosophical determinant of Mersenne's mature epistemology in that the latter is held to be, before all else, a practical solution to the foundational problems posed by Pyrrhonism.[10]

As much a moral stance as a philosophical position (in common with other Hellenistic schools such as those of the Stoics or Epicureans), Pyrrhonism drew its name from Pyrrho of Elis (c. 360–275 B.C.) but owed its full intellectual development to Aenesidemus in the first century B.C. The scepticism of the Pyrrhonists became known in the sixteenth century primarily through the works of Sextus Empiricus, dating from around 200 A.D.: the *Outlines of Pyrrhonism* and the assaults on various branches of knowledge (including geometry, dialectic, and physics) known collectively as *Adversus mathematicos*. These works were translated and published in Latin in the 1560s and

7. Mersenne, *L'impieté*, 1:414–16.
8. Ibid., 2:450.
9. Ibid., 450–69.
10. Popkin, *History of Scepticism*, esp. chaps. 5–7; Richard H. Popkin, "Father Mersenne's War against Pyrrhonism," *Modern Schoolman* 34 (1956–57), 61–78.

became thereafter widely known, serving as an important source for Montaigne and his followers. The Pyrrhonists attempted to undermine all claims to certain knowledge and to bring about a suspension of judgment on every issue, including the validity of their own position; they refused to be dogmatic even on the question of whether we can know that we know nothing. The ethical function of such antidogmatism was to avoid conflict and disagreement over social and moral issues and thus to promote a calm, contented indifference as the basis for living one's life. In the absence of any reliable criteria for judgment on such matters, the Pyrrhonist should simply obey the customs and laws of his society.[11]

The attractiveness of such a message for Montaigne and others in the France of the later sixteenth century, divided by seemingly irresolvable religious wars, is immediately comprehensible, and Pyrrhonist arguments were seen by some as a basis for the preservation of orthodoxy in religion. But Popkin has shown how this last position, represented most importantly by the tracts of Pierre Charron at the opening of the new century, came under attack from certain orthodox Catholics because its denial of any rational basis for religion could be portrayed as a veiled atheism and conducive to libertine denial of absolute moral standards.[12] In the early 1620s attacks on Pyrrhonism from such an apologetic standpoint increased, as did opposed defenses of Charron's Catholic fideism. This has been seen as part of a general cultural and intellectual "crisis" characterizing the decade in France, and Mersenne's concern in his early publications to defend orthodox and rational theology by destroying the threat of a wide range of deviant philosophies exemplifies the turbulent atmosphere. Confronting Pyrrhonism in *La verité des sciences* formed a part of his overall project.[13]

---

11. On ancient Pyrrhonism, see Popkin, *History of Scepticism*, pp. xiv–xvi; for a more detailed examination of the whole subject, see Charlotte L. Stough, *Greek Scepticism* (Berkeley, 1969). David Sedley, "The Motivation of Greek Skepticism," in Myles Burnyeat, ed., *The Skeptical Tradition* (Berkeley, 1983), pp. 9–29, details the ethical character of ancient scepticism. Ian Mueller, "Geometry and Scepticism," in Jonathan Barnes et al., eds., *Science and Speculation* (Cambridge, 1982), pp. 69–95, provides a philosophical commentary on some of Sextus's arguments against mathematics. On reception in the sixteenth century, see Popkin, *History of Scepticism*, chap. 2; Charles B. Schmitt, "The Recovery and Assimilation of Ancient Scepticism in the Renaissance," *Rivista critica di storia della filosofia* 27 (1972), 363–84 (revised as "The Rediscovery of Ancient Skepticism in Modern Times" in Burnyeat, *Skeptical Tradition*, pp. 225–51). For Montaigne and Pyrrhonism, see Popkin, *History of Scepticism*, chap. 3; and for an interesting alternative interpretation, Zachary S. Schiffman, "Montaigne and the Rise of Skepticism in Early Modern Europe," *Journal of the History of Ideas* 45 (1984), 499–516.

12. Popkin, *History of Scepticism*, chaps. 3–6.

13. Ibid., chaps. 5–6, gives the best general treatment for my purposes; I have also found very useful, as a synthetic account of the situation in the Paris of the 1620s,

Popkin maintains that Mersenne found himself unable to overcome the force of certain basic Pyrrhonist arguments and was obliged in consequence to adopt a pragmatic, operational science of appearances that eschewed dogmatism about the true nature of things.[14] This "mitigated" or "constructive" scepticism, concentrating on the mathematical sciences, underlay Mersenne's approach to natural philosophy for the rest of his career; it is summed up neatly in this passage from the *Questions theologiques* of 1634: "It seems that the capacity of men is limited by the outside and surface of corporeal things, and that they cannot penetrate further than quantity with complete satisfaction. That is why the ancients could not give any demonstration of what appertains to qualities, and restricted themselves to numbers, lines and figures, if one excepts weight, of which Archimedes spoke in his *On the Equilibrium of Planes [Isorropiques]*."[15]

Popkin is undoubtedly correct in identifying Mersenne's attempt to circumvent Pyrrhonism in *La verité* as a crucial factor in the genesis of his epistemological position and its associated natural philosophical agenda, but his account cannot be regarded as a complete explanation. Mersenne wished to defuse what he saw as a Pyrrhonist threat, but his strategy is comprehensible only when, in addition to the character of the arguments he opposed, the conceptual resources on which he drew are considered. Just as the content of Pyrrhonism provided parameters within which its confrontation had to be constrained, so the materials employed against it served to shape the final outcome. An examination of these shows the extent to which Mersenne's thought followed patterns found in the school doctrines he had received from the Jesuits.

Schuster, "Descartes," chap. 3. René Pintard, *Le libertinage érudit dans la première moitié du XVIIe siècle* (Paris, 1943; rpt., Geneva, 1983), is the classic treatment of this subject generally; see also J. S. Spink, *French Free-Thought from Gassendi to Voltaire* (London, 1960), chap. 1. The now very extensive literature on "libertinism" throughout the seventeenth century is discussed, with exhaustive bibliographical notes, by Françoise Charles-Daubert, "Le libertinage et la recherche contemporaine," *XVIIe siècle*, no. 149 (1985), 409–32.

14. Popkin, *History of Scepticism*, pp. 129–41.

15. Marin Mersenne, *Questions theologiques* (Paris, 1634), "Epistre," p. iii. In his first publication, *L'usage de la raison*, Mersenne had commented on the lack of certitude in our knowledge of the natural world: "The greatest [*plus rares*] minds confess ingenuously that they know nothing with evidence and certitude about anything that we see: for whether we consider the heavens, or lower our view to the earth, we are constrained to admit that everything is unknown to us. Natural being, which is the closest to us, and the best proportioned to our senses, is an irreproachable witness to our very great and very profound ignorance, since we don't know the nature of anything either in general or in particular" (dedication, "À Madame la Mareschale de Vitry," [pp. 2–3]).

II

The previous chapter described how Jesuit texts like that of Fonseca reflected the humanist view of dialectic, with its emphasis on persuasive and probabilistic argumentation. The move from demonstrative logic to a Ciceronian *ratio disserendi* represented more than just a preference for the forensic capabilities of rhetoric, however; it also embodied new epistemological assumptions. Lisa Jardine has argued that Rudolf Agricola's foundational *De inventione dialectica* was a realization of the program set out in a work by the influential quattrocento humanist Lorenzo Valla, the *Dialecticae disputationes*. Valla read Cicero's philosophical and oratorical works as complementary aspects of an overall theory of language and knowledge, the philosophical side finding practical exemplification in the rhetorical writings. Together they appeared to Valla to put forward a view of reasoning as a process of persuasion and probable argument within the context of discourse, and the philosophical justification for this came from works like Cicero's *Academica,* one of the major sources in the Renaissance of Academic scepticism.[16]

This, and the other principal sources by which the arguments of the ancient Academy reached the Renaissance, namely Saint Augustine's *Contra Academicos* and Diogenes Laërtius's *Lives of the Philosophers,* portrayed the Academics of the third to the first century B.C. as supporting the position that nothing could be known with certainty, owing to the fallibility of sensory evidence and the inconclusiveness of reasoning processes. Carneades (second century B.C.) was credited with endorsing probabilistic judgment as a substitute for certainty, permitting the justification of practical action on the basis of considered opinion. These doctrines therefore had direct moral implications. Indeed, the major difference between Pyrrhonian and Academic scepticisms, at least as seen in the Renaissance, lay in their respective moral purposes: for the Pyrrhonist, the Academic appeared as just another dogmatist, arrogantly asserting that there is no certainty in anything instead of suspending judgment even on that.[17] Thus Mon-

16. Lisa Jardine, "Lorenzo Valla and the Intellectual Origins of Humanist Dialectic," *Journal of the History of Philosophy* 15 (1977), 143–64 (revised as "Lorenzo Valla: Academic Skepticism and the New Humanist Dialectic" in Burnyeat, *Skeptical Tradition,* pp. 253–86). For a broader treatment of sixteenth-century dialectic, see also L. Jardine, *Bacon,* chap. 1. For a discussion of humanist rhetoric, emphasizing its links with Academic scepticism, see Victoria Kahn, *Rhetoric, Prudence, and Skepticism in the Renaissance* (Ithaca, 1985), chap. 2. Siegel, *Rhetoric,* chap. 1, is a good treatment of Cicero and the Academic aspects of his thought.

17. Popkin, *History of Scepticism,* pp. xiii–xvii and chap. 2; Schmitt, "Recovery and Assimilation," which concentrates esp. on scepticism before the printing of Sextus

taigne, who favored Pyrrhonism, criticized the Academics for allowing probable judgment, which could no more be justified than dogmatic assertion.[18]

Valla therefore understood Cicero's oratory to be a practical consequence of the probabilism set out most notably in the *Academica*,[19] itself drawn from the teachings of the Academy (where Cicero had studied). Valla's view informed Agricola's seminal textbook, and "Ciceronian probabilism," the humanist reading of Cicero's version of Academic scepticism, formed an essential part of the new humanist dialectic.[20] Cicero the orator and jurist, concerned above all with swaying an audience, became the model for the humanist dialectician. The moderate sceptical position that very few issues, if any, could be resolved with demonstrative certainty meant that the syllogism, the form of demonstration central to scholastic logic, had little practical applicability. Humanist dialectic textbooks, in placing a much greater stress on techniques of persuasion and probable argument, therefore promoted an attitude unsympathetic towards dogmatic knowledge claims.[21]

Dialectic was a general art of controlling discourse and hence applicable to all kinds of subject matter, including natural philosophy. Patricia Reif has noted the tendency among early seventeenth-century authors of scholastic philosophy textbooks to weigh conclusions in terms of relative probabilities, the preferred conclusion being presented as "the most probable opinion";[22] she notes: "The prevalence of this mode of argumentation shows the extent to which dialectic has influenced textbook natural philosophy."[23] Melanchthon, one of the leading promoters of humanist dialectic, displays a moderate scepticism in several of his philosophical works, stressing the limits on

---

Empiricus; Schmitt, *Cicero Scepticus*. It is now considered doubtful that Carneades himself endorsed a probabilistic scepticism: cf. Burnyeat's introduction to *Skeptical Tradition*, p. 7n.8, referring to a forthcoming article. This recent argument that, strictly speaking, there was no such thing as Academic scepticism does not affect accounts of Renaissance perceptions of the matter.

18. Popkin, *History of Scepticism*, p. 49.

19. It is present also in *De natura deorum*. Valla drew on other sources as well for his approach: see Letizia A. Panizza, "Lorenzo Valla's *De Vero Falsoque Bono*, Lactantius and Oratorical Scepticism," *Journal of the Warburg and Courtauld Institutes* 41 (1978), 76–107.

20. I take the term from C. J. R. Armstrong, "The Dialectical Road to Truth," in Peter Sharratt, ed., *French Renaissance Studies, 1540–70* (Edinburgh, 1976), p. 49n.33. For an overview of these issues, see also Douglas Lane Patey, *Probability and Literary Form* (Cambridge, 1984). pp. 13–19.

21. See Chapter 2, above.

22. Reif, "Natural Philosophy," pp. 290–94.

23. Ibid., p. 293n.61.

man's potential knowledge of nature: "Even though the nature of things cannot be penetrated by the human mind, yet God wished it to be considered by men so that they should take account of the evidence in it about Him, which shows that there is indeed a God, and what His nature is."[24] The Jesuits too adopted a probabilist stance. Fonseca observed, in his commentary on the *Metaphysics*, the relevance of probabilist discourse to philosophy;[25] and the Coïmbra commentary on Aristotle's logical works (one of a series of commentaries on Aristotle designed for use in the Jesuit colleges) remarked that physics, which concerns the probable material of natural things, cannot rely on a view of dialectic confined to certainty, "for few demonstrations and essential definitions are found in it."[26] Accordingly, when treating the *Physics*, the commentators use the language of probabilities with great frequency and even employ the Ciceronian phrase "in utramque partem," designating the judgmental weighing of both sides of a question. Considering whether the senses perceive substance directly or only accidents, they present both sets of arguments but decline to commit themselves: "And this judgment [*sententia*] is probable on both sides [*in utramque partem*]"—although Aquinas and others did see fit to say that the senses *can* perceive substance.[27] The Conimbricenses are quite prepared to make judgments as long as the status of the conclusion is clear; thus their preference on one question, whether the parts of a thing are distinguished simultaneously with the perception of the whole, is headed "That the controversy seems probable on both sides, the affirmative, however, being truer" (Utranque partem controversia videri probabilem, veriorem tamen affirmativam).[28]

24. See Nicholas Jardine, "The Forging of Modern Realism: Clavius and Kepler against the Sceptics," *Studies in History and Philosophy of Science* 10 (1979), 147–49.

25. Fonseca, *Commentariorum . . . tomi*, 1:525.

26. *Commentarii Collegii Conimbricensis e Societate Iesu: In universam dialecticam Aristotelis Stagiritae* (Cologne, 1607; facsimile rpt., Hildesheim, 1976), 1:29 (hereafter cited as Coïmbra *Dialectic*).

27. *Commentariorum Collegii Conimbricensis Societatis Iesu, in octo libros physicorum Aristotelis Stagiritae . . . tomi* (Cologne, 1596), 1:96 (hereafter cited as Coïmbra *Physics*).

28. Ibid., 1:109. For the special premodern sense of "probability" involved here, see Ian Hacking, *The Emergence of Probability* (Cambridge, 1975), chaps. 1–5; and Patey, *Probability*, chap. 1, which provides an excellent and detailed short treatment. N. Jardine, *Birth*, p. 251, examines Kepler's use of the term *probabilis*, its meanings clustering around such concepts as "acceptability" and "worthiness." The use of "probability" in philosophical, including natural philosophical, discourse was not new in the sixteenth century and cannot be attributed entirely to the impact of humanist dialectic; the difference is one of emphasis. Scholastic philosophers of whatever stripe had never regarded the achievement of true scientific (that is, necessary) demonstration in natural philosophy as an easy task. See William A. Wallace, "The Certitude of Science in Late Medieval and Renaissance Thought," *History of Philosophy Quarterly* 3 (1986), 281–91.

All this conformed with other aspects of Jesuit thought. The ethical theory of probabilism, notorious for its portrayal in Blaise Pascal's *Provincial Letters,* held that an action is morally justified as long as it can be supported by a "probable opinion" (*opinio probabilis*). An opinion is probable if it is held by an authority of weight (such as Saint Thomas Aquinas), regardless of the conflicting judgments of many others; furthermore, if one is a person of "learning and uprightness," then for one's own guidance an opinion is "assuredly probable" if one is "conscious of having thought it out diligently."[29] Probabilism thus compensated for the absence of criteria of certainty. The importance of avoiding dogmatism—though this is not the place to consider the reasons for Jesuit insistence on the point—led a sixteenth-century teaching guideline to recommend that masters in the colleges ought "not to conjecture boldly overmuch, but to realize that one can deceive oneself, and to judge and speak with humility."[30] The attitudes represented by humanist dialectic shaped the whole of Jesuit pedagogy, and they formed the background to Mersenne's reconsideration of natural philosophical priorities.

Several of the discussions in *Quaestiones in Genesim* clearly employ Ciceronian probabilism, and an understanding of that fact helps to reveal the nature of Mersenne's subsequent stance against Pyrrhonism. Near the beginning of the work Mersenne lists thirty-six different reasons for believing in the existence of God, each of which is subsequently discussed at some length.[31] As Lenoble comments, Mersenne is trying to make a sale rather than provide a demonstration.[32] The point, of course, is that had Mersenne regarded any of these arguments as demonstratively certain, he would not have had to give thirty-six of them. Every one is *probable*—that is, has authority behind it—so that even though there are inconsistencies between

---

29. For fairly straightforward accounts of probabilism, see Hacking, *Emergence of Probability,* pp. 23–24; and W. C. Cartwright, *The Jesuits* (London, 1876), pp. 149–52 (quotations are from the latter, p. 150).

30. *Monumenta Paedagogica Societatis Iesu quae Primam Rationem Studiorum anno 1586 praecessere* (Madrid, 1901), p. 486. See also the quotation concerning the value of disputation for teaching given in Dainville, *Naissance,* p. 137. The possibility of a relationship between probabilism in Jesuit natural philosophy and probabilism in Jesuit moral philosophy is noted in William B. Ashworth, Jr., "Catholicism and Early Modern Science," in David C. Lindberg and Ronald L. Numbers, eds., *God and Nature* (Berkeley, 1986), pp. 157–58. Wallace, "Certitude of Science," sees the theological disputes of the Counter-Reformation, both within and between Catholic orders, as encouraging probabilism in theology and moral philosophy to avoid rifts; he suggests that this carried directly over into natural philosophy and cites late sixteenth-century Jesuit philosophers of the Collegio Romano on cosmology and the physics of projectile motion.

31. Mersenne, *Quaestiones,* cols. 25–26.

32. Lenoble, *Mersenne,* p. 247.

them, they all have complementary persuasive value because they all argue for the same conclusion.[33]

Mersenne's approach to astronomical and cosmological matters in *Quaestiones* also betrays the influence of probabilism. William Hine has taken issue with Lenoble and others over whether Mersenne here rejected Copernicanism or merely considered both sides and declined to commit himself.[34] Hine takes the second alternative, but in fact, the nature of Mersenne's discussion seems to lie somewhere in the middle. While Mersenne says, time and again, that many such issues cannot be decided with certainty, he does not suspend judgment; instead he makes *probable* judgments.

He had discussed the issue of making probable judgments in his earliest work, *L'usage de la raison* (1623), with specific reference to cosmological issues. If a particular question, such as whether the sun moves around the earth or vice versa, cannot be settled by evident reasons, he says, it might seem that one could simply choose freely which to believe or else suspend judgment entirely.[35] He clearly finds both alternatives unattractive.

> It is necessary, however, that the understanding have some probable reason in order to judge something false or true [*veritable*]; otherwise the will would command the understanding in vain [*autrement la volonté auroit beau commander, ce seroit en vain*]; as, for example, if the will commanded it to judge and conclude that the heavens were solid, and it had no reason however little probable for that conclusion, it could not do it, for it would have no grounds of truth. . . . Whence it follows that [the understanding] will never conclude that the heavens are liquid, or solid, if it has no reason which renders that truth believable to it.[36]

When he addressed this same issue in *Quaestiones*, Mersenne considered that reasons did indeed exist for making a probable judgment. He comments that when "we consider that controversy about the solidity of the heavens, at length it is to be pronounced what, among all the obscurity, is the most probable."[37] This, he continues, is primarily a job for reason, insofar as scripture is not clear on the matter. After considering the paths of the sun and planets, the nature of their epicycles and deferents, and so forth, he presents his "first conclusion: every heaven [i.e., sphere] in which the stars seem to be moved

---

33. Lenoble (ibid., p. 252) notes that Anselm's proof is included as well as one from Aquinas, even though Aquinas had rejected the former.

34. William L. Hine, "Mersenne and Copernicanism," *Isis* 64 (1973), 18–32.

35. Mersenne, *L'usage de la raison*, pp. 144–45.

36. Ibid., pp. 145–46.

37. Mersenne, *Quaestiones*, col. 841.

seems to me not improbably to be fluid, of the likeness of air, of which the parts unite steadily when the stars pass from place to place by their own motion."[38] The "first conclusion" is not, then, the last word on the matter; it is merely "not improbable." Having next discussed the fixed stars, Mersenne gives his "second conclusion": "It seems to be most probable that the eighth sphere, in which the [fixed] stars reside, is solid, and neither is it absurd if we retain the solidity of the remaining spheres of the planets."[39] The source of probability regarding the solidity of the eighth sphere is the authority of the Bible,[40] since reason has left the question open. As for the planetary spheres, Mersenne can decide that it would not be "absurd" to retain their solidity even though he has previously placed the weight of probability on their being fluid: no firm decision is called for.

Later on, when giving the full text of the decree of 1616 against Copernicanism, Mersenne does not present it as a definitive condemnation.[41] His sceptical, or probabilist, attitude towards astronomical hypotheses in general, however, leads him to accept geocentrism through weight of probability, and the Church's authority is a factor in that judgment. That his was indeed a probabilistic and not a fideistic acceptance of geocentrism[42] is indicated by his remarks concerning "the Ptolemaic hypotheses, which I am scarcely bound to follow; it is, in fact, enough that by some other probable hypotheses we at least save all the phenomena."[43] This attitude never changed throughout Mersenne's career, although for him the weight of probability did shift towards Copernicus.[44] The next year, in *L'impieté des deistes*, he

---

38. Ibid., col. 843.

39. Ibid., col. 845. On the solidity of the heavens in sixteenth- and seventeenth-century thought, see Nicholas Jardine, "The Significance of the Copernican Orbs," *Journal for the History of Astronomy* 13 (1982), 168–94; and esp. William H. Donahue, *The Dissolution of the Celestial Spheres 1595–1650* (New York, 1981). Wallace, "Certitude of Science," pp. 287–88, quotes late-sixteenth-century Jesuit philosophers on the constitution of the heavens (in discussions of *De caelo*), and these writers exhibit exactly the same kinds of forms of expression as those we have quoted from Mersenne.

40. Mersenne, *Quaestiones*, col. 845.

41. Ibid., col. 904; see also col. 919.

42. Nicholas Jardine characterizes the prevalent sixteenth-century attitude towards astronomical hypotheses, evidenced by such as Osiander or Ursus, as probabilistic, *contra* Duhem's "instrumentalism": see N. Jardine, "Forging of Modern Realism," pp. 144, 149, and passim; idem, *Birth*, chap. 7; idem, "Scepticism in Renaissance Astronomy: A Preliminary Study," in C. B. Schmitt and R. H. Popkin, eds., *Skepticism from the Renaissance to the Enlightenment* (Wolfenbüttel, forthcoming). The latter two pieces, however, esp. the last, involve significant qualifications to the first.

43. Mersenne, *Quaestiones*, col. 917. Throughout this discussion it is important to bear in mind the complicating factor of the distinction between cosmological (i.e., physical) and astronomical questions. Geocentrism, of course, straddles the two.

44. Hine, "Mersenne and Copernicanism"; Lenoble, *Mersenne*, pp. 394–97; Armand Beaulieu, "Les réactions des savants français au début du XVIIe siècle devant l'hélio-

concluded a discussion of Copernicanism by saying that we cannot tell whether it is true or not, advising that it would be better to confess our ignorance on the subject.[45] He scrupulously avoided dogmatic adherence to propositions amenable only to probable judgment.

Probabilistic arguments had the disadvantage, however, of being inadequate counters against Pyrrhonism. Mersenne had already announced his intention to combat the Pyrrhonists in *Quaestiones*,[46] and clues to the structure of his strategy in *La verité* begin to emerge from his treatment of dialectic in that earlier work. *Quaestiones* contains a large table, covering the equivalent of two folio pages: down the left-hand side is a list of the principal divisions of knowledge from theology (at the top) to "artes"—such matters as agriculture—with each major category subdivided to yield a neat total of one hundred subjects; on the right-hand side appear the names of the best authors, ancient and modern, in each.[47] The various mathematical and mechanical disciplines take up most of the space, but it is the eleventh category, "scientia sermocinalis," that contains something of a surprise:[48]

		Grammatica
XI.	Scientia	Rethorica
	Sermocinalis	Dialectica
		Logica
		Poetica

In distinguishing between dialectic and logic, Mersenne here deviates from generally accepted usage, including that of the Jesuits from whom he had originally learned the terms. We saw in the previous chapter that Fonseca described "dialectic" and "logic" as equivalent terms, and in this he adhered to an absolutely orthodox position. All through the Middle Ages they had usually been interchangeable; hu-

---

centrisme de Galilée," in Paolo Galluzzi, ed., *Novità Celesti e Crisi del Sapere* (Supplement, *Annali dell'Istituto e Museo di Storia della Scienza*, 1983, fasc. 2), pp. 373–81. Beaulieu characterizes the attitudes of Mersenne's correspondents such as Gassendi and Roberval as similarly tentative. See also Frederick J. Baumgartner, "Scepticism and French Interest in Copernicanism to 1630," *Journal for the History of Astronomy* 17 (1986), 77–88.

45. Mersenne, *L'impieté*, 2:200–201.

46. Mersenne, *Quaestiones*, cols. 909–10.

47. Ibid., cols. 1205–10.

48. Ibid., cols. 1209–10. The bracketing of all these subjects under "scientia sermocinalis" is typical humanist practice; see E. J. Ashworth, *Language and Logic in the Post-Medieval Period* (Dordrecht, 1974), pp. 32–33. The grouping is effectively that of the trivium with the addition of poetics: on the career of such classifications see Paul Oskar Kristeller, "The Modern System of the Arts," in *Renaissance Thought and the Arts* (Princeton, 1980), pp. 163–227, esp. 163–89.

manist dialectic, intended to supplant or absorb scholastic logic, retained the identity.[49] Ramist dialectic textbooks began with some such definition as "Logick is an Art of reasoning well. It is also called Dialectick."[50] And even in a late-sixteenth-century work of moral guidance by Pierre de la Primaudaye, translated into English as *The French Academy*, one reads of "Dialectike or Logicke, which is to learn the truth of althings by disputation."[51]

What Mersenne had in mind is made clear in the discussion of the sciences that precedes the table. After dealing with mathematics and mechanics, he continues: "There remain other sciences with which we ought especially to deal in relation to the others: dialectic, for example, supplies the ability to arrange in order [i.e., for the purposes of discussion] and the material to be discoursed of;[52] logic supplies the forms of argumentation: the former deals with probable subject matter, the latter with syllogisms."[53] Dialectic as Mersenne had learned it dealt with probable matters and persuasion, and while humanist dialecticians themselves had cheerfully admitted that syllogistic logic could provide rigorous demonstration, they had not seen fit to grant it a separate status. Mersenne describes dialectic as Soarez did with respect to rhetoric; it is made up of *inventio* and *dispositio*, as the Ramists also taught.[54] Mersenne views both "dialectic" and "logic" as parts of discourse, and while syllogisms could provide rigor in the arguments made therein, the subject matter—and thus the conclusions—remained only probable.

Since Mersenne regarded "dialectic" and "logic" as concerned with the same overall enterprise, his motive for separating them termi-

49. On the medieval period, see Heath, "Logical Grammar," p. 46n.157; on humanist practice, Rita Guerlac, *Juan Luis Vives against the Pseudodialecticians* (Dordrecht, 1979), p. 31. Franciscus Toletus at least matched Fonseca among the most prominent Jesuit authors of dialectic textbooks; I have consulted the following edition: *Introductio in dialecticam Aristotelis, libri quinque* (Rome, 1601). Bk. 1, chap. 1, "De nomine dialecticae," considers the etymologies of "dialectic" and "logic" and concludes that whatever distinctions might be made between them, "it has now . . . been commonly accepted that whenever 'logic' is talked of, it is understood as the same as 'dialectic'" (p. 5).

50. Wotton, *The Art of Logick . . . by Peter Ramus*, p. 1.

51. Peter de la Primaudaye, *The French Academy*, trans. T.B. (London, 1602), p. 72.

52. The verb is *disserere*; for Ramus, this term was interchangeable with *disputare*: Ong, *Ramus*, pp. 179–80. The usual translation, retaining the breadth of meaning, is "to discourse."

53. Mersenne, *Quaestiones*, col. 1206. This distinction is different from Aristotle's in *Topics* I.1, where "dialectic" and "demonstration" are distinguished solely by virtue of the certainty of the *premises* of the argument. Aristotle's distinction did not inform medieval usage of the terms "dialectic" and "logic" (see n. 49, above), and in any case Aristotle himself did not always make it, as Fonseca pointed out (*Institutiones*, p. 10). On Aristotle and demonstration, see also G. E. R. Lloyd, *Magic, Reason and Experience* (Cambridge, 1979), chap. 2.

54. See Chapter 2, above.

nologically deserves attention. In effect, he put the syllogism in a class by itself because of its demonstrative properties; clearly, then, certain demonstration was of special interest to him. Descartes later made a similar distinction for similar reasons—but only when pressed. His natural tendency to speak of logic and dialectic indifferently had led him to assert, in the *Discourse on Method,* that "in logic, its syllogisms and most of its other rules serve to explain to others the things one already knows—and even, in the art of Lull, to speak with apparent authority about things of which one is ignorant—rather than to learn them."[55] When queried by Burman on this remark, however, Descartes availed himself of the unusual distinction found in Mersenne: "This [objection] really applies not so much to Logic, which provides demonstrative proofs on all subjects, but to Dialectic, which teaches us how to hold forth on all subjects. In this way it undermines good sense, rather than builds on it. For in diverting our attention and making us digress into the stock arguments and headings, which are irrelevant to the matter under discussion, it diverts us from the actual nature of the thing itself."[56] Distinguishing syllogistic logic from dialectic, it appears, was a means of recognizing certain demonstration as a particularly desirable goal. Mersenne's assault on Pyrrhonism in *La verité des sciences* necessarily employed just such an evaluation.

As the case of the syllogism indicates, the Ciceronian probabilism underpinning humanist dialectic did not extend its denial of certainty to all forms of knowledge; it was not the same as the Academic scepticism reflected in Cicero. There were, in fact, three commonly accepted sources of certain knowledge, all of which can be found in Saint Augustine's *Contra Academicos.*[57] Augustine's dialogue, itself a major source in the Renaissance for knowledge of Academic scepticism,[58] attempted to moderate sceptical claims but did so by putting forward a position itself conducive to a mild scepticism in philosophy and consonant with Valla's interpretation of Cicero. The chief sources of certainty proposed by Augustine appear, for example, in Melanchthon, following his statement of the limits of human knowledge quoted earlier. Leaving aside revelation, we can, first, acquire knowledge of corporeal bodies through application of the senses to their proper objects under normal circumstances: thus we know that fire is

---

55. Quoted in Desmond Clarke, *Descartes' Philosophy of Science* (Manchester, 1982), p. 63.

56. Quoted in ibid., p. 64.

57. N. Jardine, "Forging of Modern Realism," p. 147n.20. For an excellent discussion of Augustine's treatise, see Alven Michael Neiman, "The Arguments of Augustine's *Contra Academicos,*" *Modern Schoolman* 59 (1982), 255–79.

58. See references in n. 17, above. Fonseca (*Institutiones,* p. 10) cites Augustine's *Contra Academicos* in connection with describing dialectic as a "doctrina disserendi."

hot. Secondly, we can know mathematical truths and "common axioms" such as "the whole is greater than its proper part." The final source of certain knowledge lies in grasp of syllogistic form.[59] Nicholas Jardine observes that Melanchthon's position represents "the widespread moderate sceptical stance promoted by the humanist dialecticians,"[60] and it is found equally in Jesuit authors.

Jesuits never, of course, questioned the validity of the syllogism. An instance of their endorsement of ordinary sense perception occurs in the Coïmbra commentary on the *Physics*. In the course of arguing against the Academic sceptics, the commentators cite Augustine's classic response from *Contra Academicos*—that if one doubts, then at least one knows that one doubts ("si fallor, sum"). They then turn to a defense of sensory cognition. The senses, they say, cannot err

> concerning a proper sensible which has been observed according to the common way [i.e., normally]. If it then happens that sometimes they do err, they are often corrected by the intellect, which, although it has by nature no inborn ideas or knowledge, has, however, imparted light by which it assents to the most common principles without any danger of error or rashness and by which it deduces through inference [*ratiocinando deducat*] some things from others, sometimes clearly and certainly, sometimes probably; also sometimes it perceives and intuits something without discourse [i.e., directly].[61]

The commentators cite as a basis for their discussion of the senses Aristotle's *De anima*. The "common principles" to which they refer are the same as Melanchthon's "common axioms"; like him, and like Aristotle, they have in mind self-evident truths for which the model lay in geometry—what Euclid called "common opinions."[62]

No Jesuit author emphasized the certainty of mathematics more than Christopher Clavius, who did so as part of his successful campaign to install the subject as an important element of Jesuit pedagogy.[63] Clavius exploited the generally accepted conclusiveness of mathematical demonstration to enhance the status of the knowledge it produced: "Truly, if the nobility and preeminence of a science be judged by the certainty of the demonstrations that it uses, there is no

59. N. Jardine, "Forging of Modern Realism," pp. 147–49.

60. Ibid., p. 149.

61. Coïmbra *Physics*, 1:25. The doubts cast by the Academics on the reliability of the senses are also explicitly countered in, e.g., the Jesuit work on optics by Franciscus Aguilonius, *Opticorum libri sex* (Antwerp, 1613), pp. 215–16.

62. See Lloyd, *Magic, Reason and Experience*, p. 111.

63. See Peter Dear, "Jesuit Mathematical Science and the Reconstitution of Experience in the Early Seventeenth Century," *Studies in History and Philosophy of Science* 18 (June 1987).

doubt that the mathematical disciplines will have the first place among all the rest. For they demonstrate and confirm everything concerning which they undertake disputation by the firmest reasons, so that they truly produce knowledge [*scientiam*] in the soul of the hearers and, in short, remove all doubt."[64] Clavius praises mathematics by describing the character of its "disputations"; his object is to bring home the contrast with the inconclusiveness of other branches of knowledge, which can strive only to persuade. Mathematics removes doubt in a way that

> we can scarcely concede to other disciplines, since in those the mind, in judging the truth of conclusions, very often remains suspended and uncertain with a multitude of beliefs and a variety of opinions. All the sects of the Peripatetics (although, however, I implicitly include other philosophers) are clearly convinced of these things, which [have] arisen from Aristotle as if branches from some trunk; they differ among themselves, and sometimes from the source, Aristotle himself, so that, in short, the person who does not know [*ignores*] what Aristotle might mean, whether concerning names or things, preferably institutes a disputation. . . . How far this is from mathematical demonstrations I think is concealed from no one. For the theorems of Euclid, and of the other mathematicians, retain today in learned discussions [*in scholis*] the same purity of truth, the same certitude of things, and the same strength and firmness of demonstrations as ever before.[65]

A little later Clavius contrasts mathematics with dialectic: "For in dialectical problems, whichever side of a contradiction has been taken up, it is confirmed only probably, so that the intellect is in doubt of it, whichever side of it be true"—whereas in mathematics, "whichever side anyone will have chosen, he will prove it by firm demonstration, so that nothing at all is left doubtful."[66]

Clavius's assault on his philosophical colleagues would scarcely have received their wholehearted endorsement, because they evidently placed a lower premium on absolute demonstrative certainty. But though they might have disagreed with his evaluations, his characterization of mathematical certitude was an accepted commonplace. The cluster of attitudes represented by humanist dialectic, Ciceronian probabilism, and the restricted areas of certain knowledge admitted by the latter, provided the framework for Mersenne's response to the

64. Christopher Clavius, *Operum mathematicorum tomus primus* (Mainz, 1611), "Prolegomena," p. 5.
65. Ibid.
66. Ibid., p. 8.

challenge of Pyrrhonism. He did not merely acquiesce in them, however; he used them.

Removing the syllogism from the province of probabilist dialectic was a significant move in Mersenne's strategy. It indicates his intention to cordon off certainty as an especially important quality clearly distinguished from the merely probable. We have seen Melanchthon and Jesuit authors respond similarly when confronting Academic scepticism; however, Mersenne's concern with certainty, the theme of *La verité des sciences,* arose from the threat of Pyrrhonism. Pyrrhonism denied the possibility of any kind of reliable knowledge, not only ruling out probable judgments but also rejecting the idea that mathematics or syllogistic logic could achieve certain demonstration. Judgment was to be suspended on *all* matters. In opposing Pyrrhonism, therefore, Mersenne determined to emphasize those things which humanist dialectic tended to play down—namely, demonstrative arguments—and leave aside probability as far as possible, owing to its greater vulnerability to Pyrrhonian scepticism. It was common in this period to see mathematics and syllogistic logic as essentially identical forms of reasoning (Clavius, for example, had made an attempt to reduce Book I of Euclid's *Elements* to syllogistic form).[67] Since both relied for the truth of their conclusions on the truth of the premises with which they started (Francis Bacon saw this as a fatal shortcoming and rejected the syllogism in favor of induction),[68] Mersenne had the problem of justifying the premises on which syllogisms were to be built and the data to be mathematically treated. He could not adopt Aristotle's solution, since that relied on knowing the inner natures of things through its theory of perception and the induction of specific natures.[69] Mersenne, working from the basis of Ciceronian probabilism and aware that such knowledge was hardly immune to sceptical doubt, attempted to formulate an alternative out of the three sources of certainty admitted by the schools.

In *La verité des sciences,* the Sceptic argues against the possibility of knowing essences. Aristotelian physics aimed at providing necessary causal explanations of properties and change through deduction from essential definitions; an essential definition revealed a thing's essential properties, and those properties explained its behavior under specified circumstances. Thus, for example, the element earth, because it possesses the essential property of gravity, will necessarily descend when it is removed from the center of the universe and left

67. Neal W. Gilbert, *Renaissance Concepts of Method* (New York, 1960), p. 90. The identification was not universally accepted, however; see Chapter 4, below.
68. L. Jardine, *Bacon,* chap. 4.
69. Aristotle *Posterior Analytics* I.24, II.19.

unimpeded. But if essences were unknowable, Aristotelian natural philosophy became unworkable. Because Mersenne could have defended it only on a probabilistic basis, he in effect abandoned it in order to ward off scepticism from more solid ground. Accordingly, the Christian Philosopher answers the Sceptic's objection to essentialism by saying that it "does not demonstrate that we know nothing; everything that you have brought against Aristotle shows only that we don't know the final differences between individuals, and between species, and that the understanding doesn't at all penetrate substance except through accidents[70] . . . now, this small amount of knowledge [*science*] suffices to serve us as a guide in our actions."[71]

As for the Sceptic's claim that to achieve true knowledge of a piece of paper one must know all the particulars of its composition, past history, and everything else connected with it in whatever way, the Christian Philosopher brushes it aside: "That would be necessary to know it perfectly as God knows it: it's enough, in order to have certain knowledge [*avoir la science*] of something, to know its effects, its operations, and its use, by which we distinguish it from all other individuals or species: we don't want to attribute to ourselves a greater or more particular science than that."[72] He then rehearses, for the Pyrrhonist's benefit, the standard arguments about the unreliability of the senses.[73]

Mersenne's admission of the unattainability of essential knowledge therefore relied on being able to identify alternative sources of knowledge regarding appearances and effects. Mersenne had them readily to hand. "Each sense is the judge of its own objects," asserts the Christian Philosopher, "the eye of light and colors, the ear of sounds, and similarly for the others." Each "must have everything requisite to its nature, and to the perfection of its operation, in order to judge its object well, for given that, it never errs." Deception of the senses, furthermore, can be avoided by the coordination of data from several senses at once by the exercise of the (perfectly Aristotelian) common sense, which "is above the exterior senses, and their operations lead to it like lines from the circumference terminating at the center, so that it can judge the sensible difference between color, sound, odor, and the other objects of the external senses." The understanding then sets

70. Cf. the remarks in Coïmbra *Physics*, text to n. 27, above.
71. Mersenne, *La verité*, pp. 13–14.
72. Ibid., pp. 14–15.
73. Ibid., pp. 15–18. Mersenne's interest in making positive use of scepticism against certain opponents while denying the efficacy of its arguments against his own favored forms of knowledge appears in his employment of the Sceptic against an Alchemist, who appears only in *La verité*'s first book; the Christian Philosopher acquiesces in the sceptical undermining of this third protagonist's position.

to work on the results.[74] Melanchthon, in setting out the same standard view, had said that though the senses might deceive, no one could deny that fire is hot. Mersenne put it more vigorously: if all the men on earth were asked whether fire was hot, they would say it was "and would burn those who doubted it, so that the heat would draw forth witness of the truth from their senses and their mind."[75]

The certainty of mathematics is the chief theme of *La verité*, the bulk of the work consisting of a presentation of undeniable mathematical truths as an antidote to Pyrrhonism; as a natural corollary Mersenne also adduced the certainty of "common axioms," choosing as his examples "it is impossible for the same thing to be and not be," and "what one says of a thing of which one speaks is true or false."[76] In such mathematical sciences as optics the certainty of ordinary sense perception thus combined with that of mathematics to provide a paradigm of a reliable science of appearances. As for the third orthodox source of certainty, the syllogism, its importance as a coordinator of true statements led Mersenne to distinguish it sharply from dialectic. The Christian Philosopher defends it against the criticisms of the Sceptic and recommends Aristotle's logical works for further enlightenment on the subject.[77]

Such, then, is the basic structure of what Popkin has called "mitigated scepticism." The position Mersenne puts forward as a bulwark against scepticism is not so much a watered-down Pyrrhonism—accepting its arguments against essentialism but finding pragmatic alternatives to that ideal—so much as a modified Ciceronian probabilism directed towards context-dependent goals. None of the elements of Mersenne's positive natural philosophical program was novel; he simply took the validity of orthodox views for granted and exploited those forms of knowledge usually maintained as certain, doing so in a manner similar to that of contemporary scholastic antisceptical strategies with which he would have been familiar. His innovation lay in his playing down of probable knowledge, and this may be partly attributed to his concern to refute the especially radical Pyrrhonian form of scepticism rather than the Academic form targeted by, for example, the Coïmbra commentators.

Probabilism does appear in *La verité*, however. Speaking of metaphysics and physics as disciplines which consider things "absolutely, without having regard to this or that,"[78] the Christian Philosopher

74. Ibid., p. 191.
75. Ibid., p. 192.
76. Ibid., pp. 52, 53.
77. Ibid., pp. 194–205.
78. Ibid., p. 51.

comments that physics "seems to be the most doubtful" of such disciplines.[79] He also makes some attempts to defend the use of Aristotle in the schools and to counter charges of slavish adherence to his doctrines: of course one must disagree with him on some points, he says—such as on whether the world is eternal—because the fact is that (as a marginal gloss puts it) some "principles of Aristotle" are "more probable than others."[80] Mersenne defended Aristotle in *La verité* not because he believed all his teachings to be true but because he found them at that time the most persuasive and probable. If it should please God to send someone more perceptive than Aristotle, says the Christian Philosopher, so be it, "but in the meantime, I am of the opinion that we should make use of Aristotle's doctrine, particularly in those places and parts that are received by all the learned and followed by them by common consent: as for other places, which are in dispute, each may follow whatever he judges most likely [*veritable*] and which is supported by the best reasons."[81]

III

Mersenne was soon to abandon Aristotle and essentialist physics altogether in favor of that vision of an operational science of appearances which formed his reply to Pyrrhonism and also, by no means accidentally, coincided with the predilection for applied mathematics seen in his earlier works. Later, freed from the immediate task of opposing Pyrrhonism, he permitted himself to admit that even the mathematical sciences of appearances, such as optics and music, could not be absolutely certain, because they necessarily made use of assumptions about the physical nature and properties of light and sound.[82] (In *La verité* such points were largely evaded for strategic reasons.)[83] But these kinds of mathematical sciences had the compensating advantage of practical applicability: "It is certain that the artisan must have an idea in order to effect his work, or he would never succeed in it";[84] being able to do something is itself proof of genuine

79. Ibid., p. 54. Nine years later, in *Questions harmoniques* (Paris, 1634), pp. 202–3, Mersenne does not even mention the possibility of "absolute" knowledge of this kind; he concentrates only on the mathematical coordination of appearances.

80. Mersenne, *La verité*, p. 125 (marginal gloss).

81. Ibid., p. 110.

82. Mersenne, *Questions theologiques*, pp. 179–82. See also Lenoble, *Mersenne*, p. 354.

83. E.g., Mersenne sometimes adopts the tactic of saying that mathematical truths are certain *whether or not* they are realized in nature: see *La verité*, p. 277.

84. Ibid., p. 14. On the ubiquity of this theme in the Renaissance, see Alistair C. Crombie, "Science and the Arts in the Renaissance," in John W. Shirley and F. David Hoeniger, eds., *Science and the Arts in the Renaissance* (London, 1985), pp. 15–26.

knowledge. Arguing in *L'usage de la raison* for the importance of putting theoretical knowledge to practical use, Mersenne cited mathematics: "Archimedes, Proclus, Hero, and many excellent geometers . . . have shown us how much the usage of the liberal arts and speculative sciences is excellent and admirable. And truly there is no reason to defend that usage if it isn't that it causes the loss, or diminishes the truth, of the theory; but since it rather proves and confirms it, [then] the visible work assures us of the invisible, which is the idea and the prototype."[85]

The utility of mathematics provided an important sub-theme in Mersenne's anti-Pyrrhonian arguments, because although a Pyrrhonist might undermine theoretical knowledge on philosophical grounds, there was little point in denying the practical value of operational knowledge. The Christian Philosopher tries to persuade the Sceptic that unity is a number, then finally acknowledges that many people disagree about it and tells his adversary to "follow what you please in this matter, for it's of very little importance"; the decision makes no practical difference to unity's function in arithmetic.[86] This concern with operational rather than speculative considerations reappears more strongly when the Christian Philosopher observes that "many people are astonished as to how it's possible that − multiplied by −, that is, *less* by *less*, makes + . . . which seems to be against every kind of reason." He responds by simply brushing the question aside: those exist who deny the proposition, but "I won't detain myself any longer, in order to make you see the fruit that can be drawn from those things we've said up to now about practical arithmetic."[87]

Mersenne's tactic employed well-established arguments. During the sixteenth century, emphasis on the practical "fruit" of mathematics had become a minor commonplace of humanist educational reform. Juan Luis Vives extolled the benefits of teaching geometry in this way:

> From geometry are developed optics or perspective, and architecture, and the art of measurement, all of which have great usefulness in ordinary life for protecting our bodies; for from geometry we proceed to all measurement, proportion, movement and position of heavy weights, whether regarded as moveable or fixed at the moment, or as immoveable. Then follows the study how to measure fields, mountains, towers and buildings. How great comfort does architecture bring to us in our

---

85. Mersenne, *L'usage de la raison*, pp. 243–44.
86. Mersenne, *La verité*, p. 284.
87. Ibid., pp. 521–22.

dwellings! How greatly perspective assists in the observation of pictures! Optics further gives the theory of the mirror: would that a theory of hearing [*auditiva*] had been discovered.[88]

Vives also retails the story of Plato forbidding all those ignorant of geometry to enter his Academy,[89] as did almost everyone in this period who engaged in such eulogies to mathematics. Petrus Ramus used arguments very similar to those of Vives when he agitated for reforms at the University of Paris designed to restore mathematics to what he regarded as its rightful place in the curriculum.[90] John Dee, in his 1570 *Preface* to Billingsley's translation of Euclid's *Elements*, aimed to bring forth "evident testimony of the use, proffit and Commodity of Arithmetike vulgar, in the Common lyfe and trade of men";[91] he points to its value for goldsmiths, leaders in battle (examples also chosen by Ramus), physicians, and lawyers.[92] The essay as a whole constitutes a survey of the various branches of mathematics, the bulk of which are practical.

In the sixteenth century these arguments for the utility of mathematics became part of a general revaluing of the subject, buttressed by the claims of Melanchthon, Sturm, and other German humanists that it was necessary for a complete understanding of Aristotle.[93] Not surprisingly, therefore, the Jesuits, in their largely successful efforts to maintain the foremost position in contemporary education, kept up with the trend. In 1556, for example, the program of studies at the college of Tournon devoted six months to the study of the astrolabe and the theory of the planets.[94] The *Ratio studiorum* of 1586 argued the case for mathematics, using what were by then well-tried tactics.

[Mathematics] teaches poets about the rising and setting of the stars; teaches historians the situation and distances of various places; teaches

88. Vives, *De tradendis disciplinis*, bk. 4, chap. 5 (Watson, *Vives: On Education*, p. 204).

89. Ibid.; Watson, p. 203.

90. See R. Hooykaas, *Humanisme, science et réforme: Pierre de la Ramée (1515–1572)* (Leiden, 1958), pp. 84–90; on Ramus and general university reform, see Peter Sharratt, "Peter Ramus and the Reform of the University," in Sharratt, *French Renaissance Studies*, pp. 4–20. Melanchthon commented at about this time on the ease with which young Germans trained in mathematics could find jobs in France; the French were accused of having to steal the mathematical textbooks of Italy and Germany: Jean-Claude Margolin, "L'enseignment des mathématiques en France (1540–70)," in Sharratt, *French Renaissance Studies*, pp. 109–55, esp. 112.

91. John Dee, *The Mathematicall Preface to the Elements of Geometrie of Euclid of Megara* (1570), intro. Allen G. Debus (New York, 1975), [p. 6].

92. Ibid., [pp. 7–12].

93. Gilbert, *Renaissance Concepts*, p. 84.

94. François de Dainville, "Foyers de culture scientifique dans la France méditerranéenne du XVIe au XVIIIe siècle," *Revue d'histoire des sciences* 1 (1948), 290.

logicians [? *analytici*] examples of solid demonstrations; teaches politicians truly admirable methods for conducting affairs at home and during war; teaches physicists the manners and diversity of celestial movements, of light, of colors, of diaphanous bodies, of sounds; teaches metaphysicians the number of the spheres and intelligences; teaches theologians the principal parts of the divine creation; teaches jurists and canonists calendrical computation, not to speak of the services rendered by the work of mathematicians to the state, to medicine, to navigation, and to agriculture. An effort must therefore be made so that mathematics will flourish in our colleges as well as the other disciplines.[95]

Very similar points were made by Clavius in a document on educational policy also dating from the 1580s. Claiming that the major problem to be faced was lack of interest on the part of both teachers and pupils, he insisted that the latter needed to be persuaded of "the utility and necessity of these mathematical disciplines" and should be shown that "philosophy and the mathematical sciences are joined, as indeed they are"; the former, meanwhile, must be prevented from criticizing mathematics as being of no value.[96] Listing those things for which mathematics is essential, Clavius argues for its importance in philosophy:

> Physics cannot be understood correctly without [the mathematical disciplines], especially what pertains to that part concerning the number and motion of the celestial orbs, of the multitude of intelligences, of the effects of the stars, which depend on the various conjunctions, oppositions and other distances between them, of the division of continuous quantities to infinity, of the tides, of the winds, of comets, the rainbow, haloes, and other meteorological matters, of the proportion of motions, qualities, actions, passions, reactions etc., concerning which the *calculatores*[97] wrote much. I omit an infinity of examples in Aristotle, Plato, and their most illustrious interpreters which can in no way be understood without some knowledge of the mathematical sciences.[98]

By the early seventeenth century, therefore, the common wisdom was well established in the Jesuit curriculum that mathematics should

95. *Ratio studiorum et institutiones scholasticae Societatis Iesu per Germaniam olim vigentes collectae* (Berlin, 1887–94), 2:141–42; translation compared with partial translation into French in Dainville, *Naissance*, p. 60.
96. Clavius, "Modus," p. 471.
97. On the "calculators" of fourteenth-century Merton College, Oxford, see, e.g., Marshall Clagett, *The Science of Mechanics in the Middle Ages* (Madison, Wis., 1959), chap. 4. For the career of these ideas in Clavius's time, see Christopher Lewis, *The Merton Tradition and Kinematics in Late Sixteenth and Early Seventeenth Century Italy* (Padua, 1980), esp. chap. 3, "The Collegio Romano"; also William A. Wallace, *Prelude to Galileo* (Dordrecht, 1981), chap. 5.
98. Clavius, "Modus," p. 472.

be taught and studied not merely for its demonstrative certainty (though this was a factor) but also for its usefulness both in everyday life and in philosophy. Jesuit teaching of mathematics, exemplified by Clavius's textbooks, laid stress on practical techniques and the use of instruments, so much so that Descartes, looking back on his school-days at La Flèche, said that he had been left with the impression that mathematics "served only for the mechanical arts."[99] Mersenne's adoption of this position transformed it from a way of arguing the importance of mathematics into both a guarantee of knowledge and a *form* of knowledge in its own right. The rhetoric came ready-made, however. In *La verité,* after having provided an inventory of the sub-branches of mathematics, the Christian Philosopher suggests: "Let us now see their necessity and utility, which are so great that Plato did not want to admit anyone into his Academy who was not a geometer." Mathematics, he says, is useful in theology, assisting one "to under-stand holy scripture, that which concerns distributive and com-mutative justice, and the Church Fathers, particularly those who ex-plain their conceptions by Pythagorean numbers."[100] Aristotle cannot be understood without it (nor can Plato, but Mersenne is more in-terested in Aristotle, "whose philosophy is taught by all the schools of Europe").[101] It is, furthermore, indispensable to medicine, surgery, Paracelsianism and Cabbalism, alchemy, politics, and jurispru-dence.[102] The implication seems to be that whatever the Sceptic's doubts about its foundations, mathematics provides a body of knowl-edge without which most human activities could not proceed.

Mersenne's strategy against Pyrrhonism thus emerges as much less naive than it might at first appear to be. While the supposed refuta-tions of specific sceptical arguments often seem weak, the overall approach involves putting the lid on radical scepticism by removing the reasons for adopting it. Pyrrhonism had no target without dog-matisms: it was used both in the ancient world and by Montaigne and his followers to defuse the arrogance and divisiveness of philosophical

---

99. René Descartes, "Discours de la méthode," pt. 1, in *Oeuvres de Descartes,* 6:7. On the teaching of mathematics in the Jesuit colleges, see François de Dainville, "L'enseign-ment des mathématiques dans les Collèges Jésuites de France du XVIe au XVIIIe siècle," *Revue d'histoire des sciences* 7 (1954), 6–21, 109–23; idem, *La géographie des human-istes* (Paris, 1940), chap. 1; Pierre Costabel, "L'initiation mathématique de Descartes," *Archives de philosophie* 46 (1983), 637–46, esp. 637–38; John L. Heilbron, *Electricity in the 17th and 18th Centuries* (Berkeley, 1979), pp. 101–14. See also references in art. cited in n. 63, above.

100. Mersenne, *La verité,* p. 233.

101. Ibid., p. 236. The identification of mathematical passages in Aristotle was one of the exercises recommended by Clavius, "Modus," p. 473.

102. Mersenne, *La verité,* pp. 242–43.

dogma. Hence, by accepting the efficacy of scepticism directed against essentialist philosophies that aspired to know the world as God knew it, Mersenne conceded to the Pyrrhonists their moral goal. This done, there remained no purpose in questioning those sources of knowledge concerning appearances, their practical management by the understanding through logic and mathematics, and their operation in the affairs of life. Mersenne meant to undercut the Pyrrhonists' claim to possession of a legitimate philosophical alternative and to reduce their doubts to mere intellectual conceits. That he did so using orthodox conceptual materials and rhetorical resources, reordering their significance but not their content, meant that his resultant mathematical agenda for natural philosophy required no dramatic break from the learning of the schools.

CHAPTER FOUR

Aristotelian Science and
the Metaphysics of Mathematics

I

Mᴇʀsᴇɴɴᴇ's was a practical epistemology, designed to underpin and justify a natural philosophical agenda concentrating on mathematical, operational, and experimental forms of knowledge. It also served to deny legitimacy to those alternative positions which appeared to threaten the delicate relationship between theology and philosophy that sustained orthodox religion and, thereby, the authority of the Church. The apologetics of Mersenne's early publications and the anti-Pyrrhonist strategy of *La verité des sciences* had resulted in a system of epistemological arguments applicable both to the emasculation of Pyrrhonism and to the exposure of unorthodox dogmatisms. Mersenne could use the Sceptic in *La verité* to undermine the position of the dialogue's third interlocutor, the Alchemist, because he had freed sceptical arguments from the matrix of philosophical scepticism in which they had previously been embedded. The exclusionary functions of his positive agenda therefore provided an important part of its characterization: it needed to be immune from whatever charges could most profitably be leveled against its rivals and to incorporate the suppositions behind those charges. The general features of "mitigated scepticism" justified the suppositions and set a cognitive agenda that even a Pyrrhonist should find morally unexceptionable.

In part, Mersenne simply defined what could not be known and advocated the pursuit of whatever was left. This kind of negative justification appears, for example, in the methodological musings of his *Questions theologiques* in 1634: "Since we cannot know the true

[48]

reasons, or the science of what happens in nature, because there are always some circumstances or instances that make us doubt if the causes that we invent [*nous nous imaginons*] are true [*veritable*], and if there are any at all or if there cannot be others, I don't see that one ought to require anything else of the most learned than their observations, and the remarks they will have made of different effects or phenomena of nature."[1]

Even when Mersenne sanctioned his agenda through the affirmation of epistemological and metaphysical doctrines, however, such positive justifications themselves often served a negative function. Because they were usually selected from orthodox teaching, they effectively displayed a lack of innovation; they proclaimed their philosophical and hence theological and social orthodoxy. One of the central epistemological questions in scholastic metaphysics concerned the relation of the known object to the concept of it in the mind. Mersenne, while denying the possibility of genuine access to essences, nonetheless dealt with this issue so as to clarify how we can acquire at least some knowledge of the external world: that is, say true things about it. In particular, what makes a concept of a thing true? Both in posing the question and in the way he answered it, Mersenne adhered to scholastic precedent. In *L'usage de la raison* he had discussed the relation between ideas in the understanding and the things producing those ideas: "The understanding forms a living [*vive*] image which expressly resembles the object, in such a way that if one saw that object represented in the intellect, one would say that there was in some way a greater union between the object and the understanding than there is between matter and form, and that the axiom *intellectus, & res intellecta sunt unum, & idem* [the intellect and the thing known (or perceived) are one and the same] would be true for the representative being of the object [i.e., the idea of the object]."[2] This statement relates directly to the issue of truth.

"Truth of cognition," according to the Coïmbra commentators, "is defined as the conformity between the intellect and the thing; that is, the intellect then knows truly when it perceives the thing as it is."[3] Fonseca, in his commentary on Aristotle's *Metaphysics*, observed that all philosophers and theologians agreed that truth "is the adequation [*adequatio*] or rather conformity between the thing and the intellect."[4] "Conformity" is a relation of one thing to another, he went on, but in

1. Mersenne, *Questions theologiques*, p. 18.
2. Mersenne, *L'usage de la raison*, p. 137.
3. Coïmbra *Dialectic*, 2:60.
4. Fonseca, *Commentariorum . . . tomi*, 1:786.

this case it cannot be a *real* relation. If it were, then "God is a being" would imply a relation between God and something separate from God, something common to all divine personages; however, since "being" is in fact inseparable from God, this cannot be the case. Consequently, said Fonseca, what is involved is a *relatio rationis,* a relation of reason. He concluded that truth "is the adequation or conformity of the thing and the intellect: the conformity, however, is formally nothing other than a relation; therefore truth also is nothing other than a relation of conformity."[5]

Matters were not that simple, however. Things are corporeal, but the intellect is not; this distinction had led some scholastics to maintain that the conformity establishing truths of cognition was not in fact directly between the thing and the formal concept of it in the mind but between the thing and the "objective concept."[6] An "objective concept" was that by which the mind considered an object in order to make a judgment of it: that is, to create a "formal concept." In the statement "that is a horse," for example, "that" represents the objective concept, since it identifies the thing of which a judgment is to be made. "Horse" represents the formal concept, the concept resulting from the judgment of what "that" is. Thus the objective concept held the status of "the thing insofar as it is known," distinct from the thing itself *or* from the idea the mind has of the thing.[7] Certain scholastics, preeminently Durandus but also Vasquez (the Jesuit colleague of Fonseca and Francisco Suarez), held that because the intellect and corporeal substance were different in kind, there could be no conformity between the thing and the formal concept; truth had therefore to consist of a conformity between the thing and the *objective* concept, "the thing insofar as it is known."[8] Suarez, as several authors have noted, rejected Durandus's idea, holding that such conformity was no conformity at all but simply an identity of the thing with itself,

5. Ibid., 1:786–87.

6. "Objective concepts" were discussed in the dialectic textbooks of Fonseca and Toletus, standard in the Jesuit colleges. The appropriate passages from each are given in Timothy J. Cronin, *Objective Being in Descartes and in Suarez* (Rome, 1966), pp. 34–35. On this topic, see R. Dalbiez, "Les sources scolastiques de la théorie cartésienne de l'être objectif," *Revue d'histoire de la philosophie* 3 (1929), 464–72, esp. 468–69; James C. Doig, "Suarez, Descartes, and the Objective Reality of Ideas," *New Scholasticism* 51 (1977), 350–71. Certain aspects of Doig's article, not directly relevant to the present point, have been questioned by Norman J. Wells, "Old Bottles and New Wine," *New Scholasticism* 53 (1979), 515–23.

7. "Objective being," concomitantly, is the "being-of-being-known"; see Wells, "Old Bottles," p. 519; see also the valuable treatment in John P. Doyle, "Suarez on the Reality of the Possibles," *Modern Schoolman* 45 (1967), 29–48, esp. 37–39.

8. Dalbiez, "Sources," 468–69.

having no bearing on truth.[9] The Coïmbra commentators adopted the same position as Suarez; Vasquez seems to have been unorthodox in his support of Durandus.[10] By contrast, the standard solution to this problem among the Jesuits held that truth ultimately resided in the conformity of the objective concept with the formal concept—to take the example given above, of the "that" with the "horse." The objective concept, in other words, played the part of the thing, because the thing itself could not be brought into relation with the formal concept except "insofar as it is known."[11] As Suarez said, science "concerns common objective concepts, which granted in reality are not distinguished from singulars [i.e., individual things], are nonetheless distinguished by reason [*in ratione*]."[12]

Mersenne educated his Sceptic in *La verité des sciences* in just these terms, explaining that

> the notions of logic, of physics, of metaphysics, of the circle and of the other figures, and even those that you have of stars, stones, houses, and all the other things that you know, are intellectual, and insensible; otherwise, it would be necessary to say that the understanding was sensible, material, and corporeal, if the knowledge that we have of corporeal things was material and corporeal, inasmuch as everything that is received in any subject is received according to the proportion of the subject, following this axiom, *quidquid recipitur, ad modum recipientis recipitur* [whatever is received, is received in the mode of the receiver].[13]

The value of this philosophical idiom lay in its ability to render certain maxims, such as the one quoted by Mersenne, self-evident and therefore available to do argumentative work without themselves requiring

9. Doig, "Suarez, Descartes," p. 357. On Suarez's metaphysics in general, see the excellent treatment in Frederick Copleston, *A History of Philosophy* (Westminster, Md., 1963), 3:353–79; also John A. Trentman, "Scholasticism in the Seventeenth Century," in Norman Kretzmann, Anthony Kenny, and Jan Pinborg, eds., *The Cambridge History of Later Medieval Philosophy* (Cambridge, 1982), pp. 818–37, esp. 822–27. For general background, see Charles H. Lohr, "Jesuit Aristotelianism and Sixteenth-Century Metaphysics," in Harry George Fletcher III and Mary Beatrice Schulte, eds., *Paradosis* (New York, 1976), pp. 203–20.

10. Coïmbra *Dialectic*, 2:60ff.

11. Doig, "Suarez, Descartes," p. 359. See also Wells, "Old Bottles," esp. p. 518, for clarification on formal and objective concepts (where Doig is sometimes suspect); and Doyle, "Suarez."

12. Translation in Doig, "Suarez, Descartes," p. 353, from Francisco Suarez, *Disputationes metaphysicae*, Disp. vi, sec. v, para. 3; I shall cite Suarez in this form, rather than by page number, since I have not used the standard (Vivès) edition but an edition with Spanish translation: *Disputaciones metafísicas*, 6 vols. (Madrid, 1960).

13. Mersenne, *La verité*, pp. 274–75.

explicit defense.[14] By adopting it, Mersenne invoked not just the sanction of convention but also the privilege of its assumptions. Because he avoided speaking with the voice of an innovator, he could justify his own philosophical agenda by grounding it in orthodox formulations, leaving less foundational work to be done. The Sceptic is made to challenge the Christian Philosopher directly concerning the fundamental Pyrrhonian issue of the criterion of truth: how is a statement to be judged for its truth or falsity? The Christian Philosopher replies that it is, in a sense, the truth itself that does the judging: "As soon as we apprehend something, and believe it true, if truth afterwards shows the contrary, as often happens in many cases, the understanding quits the opinion which it had and embraces the truth of that which is in question, which is nothing other than the conformity of that which is proposed with the understanding."[15] "That which is proposed" is, in scholastic terms, the objective concept. It could not be the thing itself because, as Mersenne said, "quidquid recipitur, ad modum recipientis recipitur."

Scholastic metaphysics also provided an appropriate definition of "transcendent" truths, which—unlike truths of cognition—concerned noncontingent, eternal verities. Fonseca, for instance, followed Aquinas's general line in holding that transcendent truth "is the conformity of things with the divine intellect, that is, with their formal reasons which are in the divine mind." In other words, Fonseca continues, those things "which we call true from all eternity" must, since truth itself exists only by virtue of conformity between a thing and an intellect, be true by conforming to some eternal intellect, "which is the divine alone." Fonseca meant that truths concerning, for example, the essential natures of created things were established by virtue of the fact that the things themselves truly conformed to the exemplary ideas of them in the mind of God.[16]

For Aquinas himself, truth, although having relation to external things, resided primarily in the intellect (as Mersenne asserted in the passages quoted earlier). Furthermore, truth and true propositions related to the *being* of things rather than to their essences: "The being of a thing is the cause of truth."[17] On two counts, therefore, all truths—including transcendent, eternal truths—depended entirely on God. First, they required an intellect within which to reside, and the divine intellect was prior to all others. Secondly, since all things

14. On scholastic philosophical maxims, see Reif, "Natural Philosophy," pp. 241–58.
15. Mersenne, *La verité*, p. 195.
16. Fonseca, *Commentarii*, 1:803, 804.
17. Armand Maurer, "St. Thomas and Eternal Truths," *Mediaeval Studies* 32 (1970), 94, 95 (quote on p. 95).

derived their being from participation in the being of God, without God there could be no "cause of truth." Aquinas distinguished between necessary and contingent truths in a similarly theocentric fashion, holding that the basic difference between them was established by God's knowing the necessary truths to be necessary and the contingent truths to be contingent.[18] Truth depended utterly on God, as did the exemplars in the divine mind; the conformity of things with those exemplars established the transcendent truths of which Fonseca spoke.

Mersenne used this orthodox Thomistic account to undermine further the claims of physics to being a genuine science. The previous chapter considered how the Aristotelian requirement that a science provide necessary demonstrations had formed a central part of Mersenne's and Clavius's attempts to elevate the status of mathematics at the expense of physics. The considerations there were epistemological: the subject matter of physics was inherently less amenable to certain demonstration than that of the mathematical disciplines. Metaphysical and theological arguments, however, provided Mersenne with grounds for an ontological dismissal of a scientific Aristotelian physics. Since we have no direct access to the mind of God, the essential natures of things remain inscrutable; they can be known only if we are assured of the conformity between them and the appropriate divine ideas. However, things are themselves created through God's exercise of His free will, and that set up a problem frequently discussed in this period. Because of this radical contingency, said Mersenne, "one knows all but nothing in physics, if one follows the definition of science Aristotle gave; for if it ought to be about eternal and immutable objects, and God can change everything that is in physics, one cannot make a science of it."[19] God could, for example, bring about the same effect by a different cause; there seemed to be no determinate way of distinguishing the actual from the possible. Mersenne had indicated a closely related problem in *La verité des sciences* when he said that since physics concerns motion in general, "it is subject to diverse changes," even when dealing with quantities.[20] Physics, therefore, working with contingent and changeable things, could never be a science.

This kind of objection to the scientific status of physics was a commonplace of the period; usually, however, a reply appeared alongside.[21] Suarez, who acknowledged that sciences should demonstrate

18. Ibid., p. 106.
19. Mersenne, *Questions theologiques*, p. 9.
20. Mersenne, *La verité*, p. 226.
21. For examples, see Reif, "Natural Philosophy," pp. 41–45.

necessary truths,[22] solved the problem of the contingency of nature by claiming that, in addition, they properly concern not actual but *possible* existence: "Sciences, which consider things abstracted from existence, do not concern entities of reason but real things, because they consider real essences, not according to the position which they have objectively in the mind but in and of themselves, or inasmuch as they are apt to exist with such natures or properties."[23] Thus, although sciences must concern real things, these things are always abstracted from existence (otherwise, they could not be considered by the mind); consequently, there can be necessary truths about them whether or not God chooses actually to create them. Physics therefore retains its scientific status. Suarez's solution echoes the usual argument that since the statements of a science should be universal, they must hold, independent of the changeability and corruptibility of individual objects. This was sometimes presented in terms of "a rose in winter": there are no roses at that time of year, so what is the status of statements then made about them?[24]

Mersenne used the standard objections raised against physics but would not avail himself of the standard replies. Instead, he treated the objections as if they were conclusive. After asserting that physics could not be a science because its subject matter is change, he contrasted mathematics: "Mathematical quantity is invariable, for it cannot come about that a triangle not be composed of three lines, and by three angles conjoined by three indivisible points: no matter that there were no perfect triangle in the world, it suffices that there can be to establish the truth of this science."[25] The stability of its subject matter allowed mathematics to aspire to scientificity. For Mersenne, the arguments directed against physics did not touch mathematical objects or mathematical truths; each was absolutely unchangeable. Clearly, there was no question of God's ability to change "everything that is in physics" extending to mathematics as well.

II

If Mersenne had extended his voluntarism to mathematics, it would have been somewhat counterproductive, given the nature of the natural philosophical agenda he wished to justify. It would also have been

22. E.g., Suarez, *Disputationes* XXXI.XII.38.
23. Ibid., XXXI.II.10.
24. William A. Wallace, *Galileo and His Sources* (Princeton, 1984), pp. 111–12.
25. Mersenne, *La verité*, p. 226.

starkly innovative. Mersenne's position rested securely within the boundaries of scholastic discourse, and nothing reveals this better than his reaction to Descartes's rupturing of those boundaries in 1630. The relevant letters have been much plundered by Descartes scholars over the years, frequently with a focus on the suggestion that Descartes's remarks on "eternal verities" represent a conscious opposition to Suarez's statements in his *Disputationes metaphysicae.* Despite disagreement among specialists over the subtleties of Suarez's, and to a lesser extent Descartes's, positions, the main outlines are clear enough, certainly as regards Mersenne.[26]

On 15 April 1630 Descartes wrote a letter to Mersenne obviously in response to a set of queries, though Mersenne's side of the whole exchange is lost.[27] Descartes mentions his projected *Physique*—he was working on *Le monde* at the time—and says that he intends to deal with some questions of metaphysics, and with one proposition in particular: that "mathematical truths, which you call *eternal,* have been established by God and depend on Him entirely just as do all the other creatures." He enjoins Mersenne to tell everyone that mathematical truths are not independent of God but have been established by Him "just as a king establishes the laws in his kingdom." God's laws of mathematics are all "mentibus nostris ingenitae" (inborn in our minds), continues Descartes (using Latin as the appropriate technical language), just as a king's laws would be imprinted in the hearts of his subjects if he had the power to do it.[28]

26. Émile Boutroux, *Des vérités éternelles chez Descartes,* trans. Georges Canguilhem from *De veritatibus aeternis apud Cartesium* (Paris, 1927); Étienne Gilson, *La liberté chez Descartes et la théologie* (Paris, 1913); Pierre Garin, *Thèses cartésiennes et thèses thomistes* (Paris, 1932); Émile Brehier, "The Creation of the Eternal Truths in Descartes's System," in Willis Doney, ed., *Descartes* (New York, 1967), pp. 192–208; Henri Gouhier, *La pensée métaphysique de Descartes* (Paris, 1962), pp. 285–91; Cronin, *Objective Being;* Geneviève Rodis-Lewis, *L'oeuvre de Descartes* (Paris, 1971), pp. 125–40; Jean-Luc Marion, *Sur la théologie blanche de Descartes* (Paris, 1981); Norman J. Wells, "Suarez on the Eternal Truths," *Modern Schoolman* 58 (1981), 73–104, 159–74; E. M. Curley, "Descartes on the Creation of the Eternal Truths," *Philosophical Review* 93 (1984), 569–97; Margaret J. Osler, "Eternal Truths and the Laws of Nature," *Journal of the History of Ideas* 46 (1985), 349–62. This general issue also sets the stage for Maurer, "St. Thomas." For a bibliographical survey to 1961, see Norman J. Wells, "Descartes and the Scholastics Briefly Revisited," *New Scholasticism* 35 (1961), 172–90. At issue are "created" eternal truths as opposed to "uncreated" eternal truths, which are the attributes of God Himself and could not, for Descartes, possibly be otherwise: see Norman J. Wells, "Descartes' Uncreated Eternal Truths," *New Scholasticism* 56 (1982), 185–99, which is one of a number of replies to H. Frankfurt, "Descartes on the Creation of the Eternal Truths," *Philosophical Review* 86 (1977), 36–57, and provides a more historically structured version of some of the points in Curley, "Descartes."

27. Descartes to Mersenne, 15 April 1630, in Mersenne *Correspondance,* 2:422–37.

28. Ibid., p. 431. On the writing of *Le monde,* see Michael S. Mahoney's introduction to his translation of René Descartes, *The World* (New York, 1979).

Mersenne, who had presumably referred to mathematical truths as "eternal" in a quite casual and routine way, appears to have been caught somewhat by surprise. A paragraph in Descartes's next letter to Mersenne—again a listing of responses to questions—begins: "As for eternal truths . . ." and goes on to review the opinion presented previously; evidently, Mersenne had asked for clarification.[29] It would seem that Mersenne, perhaps having discovered from this reply that he had not mistaken the unsettling character of his correspondent's position, was sufficiently taken aback to pester Descartes with a number of objections and queries on the point, because another letter from Descartes a month later addresses the same issue more fully, ticking off Mersenne's questions one by one. "You ask me *in quo genere causae Deus disposuit aeternas veritates* [in what kind of cause God has disposed the eternal truths]. I reply to you that it is *in eodem genere causae* [in the same kind of cause] that He has created everything, that is, *ut efficiens et totalis causa* [as efficient and total cause]." And again: "You also ask what has necessitated God to create these truths." Nothing, says Descartes; God was completely free, for example, to have made the lines drawn from the center of a circle to its circumference unequal. And a third time: "You ask what God has done to produce them"; Descartes answers by pointing out the identity in God between willing, knowing, and creating.[30]

As noted earlier, Aquinas's, and apparently Fonseca's, view of the dependence of truth on God allowed that there was a genuine distinction between "necessary" and "contingent" truths in that God knew each of them to be either the one or the other. The suggestion that the former could somehow hold *independent* of God would have run against the general tenor of the argument. Descartes, however, seems to have found such an opinion, which he here counters, in Suarez's *Disputationes*. The crucial passage from Suarez usually cited in modern discussions of the matter[31] reads as follows: "Neither are those statements [i.e., eternal, necessary truths] true because they are known by God, but rather therefore they are known because they are true; for, if their truth came from God himself, it would arise from the intervening will of God; whence it would emerge not by necessity, but by will."[32] In the case of such a statement as "man is a rational

29. Descartes to Mersenne, 6 May 1630, in Mersenne *Correspondance*, 2:481.

30. Descartes to Mersenne, 3 June 1630, in ibid., pp. 490, 491. Descartes's last response is quite Thomistic: see Étienne Gilson, *The Philosophy of St. Thomas Aquinas*, trans. G. A. Elrington (Cambridge, 1924), p. 99. On this whole exchange see Marion, *Sur la théologie*, pp. 162–63 etc.

31. Most notably in Cronin, *Objective Being*, and Marion, *Sur la théologie*.

32. Suarez, *Disputationes* XXXI.XII.40.

animal," for example, there is a logical necessity requiring its truth; the term "man" unavoidably implies "rational animal" because that is the essence of man. This holds independent of divine causality and hence provides a clear and fundamental distinction between necessary, eternal truths and contingent truths (the latter are eternal only in the sense that God knows them eternally).

It is important to note that the long-standing attribution of this position to Suarez has recently been cast into doubt by Norman J. Wells.[33] Wells has unraveled the complex structure of Suarez's argument in the thirty-first disputation and has attempted to explicate its overall strategy. He provides the following account of the Jesuit's intentions. Suarez wished to refute the views of those who maintained that the essences of creatures are actual even when those creatures do not exist (when God has not chosen to create them), because such a view appeared to make essences real things separate from God, analogous to Platonic forms. Actual essences that did not actually exist would have being in and of themselves, but only God is *ens ex se necessarium* (i.e., a being necessary in and of itself).[34] Suarez therefore identified essence and existence: essences are actual only when they actually exist. The effect was that, like Aquinas, Suarez rooted even necessary, eternal truths in God. However, such essential propositions as "man is a rational animal" could be regarded as eternal truths only if their connection of terms was not seen as *actually* eternal: all such connections required an efficient cause, but actually eternal essential propositions would be outside God and thus lack the causal agency needed to sustain them.[35] For Suarez, the copulative in the essential proposition representing the eternal truth did not indicate actual existence; there could be no essential propositions with actual eternal truth. However, essences having only potential existence could be sustained by a potential efficient cause, which is God. Essential propositions could be eternally true in the sense of a nonexistential copulative, and they would then be reducible to a conditional, of the form "if man exists, he is a rational animal." That conditional itself required a potential efficient cause (the only exceptions were fictions such as "a chimaera is a chimaera"); its terms always had to be capable of actual production by a causal agency.[36]

Wells thus presents Suarez, contrary to the received opinion, as arguing single-mindedly for God's indispensability in grounding eter-

---

33. Wells, "Suarez."
34. Ibid., p. 76.
35. Ibid., p. 163.
36. Ibid., p. 165–66.

nal truths as well as His being the only independently existing essence. The oft-quoted passage from Suarez emerges as simply the exposition of an opposing viewpoint within the context of the disputation.[37] The subtlety of these arguments, however, introduces an important issue relating to the establishment of mathematical truths, which Descartes's position reveals clearly. Although apparently addressing himself to the antivoluntarist passages in Suarez, Descartes interpreted them in a way that begged a crucial question: did the eternal truths considered there include those of mathematics? That is, were mathematical propositions essential propositions; did mathematical objects have essences? Descartes seems not to have noticed this point, but Mersenne certainly did.

Mersenne no more saw necessary, eternal truths as independent of God than did Suarez or, indeed, Aquinas. In *Questions theologiques* he calls God the source of all the sciences and says that the center of all creatures is "the divine goodness, on which all things, *as much actual as possible,* depend much more than streams depend on their source" (my emphasis).[38] So even essential propositions that related only to possible creatures could not possess truth without God. Similarly, in the *Traité de l'harmonie universelle* of 1627 Mersenne writes: "I consider, therefore, the divine essence as an eternal and infinite sun, which darts an infinity of rays on which depend all our perfections: the goodness of God is one of these rays, whence come our good inclinations, our virtues, and our good works: the other is eternal truth, whence proceed all our truths and our sciences."[39] For Mersenne, just as for Aquinas, all truth is established in God.

This conclusion disagrees with that of Jean-Luc Marion in his study of Descartes's theological thought. Marion, from the starting point of the correspondence we considered earlier, has claimed that Mersenne adhered to the position commonly attributed to Suarez, whereby necessary, eternal truths held without requiring divine causality; moreover, Mersenne supposedly regarded mathematics from the same perspective. Marion supports the more general part of this argument solely on the basis of a passage in *Quaestiones in Genesim,* which he presents in two separate but interlocking fragments on different pages (I translate from Marion's own French translation): "The power of God considers the possibles . . . because they are necessary and eternal . . . ; things in themselves independent of all causes are

37. Ibid., p. 161.
38. Mersenne, *Questions theologiques,* "Epistre," pp. iv–v.
39. Marin Mersenne, *Traité de l'harmonie universelle* (Paris, 1627), pp. 59–60. For background on the *Traité,* see De Waard's note in Mersenne *Correspondance,* 2:41–42.

possible"; God has to take the possibilities of the possibles into account "because they are eternal and, as other authors say (*ut alii loquuntur*), things are possible in themselves, independently of all cause (*ex se, independenter*), by virtue of the necessary connection or rather the noncontradiction (*connexio, non repugnantia*) of terms that concern the nature of a thing."[40] This material presents the view found in Suarez and certainly opposes Aquinas and Fonseca—and, on Wells's reading, Suarez himself.

A consideration of the entire passage, however, makes it doubtful that Mersenne intended to endorse that view. God, Mersenne has been saying, is free to create anything not involving a contradiction (in itself a standard Thomistic position): "We also add that the divine power therefore by nature considers the possibles, not merely [*non tantum*] because they are necessary, and eternal, and, as others say, things in themselves independently of whatever cause are possible on account of the necessary connection, or nonrepugnance, of terms that concern the nature of any thing whatever; not merely because from the knowledge of possibles the Son, and from the love of possibles the Holy Spirit, proceeds, as theologians say,[41] but because they are infinite [i.e., there is an infinite number of them]," and so not all possible creatures can actually exist at the same time. God thus has dominion over "infinite, eternal, and necessary" ideas, or possible beings, which are "God Himself."[42]

Mersenne did not assert the independence of necessary truths, therefore; he mentions the doctrine in passing without making any commitment to it. Indeed, since the "infinite, eternal, and necessary truths" are "God Himself" they can scarcely be independent of Him, although Marion takes this identification as implying that God is obliged necessarily to consider them—an interpretation lacking any textual support.[43] In fact, as we have seen, Mersenne grounded truth in God in a broadly Thomistic fashion; there can be no truth without God, and the "necessity" of a necessary truth holds by virtue of God's causality. In 1624 Mersenne remarked that "the object of the divine power is everything that does not enclose and contain any repugnance or contradiction (which is called *possible*): but the object of the divine will is the small number of things that God chose and that He wishes to create among an infinity of similar and different things that He leaves

40. Marion, *Sur la théologie*, pp. 174, 175–76.

41. For an account of Aquinas's statements of this point, see Mark D. Jordan, "The Intelligibility of the World and the Divine Ideas in Aquinas," *Review of Metaphysics* 38 (1984), 30–31.

42. Mersenne, *Quaestiones*, col. 436.

43. Marion, *Sur la théologie*, p. 176.

only in *possibility* and *nonrepugnance*."[44] This very possibility itself required that God could, if He so chose, create those things; it would not exist without God as potential efficient cause. When, in the previous year's *L'usage de la raison*, Mersenne said that "God Himself is not free in the essential and notional actions which are called *ad intra*," he was implying a kind of necessity different from that which would render God subject to truths independent of Him: examples of such actions *ad intra* were that "God loves Himself necessarily, the Father produces the Son and the Holy Spirit necessarily." Nonetheless, Mersenne continued, "all three have created the world with complete [*tres-pleine*] freedom."[45]

Descartes apparently saw the matter as a straight choice between necessary truths holding simply because God knew them (having willed them) and God's knowing them because they were independently true; he opted for the former. Within the Thomistic tradition providing the framework of Jesuit metaphysics, however, the relevant issue and the appropriate conceptualization of the problem were quite different: such truths held because God knew them *and* God knew them because they were true, but truth itself depended radically on God. Descartes seems not to have understood things in this way. Perhaps it might be said that, while striving to make the truth of any proposition dependent on God's will, he made truth itself *independent* of God.

Mersenne's exchange with Descartes in 1630 concerned specifically the truths of mathematics, and Marion has attributed to Mersenne precisely the position opposed by Descartes: namely, that mathematical truths hold independent of God and that God is therefore obliged necessarily to consider them—is, in fact, unavoidably constrained by them. Marion says that for Mersenne mathematics was "univocal," the same for man as for God. Man and God knew mathematical truths, like the Pythagorean theorem, in the same way; they did not subsist in God, who therefore had no causal relationship with them and considered them just as man did.[46] Now, it is questionable whether the use of the word "univocal" is appropriate here, given that

44. Mersenne, *L'impieté*, 2:311–12. Gilson, *La liberté*, pp. 149–56, discusses Mersenne's views on divine freedom, characterizing them as reproducing "faithfully, in spirit and in letter, the conception of St. Thomas" (p. 151).

45. Mersenne, *L'usage de la raison*, p. 31. The necessity of God's attributes and actions *ad intra* refers to a standard Thomistic idea equivalent to Descartes's "uncreated" eternal truths (see Wells, "Descartes' Uncreated Eternal Truths," esp. pp. 193–96); i.e., Descartes would not have differed importantly from Mersenne on this point.

46. Marion, *Sur la théologie*, pp. 170–71 etc. For Marion, Galileo and Kepler also saw mathematics as "univocal."

in scholastic parlance it is only properly applicable to predicates.[47] Furthermore, in the case of propositions, Aquinas himself (as we considered earlier) held that God knew necessary truths to be necessary, just as man did, but that assertion did not imply that such truths were independent of God's causality. Mersenne believed quite the opposite, as is shown by his previously quoted remarks about the dependence of all sciences on God.

That Mersenne appears to have called mathematical truths "eternal" when writing to Descartes is not in itself significant. Fonseca spoke of "eternal truths" being dependent on God, and the expression need in no way be taken as meaning anything other than "coeternal with God." Marion largely relies for his inference on the assumption that Mersenne straightforwardly applied to mathematics the doctrine of possibles found in Suarez and failed to consider that "the specificity of mathematics profoundly modifies these theological orientations."[48] Unfortunately, Marion does not explain *why* mathematics might be different; he does not demonstrate that Mersenne actually made the conflation to begin with; and since he seems to be incorrect in attributing Suarez's supposed position to Mersenne, the argument cannot be accepted on those grounds anyway. It does remain true that Mersenne, as Marion shows, frequently compares God to mathematical objects and describes Him as a geometer or architect.[49] It is not true, however, that these instances are evidence of the view that mathematics is independent of and outside God.

In *L'impieté des deistes* Mersenne compares God to unity. He gives ten different ways in which unity is like the divine act of creation, producing an infinity of different numbers, so as to clear up the apparent paradox of a perfectly simple Creator producing a diverse multitude of creatures.[50] Marion uses this comparison to argue that Mersenne thought God utilized but did not cause mathematics, which therefore existed with a kind of Platonic separateness. In fact, Mersenne merely drew an analogy; immediately preceding the comparison with unity, he had tried to make the same point by considering light reflected in a parabolic mirror, where an infinity of rays can be united at the focus.[51] Clearly, Mersenne did not mean to imply that God is somehow separate from or subject to the laws of optics, with their dependence on the physical properties of light. No such

---

47. See the excellent account of this scholastic term in Jorge J. E. Gracia, *Suarez on Individuation* (Milwaukee, Wis., 1982), under "Univoce" in the glossary, pp. 277–78.
48. Marion, *Sur la théologie*, p. 177.
49. Ibid., pp. 171–72, 170–71.
50. Mersenne, *L'impieté*, 1:417–26.
51. Ibid., 414–16.

inference can therefore be made from the comparison with unity. The next chapter considers the meaning of Mersenne's use of the metaphor of geometer or architect in describing God; for the moment it is enough to note that this was so much a commonplace of the period that it cannot act as evidence of any strict Platonic view of mathematics.

A fuller examination of Mersenne's metamathematical discourse reveals not only a radically theocentric view of mathematical objects but also a selective use of conceptual resources to bolster his particular philosophical program. By following Clavius in stressing the certainty of mathematics as its supreme advantage over physics—a tactic employed especially in *La verité des sciences*—Mersenne took sides in a debate within Jesuit circles concerning the scientific status of mathematics. That scholastic debate provided both the general terms within which Mersenne argued and the issues that he addressed. The position he adopted, however, was decidedly partisan and possessed direct implications for the status of mathematical truths.

III

The overall structure and relationship of the mathematical disciplines caused no controversy. Christopher Clavius presented the accepted scholastic view in the "Prolegomena" to his edition of Euclid, describing the usual division of mathematics into the four branches of the medieval quadrivium: arithmetic, geometry, astronomy, and music. The categorization could be justified by the kinds of objects each quadrivial discipline treated: arithmetic dealt with discrete quantity in and of itself, whereas music did so with respect to something else, specifically sounds; geometry concerned continuous quantity in and of itself, whereas astronomy did so with respect to *mobile* continuous quantity. "All other [mathematical sciences] dealing with quantity in whatever way, however, such as perspective, geography, and others of that kind, can be reduced, as if to headings from which they depend, to these four mathematical sciences, of which arithmetic and geometry are called 'pure,' music and astronomy 'mixed'."[52] Clavius's list of such sciences, including optics and mechanics, does not differ in any essential respects from Mersenne's choice of topics in *La verité des sciences* or his table of disciplines in *Quaestiones in Genesim*.[53] As we

52. Clavius, *Operum mathematicorum tomus primus*, "Prolegomena," p. 3; Mersenne echoes this discussion in *Traité*, pp. 5–6. The "Prolegomena" are summarized in Wallace, *Galileo*, pp. 137–39.
53. Clavius, "Prolegomena," p. 4.

have seen, Clavius's textbooks on mathematics were standard in the Jesuit colleges, and Mersenne had certainly used them: Clavius's name appears frequently among the mathematical authors listed in *Quaestiones.*[54]

Those mathematical disciplines dealing with subject matter other than pure quantity formed the basis of the utility of mathematics so much vaunted by pedagogues like Clavius and by Mersenne himself; they were variously known as "mixed," "middle," or "subordinate" sciences. Although the last term had a slightly wider reference, beyond mathematics, it does indicate the logical basis for the category. Subordinate sciences emerged from an anomaly within Aristotle's exposition, in the *Posterior Analytics,* of the proper form of a demonstrative science.[55] A science, he said, should have its own unique principles, from which it is developed by rigorous demonstration; Aristotle envisaged a structure analogous to that of geometry, employing the tools of syllogistic logic rather than geometrical inference. When, in *Traité de l'harmonie universelle,* Mersenne wished to show that music was a science, he did so by arguing that "it has true [*veritables*] demonstrations which it founds on its own principles."[56] However, in such a science as music a problem arose requiring a special modification of the criteria.

Aristotle explained it in this way: "It is not for one science to prove something belonging to a different science, except when the things are so related that one is subordinate to the other, that is to say, as e.g. theorems in optics are to geometry, and theorems in harmonics [i.e., music] to arithmetic."[57] Because optics and music used demonstrations borrowed from other disciplines—namely, geometry and arithmetic—they might be said to violate a cardinal rule of scientificity. A basic logical consideration justified that rule: the subject matter of a particular science could be explained only through principles of the *same kind,* because otherwise no deductive link could be established between the principles and the propositions they were to demonstrate; there could be no comparison between terms denoting generically different things.[58] Mersenne understood this perfectly well, re-

---

54. Mersenne, *Quaestiones,* cols. 1207–8.

55. See Richard D. McKirahan, "Aristotle's Subordinate Sciences," *British Journal for the History of Science* 11 (1978), 197–220; Stephen Gaukroger, *Explanatory Structures* (Atlantic Highlands, N.J., 1978), pp. 103–4; G. E. L. Owen, "Aristotle: Method, Physics, and Cosmology," in *Dictionary of Scientific Biography* (New York, 1970–80), 1:250–58, esp. 256–57 (hereafter cited as *DSB*).

56. Mersenne, *Traité,* p. 6.

57. Aristotle *Posterior Analytics* A.7.75^{b}14–17, trans. in Thomas Heath, *Mathematics in Aristotle* (Oxford, 1949), p. 11.

58. See, e.g., Owen, "Aristotle," p. 252.

marking on it in a discussion in *Questions theologiques*. It is not permissible, he said, to assert that the sounds making up an octave are in the ratio 2:1 simply on the basis of associated string lengths, because "in good logic, it isn't permitted to pass from one genus to the other without infringing the law of homogeneity."[59]

In order to retain disciplines like optics and music as sciences, therefore, Aristotle used the concept of subordination, as he explained in the *Metaphysics*: these subjects fitted the definition of a science to the extent that "neither considers its objects *qua* sight or *qua* voice but *qua* straight lines and numbers, which latter are proper attributes of the former; similarly with mechanics."[60] This point, legitimating the employment of results taken from pure mathematics, remained unquestioned in scholastic teaching like that of the Jesuits. Thus Mersenne set it out in his *Traité de l'harmonie universelle*, describing how, among the various sciences, "if they have a common [*mesme*] formal object, they will be *subordinate* and *subordinating*, although their material objects be different; this happens with mathematics, as when optics and music make use of demonstrations from geometry and arithmetic, for when its demonstrations are joined to sensible matter, it doesn't lose its formal cause [*raison*]."[61] That is, the demonstrations of pure mathematics are equally valid whether or not the magnitudes with which they deal inhere in material things.

There was also general agreement among scholastic writers on the character of the respective objects of arithmetic and geometry, the two branches of pure mathematics, and again the doctrine derived from Aristotle. Arithmetic concerned discrete quantity, and geometry concerned continuous quantity. Fonseca paraphrased "the most learned Saint Thomas" on the logical relationship between the two: "For, because the characteristic of quantity is to have parts, by some intrinsic or essential situation distinct among themselves; that is, so disposed that one is separate from another [*una sit extra aliam*]; it thence follows, that all things the quantities of which can be parts of one whole quantity, are necessarily judged to be diverse."[62] This can be made somewhat clearer by considering Mersenne's account in *La verité*, where the Christian Philosopher requests the Sceptic to note what Boethius said about "*continuous* quantity, which, according to his opinion, depends on *discrete* quantity, inasmuch as the idea that we have of the *continuity* of the continuous is nothing other than the

59. Mersenne, *Questions theologiques*, p. 182.
60. Aristotle *Metaphysics* M.3.1078ª14–17 (Heath, *Mathematics*, p. 11).
61. Mersenne, *Traité*, p. 5.
62. Fonseca, *Commentarii*, 2:378.

continuation of *discrete* and divided things."[63] The marginal gloss sums up the overall conception promoted here: "That continuous quantity depends on discrete quantity, and that both depend on unity."[64] Continuous quantity could not be recognized without the prior concept of discrete quantity, because quantity is characterized by its having parts, and so the logical basis of geometry reduces to arithmetic. Arithmetic in turn rests on the concept of unity, in accordance with Euclid's definition, presented by Mersenne, that "number is a multitude, which is composed of unities."[65] "The basis of arithmetic," said Mersenne elsewhere, "is numerical unity."[66]

A scholastic commonplace, this picture nonetheless failed to provide a suffucient basis for universal agreement on the nature of mathematical objects, and the Jesuit camp divided sharply between mathematicians on the one hand and some metaphysicians, often together with natural philosophers, on the other. The latter group denied that the objects of mathematics had any objective reality: if numbers were composed of unities, something else had to be doing the composition; that something was, of course, an intellect. A number, argued Fonseca, was therefore not a real being, *ens reale,* but only a being of reason, *ens rationalis,* and the Coïmbra commentators took the same position: a number "is not a real being" because a real being is "that which does not depend on the operation of the intellect." As a result of these considerations, the Conimbricenses felt able to state that mathematicians "consider the nature and essence of no real being."[67] Jesuit philosophers, as we shall see later, accepted that real things existing in the world possessed individual or numerical *unity* such that they were indeed individual objects. Attaching a number to a collection of individuals, however, was a purely intellectual act rather than a simple recognition of what was already there; a group of seven individuals might be regarded as comprising two groups of three and four, or of five and two, or just as separate individuals, depending on how the mind chose to apprehend them.

In this view, definitions of mathematical objects could not be essential propositions, because those objects lacked the potential for real existence. By contrast, "man is a rational animal" could be, because a man can have real existence if God creates him. The intimate connection between essences and causation that appeared in discussions of

---

63. Mersenne, *La verité,* pp. 282–83.
64. Ibid., p. 283.
65. Ibid., p. 285. This definition is also given in, e.g., the Coïmbra *Dialectic,* 1:432, and Fonseca (citing Aristotle), *Commentarii,* 2:763–64.
66. Mersenne, *La verité,* p. 251.
67. Fonseca, *Commentarii,* 2:667; Coïmbra *Dialectic,* 1:432, 2:507.

eternal truths and their relationship to God therefore allowed implications to be drawn about the causal nature of mathematical demonstrations. In the sixteenth century, a number of Italian philosophers, starting with Alessandro Piccolomini and including such Jesuits as Pereira in Rome and the Coïmbra commentators, had maintained that arithmetic and geometry were not true sciences in the Aristotelian sense, because they lacked causal demonstrations.[68] For Aristotle, *scientia,* scientific knowledge, in addition to possessing those formal requirements considered earlier, emerged from the demonstration of necessary effects through their immediate causes. The ideal unit of a scientific demonstration was a syllogism, the minor premise of which stated a causal relation—whether efficient, material, formal, or final. The explanatory cause should be necessary and sufficient to produce the conclusion. The argument that pure mathematics did not produce scientific knowledge relied on the claim that its demonstrations did not employ causes; thus, a demonstration in geometry would be no more than an exposition of logical relations between propositions, with no order of causal priority. There could be no essential knowledge of mathematical objects because those objects were no more than constructed fictions, lacking real being.

These doctrines jarred with the disciplinary aspirations of Jesuit mathematicians, whose subject was thereby denied the status of science, the highest form of knowledge. In the 1580s, during the debate over the curricular structure of the colleges that ultimately produced the definitive 1599 *Ratio studiorum,* Clavius (who held the chair in mathematics at the Collegio Romano until his death in 1612) fought hard to secure for mathematics what he considered to be its rightful place. In one advisory document he severely criticizes those teachers in the colleges who tell the pupils that "mathematical sciences are not sciences, do not have demonstrations, abstract from being and the good etc." Clavius objects that "these questions are a great hindrance to pupils and of no service to them; especially since teachers can hardly teach them without bringing these sciences into ridicule."[69] He goes on to suggest ways to improve the image of mathematics; these include emphasizing its utility for philosophy, as we saw in the last chapter.[70] Clavius tried to counter the metaphysicians' denials of scientific status to mathematics by claiming for it a position of preeminence among the sciences, on the basis of its superior certainty, but

68. For a longer discussion with full references of the issues in this and the following paragraph, see Dear, "Jesuit Mathematical Science." See also Wallace, *Galileo,* pp. 136–37.

69. Clavius, "Modus," pp. 471–74 (quotes on p. 471).

70. Ibid., p. 472.

for the most part he failed to translate his opposition into explicit philosophical repudiation. The fullest attempt at this task was made by his pupil Josephus Blancanus in a work of 1615.[71]

Blancanus explains, along Aristotelian lines, how the subject of pure mathematics is intelligible matter, the result of abstracting quantity from sensible matter. The ideas of mathematics thus have their origin in the senses, as all ideas, according to Aristotle, must. This abstracted, intelligible matter, continues Blancanus, has a "mathematical perfection" not found in sensible matter (the matter of the physicist): a perfect triangle is seldom found "in the nature of things"—which, he says, has led some people to claim that mathematical entities exist only in the intellect. Blancanus is here confronting a version of the argument described earlier with reference to numbers, and in giving an answer for geometry he also indicates one for arithmetic. Admitting that geometrical entities do not exist in the world with the perfection they have in the intellect, he observes that this does not alter the fact that they *are* realized in sensible matter, even though imperfectly. "For it is well known," he goes on, "that nature and art chiefly intend mathematical figures, although on account of the crassness and imperfection of sensible matter, which is unable entirely to receive perfect figures, they are frustrated in their aim."[72] Thus the sun and the eye endeavor towards sphericity; plants often display cylinders and planes; seashells exhibit spirals. Mathematical entities may not exist perfectly in sensible things, therefore, but they clearly exist such that *copies* of them can be realized in corporeal matter.[73] In sum, "the Ideas of [mathematical entities] exist, as much in the mind of the Author of nature as in the human [mind], as the most exact types of things, and also as exact mathematical entities." These "Ideas" are the mathematician's true subject matter.[74]

Blancanus's account at this point appears to have taken a Platonic turn, but he is in fact exploiting the ordinary scholastic interpretation of the "forms" of things as corresponding to "ideas in the mind of God." This was an inseparable and uncontentious part of Christianized Aristotelianism;[75] Blancanus tries here simply to justify its application to mathematical entities. The mathematician will then be

---

71. Josephus Blancanus, *De mathematicarum natura dissertatio* (Bologna, 1615). This is always bound together with Blancanus's *Aristotelis loca mathematica ex universis ipsius Operibus collecta, & explicata*, which carries out, over 283 pages, the exercise recommended by Clavius (see Chapter 3, above). For a summary of the *dissertatio*, see Wallace, *Galileo*, pp. 141–44; see also Dear, "Jesuit Mathematical Science."

72. Blancanus, *De mathematicarum natura*, p. 6.

73. Ibid., pp. 6–7.

74. Ibid., p. 7.

75. See, e.g., the account in Jordan, "Intelligibility."

seen to discuss not merely figments of the intellect associable with physical objects but archetypes in the mind of God that find realization (however imperfect) in sensible matter. This conceptualization further provided a way of answering the charge that mathematical demonstrations were not causal, a charge that Blancanus bitterly attacks for its derogation of his discipline. Geometry, he argues, typically employs both formal and material causes. The latter arise because terminated quantity, or intelligible matter, has parts; parts constitute a material cause since they are that from which a geometrical magnitude is made. More significantly, geometrical demonstrations use formal causes because the definitions of mathematical objects are *essential* definitions—and Blancanus can make this assertion only because he has already established that mathematical objects really are entities for which talk of essences is appropriate, with prototypes in the mind of God paralleling those of physical beings.[76]

Descartes's assumption that talk of the eternal truth of essential propositions applied equally to mathematical truths appears in the light of this controversy to have been somewhat hasty. Only if mathematical truths were themselves taken to be essential propositions would this be true, and many metaphysicians denied it. Mersenne, unlike Descartes, both recognized the issue and chose one side rather than the other in support of his own position that mathematics produced scientific knowledge about the world. Not surprisingly, he adopted an approach similar to that of Clavius and Blancanus.[77]

We have already seen ways in which Mersenne echoed Clavius's pronouncements on mathematics relating to certainty and utility. He also discussed causality and number in terms like those used by Blancanus concerning geometry. The material cause of number, he asserted in *La verité*, is unity, since numbers are collections of unities. The efficient cause, acting to conjoin those unities to produce something new—namely, numbers themselves—is the understanding.[78] In describing the understanding as the efficient cause of number, Mersenne appropriated the usual view that numbers existed only in an intellect; he turned a view that often appeared as grounds for denying causality and essences to mathematical objects into *support* for causation in mathematics.

76. Ibid., pp. 13–18; the arguments for geometry are asserted for arithmetic as well on p. 18. That mathematical definitions are *essential* definitions is argued on pp. 7–10.

77. Mersenne refers to Blancanus's *Aristotelis loca mathematica* in *Quaestiones* and elsewhere (see Chapter 6, below); he may very well have been directly familiar with Blancanus's own views on these matters.

78. The final cause is being able to count things, and the formal cause is "the last unity, for it cannot be taken away or added without changing the species of the number": Mersenne, *La verité*, p. 284.

La verité's Christian Philosopher replied to the Sceptic's paradoxes concerning "le binaire" on just these grounds. The paradoxes revolved around treating "le binaire" as one thing, thereby confusing even simple processes of addition by a conflation of two different kinds of "individual" subjects, ones and twos. The problem vanished, according to the Christian Philosopher, if one bore in mind that "the binary is nothing other than the assemblage and conjunction of two unities." Considered independently, these could never be more than themselves, "for union is necessary if we want to produce the binary." However, "it suffices that this union is made by reason, which compares two or several unities when it pleases; in such a way, however, that it cannot prevent two conjoined unities from producing the binary, and three the ternary, &c."[79] A little earlier he had denied that the certainty of arithmetic was compromised by the fact that "four can be one and three, or two and two, or that each number can be divided in several ways"; these divisions could not prevent four unities from making four.[80]

Two overriding points emerge from Mersenne's arguments here: first, mathematical truths were certain, because necessary; secondly, they could have no existence outside an intellect: "$2 + 2 = 4$" would have no truth-value at all without the existence of the numbers acting as its terms, but given an intellect, it became necessarily true. Furthermore, he said, "formal numbers [as opposed to numbers of actually existing things] have need of no other existence than that which they receive in the understanding,"[81] reflecting Blancanus's contention that their possession of essential natures followed from the consideration that the preeminent intellect giving them existence was that of God. Thus, Mersenne's position on this issue shows categorically that he did not regard mathematical truths as independent of God. Numbers, as distinct from collections of unities, would not exist without God.

Mersenne's position on the question of eternal truths and their relation to mathematics can therefore be stated clearly. Those necessary, eternal truths represented by essential propositions (the only kind considered by Suarez) depended absolutely on God's causality. This in no way compromised their necessity. Mathematical truths also counted as essential propositions, contrary to the view of many metaphysicians but according with that defended by Blancanus; they too depended entirely on divine causality. Mersenne thus agreed with

79. Ibid., pp. 277–78.
80. Ibid., p. 274.
81. Ibid., p. 275.

Aquinas's contention that arithmetical truths were propositions known eternally by God.[82]

IV

The close similarity between essential propositions about real creatures and statements about mathematical objects, by which Mersenne maintained the causal, scientific status of mathematics, could be rendered additionally plausible through another Thomistic doctrine. That was the real purpose of the analogy, in *L'impieté des deistes*, between God and unity. Aquinas had described God as an absolutely simple intellect that nonetheless comprehends the diversity of all possible essences, which it can bring into actual being as analogues of the divine being. This is because it knows all possible ways in which its own divine essence can be imitated. The apparent paradox of perfect simplicity producing a diversity of creatures thus disappeared.[83] Likewise, said Mersenne, taking up an analogy made by Aquinas himself, the simplicity of unity underlay the infinite diversity of numbers and in that way resembled the divine act of creation, since "if you want to compare all the diverse kinds [*especes*] to diverse numbers, which conserve themselves by the indivisibility of their differences, like the essence of things (whence comes the maxim, *essentiae sunt sicut numeri* [essences are just like numbers]), you will see that unity produces diverse kinds."[84] Creatures draw their perfections from God just as numbers draw theirs from unity, "to which they add nothing new";[85] as the being of creatures represents participation in the divine being, so the numerality of numbers represents the participation of unity, "on which they depend, such that it is impossible that they exist [*soient*] without it."[86]

The production of diverse creatures from an absolutely simple Creator depended on the existence of an intellect, the divine intellect.

82. Maurer, "St. Thomas," p. 97.
83. Julius R. Weinberg, *A Short History of Medieval Philosophy* (Princeton, 1964), pp. 194–95; Jordan, "Intelligibility"; Gilson, *Philosophy of St. Thomas Aquinas*, pp. 94–95, 112–14.
84. Mersenne, *L'impieté*, 1:425–26; see also *Quaestiones*, cols. 437–40. Cf. the formal cause of numbers, n. 78, above. Jordan, "Intelligibility," pp. 26–27, discusses Aquinas's similar use of Aristotle's comparison (*Metaphysics* VIII.3) between forms and numbers, wherein the addition or subtraction of a single unit changes the species: Aquinas develops this in relation to God and the production of His creatures (*Contra gentiles* 1.54) to show "how an indefinite series of distinct forms can be generated by imitation of a single substance."
85. Mersenne, *L'impieté*, 1:424.
86. Ibid., p. 419.

Similarly, the production of numbers from unity depended on an intellect, be it human or divine; without it, the potentiality of number contained in unity could not be actualized. This analogy between things and numbers did not exhaust their relationship, however, and Mersenne brought other elements of the scholastic metaphysical armory to bear in an attempt to establish mathematics even more strongly as a form of knowledge relevant to the study of the physical world. The task demanded little more than setting out the standard doctrine on the nature of number, derived from the Greek concept of *arithmos*, a numbered assemblage: numbers were that which could be predicated of a collection of things.[87]

In this view, numbers could not merely be applied to things but were in a sense ontologically inseparable from them: numbers existed only by virtue of the possible existence of *things to be numbered*. Mersenne put it like this: "Each number is produced by position alone [i.e., by being posited], and by the actual or possible existence of things that are distinct or separated each from the other; for it isn't necessary that there *be* different things to establish numbers; it suffices that they *can* be, just as it suffices that there can be several men in order to establish the truth of human nature, even though they don't actually exist."[88] The concept of number therefore derived from the possibility of separate, numerable things being created (once again necessitating the existence of a potential efficient cause: that is, God).

Mersenne went on to say that although Aristotle held that number was nothing if the soul did not number it, he should be understood to mean only "numbering number [*nombre nombrant*], which is nothing else than the understanding, which conceives what is at present outside of itself, and what is real and true [*veritable*] in exterior objects."[89] For Mersenne, as for Blancanus, the objects of mathematics, although manifested as what is "real and true in exterior objects," had a prototypical existence in the intellect, preeminently that of God. They were sustained by the possibility of creation, not by its actuality. When

---

87. See Jacob Klein, *Greek Mathematical Thought and the Origin of Algebra* (Cambridge, Mass., 1968), pp. 46–60, 150–63; the theme is taken up in Michael S. Mahoney, "The Beginnings of Algebraic Thought in the Seventeenth Century," in Stephen Gaukroger, ed., *Descartes* (Brighton, Sussex, 1980), pp. 141–55. See also the clear account in Gaukroger, *Explanatory Structures*, pp. 98–102. Fonseca, *Commentarii*, 2:667, makes the point that arithmetic has its origin in numerable things.

88. Mersenne, *La verité*, p. 272. In saying that the truth of human nature requires the possible existence of men, Mersenne again indicates that essential propositions depend on a potential efficient cause: i.e., God.

89. Ibid.; see also Mersenne's remarks on this theme in Marin Mersenne, *Questions inouyes* (Paris, 1634), pp. 71–74. Cf. Kepler's use of these ideas to justify geometrical rather than arithmetical archetypes for the universe: Judith V. Field, "Kepler's Rejection of Numerology," in Vickers, *Occult and Scientific Mentalities*, pp. 273–96.

Suarez countered the idea that truths about creatures held only when those creatures actually existed, he quoted Saint Augustine's observation: "Three and four are seven is perpetually true, even if there be nothing which is numbered"; possible existence, as Mersenne said, sufficed.[90] Furthermore, the logical dependence of the objects of geometry on those of arithmetic meant that whatever held for the latter held also for the former.

V

This examination of Mersenne's scholastic apologia for mathematics shows both a determined and a selective use of argumentative and conceptual resources. All of his positions, equipped with standard arguments, conspired to justify a high estimation of the mathematical disciplines and the kind of knowledge they produced. Mathematical demonstrations were certain; they were also causal and thus scientific; their objects existed archetypically in the mind of God like those of physics; and their objects were necessary concomitants of God's creative power. Physics could be made to suffer by comparison, as Clavius had shown: if mathematics fulfilled all these desiderata while physical demonstrations typically failed to achieve that of certainty, a good foundation seemed established for an alternative mathematical natural philosophy to replace essentialist physics.

The scholastic-Aristotelian ideal of a scientific natural philosophy, however, incorporated essentialist explanation as its principal goal, and mathematics appeared from this perspective to be a necessarily inadequate natural philosophical tool. Aristotle described quantity as an accidental property unrevealing of a thing's essential nature, and the Coïmbra commentators (who even denied mathematics scientific status in its own right) outlined its shortcomings uncompromisingly: "Mathematics detaches [*praescindit*] quantity from every subject and efficient principle; therefore, it is not able to know what is real being, what accident, [or to know] whatever endows a substance with a nature [*ratione*]."[91] Such a view implied a very lowly status for the mixed mathematical disciplines at the heart of Mersenne's philosophical agenda, and he needed arguments with which to counter it.

---

90. Suarez, *Disputationes* XXXI.XII.39; for the context of this quotation see Wells, "Suarez," p. 160.

91. Coïmbra *Dialectic*, 2:504. Mathematics concerned itself with terminated, or determinate, quantity, unlike the indeterminate quantity of the physicist. For late scholastic discussions, see Reif, "Natural Philosophy," pp. 134–35, and esp. Blancanus, *De mathematicarum natura*, pp. 5–6.

Robert Lenoble remarked that for Mersenne, mathematics was a science of the possible; it constrained what could and could not be the case without determining it.[92] Having seen how deeply implicated scholastic considerations of the "possible" were in Mersenne's justification of mathematical knowledge, we can perhaps extend this insight in order to understand his attempts at presenting mathematics not as a study of accidents but as a science of metaphysically necessary attributes. The resources of scholastic metaphysics provided the language and most of the conceptual building blocks for this rather ambitious task, and Mersenne used them to their greatest potential.

According to Suarez, "science is said to deal with universals and not with singulars,"[93] and Mersenne possessed a conventional conception of the nature of a science. He seems, in fact, to have adopted the usual Thomistic teaching on universals, which ran as follows. A nature such as whiteness or humanity, which is predicable of individual things, is, considered in itself, neither one (a universal) nor many (the sum of its individual instantiations). However, when considered in relation to the things of which it is predicated, a nature is many; and when considered in relation to the mind possessing the concept (created by abstraction from individual things), it is a universal. This does not mean, as a nominalist would say, that universals are not real, being only intellectual constructs. Any quality, or nature, really does exist in its individual instantiations, but not *qua* universal as it does in the mind.[94] Mersenne had no quarrel with the concept of universals, and in these terms his principal objection to physics simply amounted to the claim that one cannot tell which properties associated with a thing are essential to it and which accidental. No essential definition can as a rule be provided for anything, therefore, and so there can be no physical demonstrations. On this level, the objection was epistemological, not ontological: we cannot know the true causes of things until God reveals them to us in Heaven, but no doubt such causes exist.[95]

In Mersenne's view, natural objects could be grouped into species only on an operational, pragmatic basis rooted in apparent similarities (see Chapter 7). Physics could not, therefore, be a science. A true *mathematical* science of the physical world, by contrast, would require a

92. E.g., Lenoble, *Mersenne*, p. 356.
93. Suarez, *Disputationes*, vi.v.3; quoted in Doig, "Suarez, Descartes," p. 353.
94. See Sandra Edwards, "The Realism of Aquinas," *New Scholasticism* 59 (1985), 79–101; Weinberg, *Short History*, pp. 202–3; Maurer, "St. Thomas," pp. 100–101. For Suarez on this issue, see introduction by J. F. Ross to Francis Suarez, *On Formal and Universal Unity*, trans. J. F. Ross (Milwaukee, Wis., 1964), pp. 6–7; Carlos P. Norena, "Ockham and Suarez on Universal Concepts," *New Scholasticism* 55 (1981), 348–62.
95. See, e.g., Mersenne, *Questions theologiques*, p. 11.

nonarbitrary, *proper* attribution of mathematical properties. Mersenne's belief in the reliability of the senses under normal conditions guaranteed the propriety of predicating the universal "whiteness" of a swan, but one could not say whether it was an essential property or not. Mathematical predicates, however, were guaranteed a more fundamental relationship to their subjects. Mathematics produced quasiessential knowledge about things in the world because all mathematics had its ontological root in unity, and unity, according to Mersenne, was a kind of universal *form*.

The Sceptic in *La verité,* having heard the Christian Philosopher's explanation that unity is the basis of number, tries to undermine the certainty of arithmetic by raising paradoxes about what makes anything "one." These center on whether unity is one or many; the Sceptic thus implicitly invokes the standard question about universals and makes it more pointed by applying it to unity, or "oneness," itself.[96] Mersenne's Christian Philosopher simply replies with the Thomistic doctrine on universals: "I say therefore firstly that numerical unity is common to everything that is one, and consequently it is like a universal, complete [*toute*] in everything that is one without any diminution, in the same way as the philosophers say that human nature is complete in each particular man: whereby you can see that unity isn't like the robe of your Empiricus [alluding to a Pyrrhonian argument], which cannot cover several people, but rather like the genus found in all species, or like the species in all individuals."[97] A little later he observes that unity is that which "makes it that each thing considered in particular is one, as whiteness makes it that the things in which it is found are white."[98]

Because the subject matter of all mathematics ultimately derived from the concept of unity, and that concept initially entered the mind—as all ideas, according to Aristotle, must—through the senses, mathematics itself was simply reason acting on ideas provided by the

96. Mersenne, *La verité,* pp. 266–68.

97. Ibid., p. 271. Note that Mersenne specifies *numerical* unity (*l'unité numerique*). This distinction invokes the division of "essential unity" into "formal" and "numerical," the first referring to unity of genus or species, the second to individual things. "Accidental unity" refers to the relation of accidents, such as saying that Achilles and Hector both exist in one and the same duration. See the discussion in Coïmbra *Dialectic,* 1:95–96. Fonseca (*Commentarii,* 2: 959–62) doubts the propriety of the distinction between numerical and formal unity and reduces them to two different kinds of numerical unity. Suarez (*Disputationes* v.1.4) devotes an entire disputation to numerical unity, holding that "all things that are actual beings whether they exist or can exist immediately [are] singulars and individuals." Gracia, *Suarez,* provides a complete translation of this disputation and, in his introduction, a useful survey of scholastic doctrines on individual unity.

98. Mersenne, *La verité,* p. 280.

external world. "A universal," as Fonseca said, "is not made unless by abstraction from particulars."[99] Mathematics could be applied to the world because it derived from the world. Mersenne, however, went further by arguing that it yielded philosophically important knowledge when so applied because unity was not just another universal; the special significance of mathematics arose from the sense in which unity appeared as a form. A "theorem" in *La verité* purports to maintain that "unity is a form by which each particular being is called one,"[100] and Mersenne there gives Boethius's definition of unity, which he describes as much more advantageous than Euclid's: "*Unitas est qua unaquaeque res una est, & est id quod est*; that is, unity is that by which each thing is one, and is that which it is."[101] Mersenne wished to argue that unity is a "form" of each particular being, "that by which each thing is one," and his confidence in doing so arose from the consideration that although the essential natures of things were unknowable, basic metaphysical properties were not.[102]

When trying to convince the Sceptic that some areas of human knowledge possess certainty, Mersenne's Christian Philosopher chooses as an example, apart from logic or mathematics, metaphysics. "Metaphysics teaches that there are beings, and natures, and that everything that is, or that has an essence, is one, true, and good; and it takes as a principle 'that it is impossible that the same thing be, and not be.'" No one, he says, can possibly doubt that, any more than one could say that a round wheel is square.[103] Mersenne held the basic terms of metaphysics to be necessarily true of things: anything that exists, for example, necessarily has being. Similarly, all beings have essences—that is, they *are* something—even though knowledge of these must await the illumination of the afterlife. Furthermore, every being is "one, true, and good" (the "oneness" here refers conventionally to individual, or numerical, unity).[104] So, although Mersenne

99. Fonseca, *Commentarii*, 1:155. Geometrical characteristics could also be abstracted from individuals as universals but not without the prior establishment of unity, since the continuous quantity of geometry had its conceptual foundation in discrete quantity, itself dependent on unity. Properties such as "triangularity" could not therefore be recognized except on the basis of a prior abstraction of the concept of unity. As for the role of "reason" in all this, Chapter 5, below, considers how for Mersenne reason itself—preeminently its manifestation in mathematics—ordered the world by virtue of God's Wisdom.

100. Mersenne, *La verité*, p. 280.

101. Ibid., p. 284.

102. Mersenne uses the term "form" a little loosely here; for the possible range of meanings in scholastic usage, see the glossary in Gracia, *Suarez*, pp. 216–17.

103. Mersenne, *La verité*, pp. 52, 53.

104. The basic tenet of scholastic metaphysics: see Gracia's introduction to *Suarez*, p. 24.

described unity as "like a universal," it was of a peculiar kind. All knowable aspects of things other than the metaphysical—whiteness or hotness, for example—might or might not be found in particular entities and might be either essential or accidental; it was impossible to say with certainty. Unity, on the other hand, represented an inseparable, necessary aspect of every thing in the world. Since mathematics derived from it, mathematical characteristics of created things, although in one sense "accidental," in another sense related to an especially fundamental property of being.

In both *La verité des sciences* and *Traité de l'harmonie universelle*, Mersenne explains the various kinds of abstraction, and he concentrates on abstraction of mathematical characteristics.[105] In the *Traité*, for example, he lists the various classes of universals and then proceeds to discuss the two appertaining to mathematics. These, the "imaginable" and the "intelligible," are analogous to considering man "or any other thing" without regard to color or "the other accidents that are proper and particular to it."[106] Clearly, mathematical aspects are not, in this view, accidental. One might conceive of a black swan, but one could never have a swan that was at the same time two swans.

Mersenne's metaphysical sanctioning of a mathematically based philosophy of nature, or "physico-mathematics," as he later came to call it, relied heavily on emphasizing the independence of mathematical objects from the contingency of physical creation. In that way, mathematics could be scientific as physics could not. At the same time, mathematics appeared suitable for the description of the physical world and for the coordination and correction of sensory data, because its subject matter was an inseparable condition of existence of physical beings. Truth, in scholastic parlance a relation of conformity, therefore existed in that conformity between mathematical relations and the observed, measurable, quantitative characteristics of things guaranteed by the latter's necessary metaphysical properties. By the same token, the truth of mathematical statements themselves devolved from the properties associated with the possible existence of created things. "It therefore suffices that the [mathematical] sciences and all their notions have a being of reason [i.e., exist in the intellect], to which they are true [*veritables*], provided that they be conformed to external objects and their properties."[107] The power of mathematics depended on this conformity: the world might be contingent, but "it

105. Mersenne, *La verité*, pp. 227–28; *Traité*, pp. 4–5.
106. Mersenne, *Traité*, p. 4.
107. Mersenne, *La verité*, p. 275.

never fails to be found that two times two men are four men, *according to the idea that reason had conceived*" (my emphasis).[108]

In *Harmonie universelle* (1636), Mersenne considered the possibility of inventing a language having a separate word for every individual thing in the world, and he concluded that by means of the alphabet and combinatorics it could be done. If God created extra individuals, one could always generate new names by increasing the maximum allowable number of letters to a word. Mersenne evidently took it for granted that individuals in nature (unlike species) presented no problems of recognition.[109] Had he denied this, unity would have become epistemologically uprooted from physical things, and mathematics would have had no advantage over essentialist physics.

Ultimately, Mersenne's portrayal of mathematics did not help it to circumvent the contingency of nature undermining Aristotelian physics; it remained, as Lenoble has said, a science of the possible. God could create *anything* not involving a contradiction, and mixed mathematics always in practice employed some physical assumptions. Lenoble presents a striking example of this view from *Questions theologiques*, where, in comparison with a work such as *La verité des sciences*, the polemical requirement to stress certainty held less sway.[110] Mersenne asks which of the two sciences of optics and music is the more certain. Neither can be absolutely certain, he says, because each involves suppositions drawn from physics as well as from mathematics. Mersenne therefore wishes only to assess relative probabilities, and the outcome of the comparison is that optics ranks above music. To the extent that optics is subordinate to geometry and music to arithmetic, he argues, both are equally and completely certain. But to the extent that each draws on physical principles based on unreliable inferences from sensory knowledge, that certainty is compromised. However, the physical properties of light are a less doubtful matter than those of sound, and so music must possess greater uncertainty than optics.[111] For all the

---

108. Ibid., p. 277.

109. Mersenne, *Harmonie universelle*, "De la voix," pp. 72–73; see also *La verité*, p. 806. See Chapter 7, below, for a fuller discussion; identifying species with certainty, of course, would require access to essences.

110. Lenoble, *Mersenne*, p. 354.

111. Mersenne, *Questions theologiques*, pp. 179–82. Lenoble expands on the problems presented by the contingency of nature: "À propos du tricentenaire de la mort de Mersenne," *Archives internationales d'histoire des sciences* 28 (1949), 583–97. Mersenne's weakening of the disciplinary integrity of mixed mathematical sciences by his assertion of their lack of complete independence from physics appears also in *Harmonie universelle*, "Nouvelles observations physiques et mathematiques," p. 17: "Now, I don't think that one can demonstrate that weights descend exactly to the center or towards the

virtues of mathematical procedures, then, ignorance of essences still stood in the way of a thoroughly satisfactory knowledge of the physical world. Nonetheless, a metaphysical justification of the mathematical sciences still served an important purpose: it legitimated the *practice* of mathematical natural philosophy as an alternative to Aristotelian physics. Mersenne's use of scholastic terms and scholastic doctrinal commonplaces indicates the context within which he wanted that legitimation to occur, as well as the context from which he himself derived his understanding of the philosophical issues.

At the end of his well-known criticism of Galileo's inclined-plane experiments, wherein he reported failure in his attempts to reproduce Galileo's results (even expressing doubts as to whether Galileo could have got them to begin with), Mersenne drew a moral. The whole business went to show that "experience isn't capable of engendering a science, and that one shouldn't rely too much [*il ne se faut pas trop fier*] on reason alone, since it doesn't always answer to the truth of appearances, from which it very often withdraws [*s'eloigne*]."[112] Experience and reason each provided an unsound foundation for a science of nature. Galileo's problem was an excessive reliance on reason, but no absolutely reliable approach existed. In countering Pyrrhonism, Mersenne had established the existence of true sciences only by claiming that it was beside the point whether "they have relation to exterior things, or not."[113] Beyond the realm of pure mathematics—arithmetic and geometry—which subsisted in the intellect, certainty ran up against contingency. Arithmetic might be applied to the Trinity or to degrees of grace,[114] but God remained inscrutable for all that: the same went for His creatures.

Contemporary scholastic metamathematics thus served Mersenne

---

center of the earth, since we have no experiences or reasons that could not be saved and explained even if they descended only four or five leagues closer to the said center. Whence one can conclude the incertitude of mechanics, and of the other parts of physics, at least in regard to men, who don't know its first principles sufficiently certainly and evidently, without which one is not assured of the conclusions." Mersenne here presents mechanics as a "part of physics" rather than a mathematical discipline (contrary to his classification in *Quaestiones*) and as correspondingly uncertain. Breaking down the boundary between mathematics and physics served at once to extend the natural philosophical scope and implications of the mathematical sciences and to compromise their claim on absolute mathematical certitude.

112. Mersenne, *Harmonie universelle*, "Des mouvemens de toutes sortes de corps," p. 112. For a discussion of Mersenne's criticisms of Galileo, see Alexandre Koyré, "An Experiment in Measurement," in *Metaphysics and Measurement* (Cambridge, Mass., 1968), pp. 89–117.

113. Mersenne, *La verité*, p. 277.

114. See, for just one example, ibid., pp. 619–20.

in creating a quasi-orthodox basis for his natural philosophical agenda. It did not go far enough, however. His lifelong interest in music theory, and its connection with his work in other mathematical sciences, involved the idea of a "universal harmony" underlying nature that justified looking for physical analogues of abstract mathematical relationships. The sanction for this idea came from Saint Augustine.

CHAPTER FIVE

Saint Augustine and Universal Harmony

I

MERSENNE may have been the first person to remark on the apparent affinities between the Cartesian *cogito* and Saint Augustine's logical swipe at the scepticism of the New Academy: "Si fallor, sum." Certainly, Mersenne's observation, made in a letter to Descartes after the appearance of the "Discourse on Method," is the first recorded instance of a seventeenth-century association of Cartesianism and Augustinianism which, finding public voice soon afterwards in Arnauld's "objections" to the *Meditations*, underlay the curious affinity of both Jansenists and Oratorians for Descartes's new philosophy.[1] In the present century, it has been suggested that the Augustinianism of Cardinal Bérulle and his fellow Oratorians in Paris during the 1620s provided an important part of the metaphysical groundwork for Descartes's system, and however that suggestion is assessed, it is predicated on an undeniable fact illustrated by Mersenne's reaction to the "Discourse": Augustinian ideas were commonplace at this time in France.[2] This chapter examines Mersenne's use of Augustinian

1. Mersenne's observation is evidenced by a remark in Descartes to Mersenne, 6 June 1637, Mersenne *Correspondance*, 6:277; Mersenne's original letter is lost. See also Henri Gouhier, *Cartésianisme et augustinisme au XVIIe siècle* (Paris, 1978), pp. 15–17, and chap. 5 for a discussion of the often observed relation between Cartesianism and Jansenism.

2. See esp. Étienne Gilson, *Études sur le rôle de la pensée médiévale dans la formation du système cartésien* (Paris, 1951), chap. 1, "L'innéisme cartésien et la théologie." Some other classic treatments of the subject by Gilson, Blanchet, and others are conveniently listed in Gouhier, *Cartésianisme*, p. 185n.1, to which one might add René Descartes, *Discours de la méthode: Texte et commentaire par Étienne Gilson* (Paris, 1925), pp. 295–98; Henri Gouhier, "La crise de la théologie au temps de Descartes," *Revue de théologie et de philosophie*, 3d ser., 4 (1954), 19–54; idem, *La pensée*, pp. 241–43, together with Gilson's

themes in establishing certain basic ideas to justify his natural philo-sophical agenda, particularly regarding the extent to which mathe-matical regularities may be anticipated in the behavior of physical processes. Mersenne emerges as a subscriber not to Renaissance Pla-tonism but to doctrines rooted in Augustine's authority as a Father of the Church and in the sanction given to the saint's teachings by con-temporary Catholic scholasticism.

Augustine's prominence in medieval and early modern theology, and not merely, in the latter period, among the Reformers, is too well known to require emphasis.[3] In addition to the better-known the-ological questions to do with grace, free will, and salvation, however, there were significant metaphysical issues. The latter divided Au-gustine from Thomas Aquinas, the official doctrinal master of the Jesuits and of Mersenne's own order, the Minims.[4] Étienne Gilson has characterized the differences as reducing to the question of "in-natism," or of "Aristotle versus Plato," and has in that connection delineated late sixteenth- and early seventeenth-century uses of the notion of "innate ideas." With one eye fixed on the *cogito,* Gilson addresses particularly those arguments purporting to demonstrate

---

review of the first edition in *Études,* pp. 281–98. See also Robert Gotwald Remsberg, *Wisdom and Science at Port-Royal and the Oratory* (Yellow Springs, Ohio, 1940), pp. 117–28, and references below.

3. The literature defies summary here. The recent treatments by Heiko Oberman, *Masters of the Reformation* (Cambridge, 1981), pp. 64–110; and Peter Iver Kaufman, *Augustinian Piety and Catholic Reform* (Macon, Ga., 1982), provide an entry to the mate-rial. For our purposes the philosophical side of Augustinianism is most crucial, and its place in the Middle Ages is discussed in, e.g., Stephen P. Marrone, *William of Auvergne and Robert Grosseteste* (Princeton, 1983), pp. 10–13; Joseph Owens, "Faith, Ideas, Il-lumination, and Experience," and Eileen Serene, "Demonstrative Science," both in Kretzmann, Kenny, and Pinborg, *Cambridge History of Later Medieval Philosophy,* respec-tively pp. 440–59 and 496–517, esp. 498–504. See also Fernand van Steenberghen's remarks in *Aristotle in the West* (Louvain, 1970), pp. 128–30, on Augustinianism in thirteenth-century theology and philosophy. Gilson discusses É. Baudin's observation on the existence in the seventeenth century of two "Augustinianisms," one philosoph-ical and the other religious: *Études,* pp. 291–92n. As Petrarch might indicate, the relation between humanism and Augustinianism was of long standing; for an ex-tremely suggestive examination of this question, see William J. Bouwsma, "The Two Faces of Humanism," in Heiko O. Oberman and Thomas A. Brady, Jr., eds., *Itinerarium Italicum* (Leiden, 1975), pp. 3–60. Bouwsma argues that the Stoic/Augustinian distinc-tion within humanist thought represents competing tendencies more authentic than any Aristotelian/Platonic distinction; he considers particularly the possible interconnec-tions within each of these two strains between natural order and social order, as well as the roles of reason and grace in theology: see esp. pages 57–58 on Augustine's place in the Counter-Reformation and his importance in seventeenth-century France. (The details of the huge literature on Jansenism and Augustinianism are not relevant here.)

4. On the Minims, see Whitmore, *The Order of Minims in Seventeenth-Century France,* p. 153.

the existence of God on the basis of innate knowledge. Aquinas's Aristotelianism maintained that *all* knowledge had its origin in the senses, and Aquinas therefore rejected any innatist proof of God's existence, including particularly the ontological proof of Anselm.[5] Gilson observes, however, that the innatist position formed a persistent undercurrent within scholastic thought, and he regards it as being greatly indebted to the writings of Augustine, the most influential repository of neo-Platonic ideas in the Middle Ages. There were therefore two opposing metaphysical positions whose long co-existence demonstrates their capability of "an infinity of accommodations."[6] It also reveals how what Espinas in 1906 identified as a rise of Platonism in the early seventeenth century[7] could emerge from late scholastic orthodoxy rather than from some Ficinean counterculture.

Gilson provides contextual reasons to account for what he sees as a "renovation of Platonic innatism," associated with Augustinianism, during that period.[8] His argument, calling to mind that of Popkin, emphasizes the prevalence of scepticism in France in the late sixteenth and early seventeenth centuries. The sceptic, if permitted to point to a lack of anything within himself that could compel belief in God, would have a powerful weapon with which to undermine faith. The usual Thomistic position served only to support such a tactic, while the sceptic already had a battery of arguments to defeat the concomitant Thomistic proposition that knowledge of God could be acquired through knowledge of His Creation.[9] Gilson shows that this sceptical threat was indeed taken seriously in some quarters, eliciting a response that supported the innateness of the idea of God; he discusses two apologists in particular: one, Silhon; the other, Mersenne. We considered in Chapter 3 Mersenne's thirty-six arguments in *Quaestiones in Genesim* for the existence of God; of these Gilson concentrates on the use of Saint Anselm's proof, designed to show that we have an intuitive, necessary apprehension of God's existence. Although, as we have shown, Mersenne's presentation of the diverse proofs relied on the recognition that none of them was demonstratively conclusive, his willingness to allow Anselm's authority to sanction the innatism of the ontological proof and thereby render it probable indicates his lack of commitment to the strict Thomistic position, as does his use elsewhere of similar innatist arguments de-

5. Gilson, *Études*, chap. 1, esp. pp. 29, 31.
6. Ibid., p. 29.
7. A. Espinas, "Pour l'histoire du cartésianisme," *Revue de métaphysique et de morale* 4 (1906), 265–93.
8. Gilson, *Études*, p. 32.
9. Ibid., p. 36.

ployed for similar ends. Gilson, like Espinas, frequently treats various versions of "innatism" together as simply "Platonic," since he is primarily concerned with establishing that ample precedent existed for Descartes's "innatist" *cogito*.[10] However, Mersenne's sanction for this and other valuable deviations from official Thomism appears actually to have derived from Augustinianism, and such deviations were frequently indulged in by the Jesuits.

In a 1938 collection of essays, *Saint Augustine and French Classical Thought*, Nigel Abercrombie took up Gilson's theme by giving further consideration to scholastic doctrines of perception and the senses, including the non-Thomistic and more Augustinian treatment of perception due to Duns Scotus.[11] Abercrombie also outlined Augustine's value as an authority in the seventeenth century for those, like the Jansenists, who required a precedent for novel theological doctrines.[12] Augustine's writings were a source of ideas in political as well as theological and philosophical thought,[13] and Abercrombie further located the cultural context of their reception by noting the importance of their consonance with the humanist penchant for good classical Latin.[14] The prominence of Augustinianism within Mersenne's cultural milieu appears therefore to have been considerable; furthermore, the ecclesiastical base of many of the philosophical doctrines supported by Augustine extended far beyond Bérulle and the Oratory.

"Scholasticism, then, cannot historically be equated with Thomism," Abercrombie concluded. "The permanence of an Augustinian and Scotist tradition, opposed to Thomist Aristotelianism, allowed to the scholastic philosopher a fairly wide range of intellectual freedom; and the Jesuit philosophers availed themselves of this toleration of originality with great effect. Particularly in regard to the theory of knowledge, the existence of innate ideas was a commonplace in certain traditions; and the axiom, *nihil in intellectu quod non prius in sensu* [i.e., nothing in the intellect which was not first in the senses] was currently extended to cover the undisguised exemplarism of a

10. See, e.g., the concluding sentence to his discussion in ibid., p. 50.

11. Nigel Abercrombie, *Saint Augustine and French Classical Thought* (Oxford, 1938), chap. 3, "Saint Augustine and the Cartesian Metaphysics."

12. Ibid., pp. 9–10. It should be remarked that Abercrombie does not regard Jansenism as using Augustine in anything other than the most sincere way. Abercrombie's introduction is a very useful survey of the important place Augustine held in seventeenth-century French thought. Saint-Cyran's legitimatory use of Augustine receives note in Popkin, *History of Scepticism*, pp. 114–15.

13. See Nannerl O. Keohane, *Philosophy and the State in France* (Princeton, 1980), pp. 183–88.

14. Abercrombie, *Saint Augustine*, pp. 8–9.

Suarez."[15] The divergences of doctrine within Jesuit scholasticism, conceived as a way of philosophizing rather than as a dogmatic system, allowed Jesuits like Suarez to adopt certain non-Thomistic positions as a matter of routine. The support of a respectable authority helped, of course, and in Fonseca's commentary on the *Metaphysics* Augustine provides and legitimates an account of the way in which "divine illumination" operates to establish truth. Fonseca's treatment reveals the doctrinal basis of Mersenne's statements on the same subject.

Fonseca concludes that "truth . . . is the conformity of things with the divine intellect, that is, with the formal reasons of those things which are in the divine mind."[16] He proceeds to consider a number of objections to his conclusion; the fifth maintains that if it were so, we could know such truths only if we knew the divine essence, which we cannot do in this life.[17] In response to this quite considerable point Fonseca has recourse to Saint Augustine. First, he observes that Augustine had said: "Truth is not known by us, unless in the eternal reasons which are in the divine mind." This, says Fonseca, "although it confirms the proposed conclusion, also seems to ruin that conclusion because it seems to conflict with experience."[18] Since the Augustinian statement appears inconsistent with basic Thomistic precepts, which the Jesuits were in principle expected to follow, Fonseca—as a preparation for fruitful employment of Augustine's doctrines in support of his position—asserts that no real conflict exists: "But the most studious observer of Augustine's words, Saint Thomas, has not yet broken away from these words which Augustine writes in *Soliloquies* 1, chapter 8, in which place he teaches: 'Truths, which are entrusted to disciplines, are known in God by eternal reasons in the same way as visible things are seen in the sun.'"[19]

Fonseca then proceeds to embrace the Augustinian doctrine of "divine illumination," paraphrasing *Contra gentiles*, chapter 47, and "many other places," where it is held that

> something is known in something else in two ways. One, as in a known object: by that agreement we see an image in a mirror, and by this agreement [we see] the truth of things in their eternal reasons, not to be known by us while we remain in this life, just as neither do we see the rest of the visible things in the sun itself, which we cannot look at directly.

15. Ibid., pp. 83–84.
16. Fonseca, *Commentariorum . . tomi*, 1:803.
17. Ibid., 806.
18. Ibid., 809.
19. Ibid. For a discussion of Aquinas's interpretation of Augustinian illumination, see Ronald H. Nash, *The Light of the Mind* (Lexington, Ky., 1969), pp. 94–97.

The other, as known from the beginning [*in principio*]: and in this way [we] know the truth of created things in the eternal reasons, inasmuch as such reasons are imparted in us by natural light, by which agreement I am said to perceive any visible thing in the sun because we perceive that thing through light imparted by the sun. And he [Augustine] teaches that the divine prophet signified this, since in Psalm 4, asking himself this: "What shows us good?" he replied: "The light of your face has been marked upon us, O Lord."[20]

Fonseca here invokes the important Augustinian account of cognition, with its traces of neo-Platonic ancestry. That account possessed certain characteristic features.[21] First of all, Augustine replaced the Platonic forms with functionally similar "ideas in the mind of God." Although this doctrine is echoed in Aquinas and other scholastics, Augustine's version is typified by its explanation of the way in which we learn about the divine ideas. For Saint Thomas, as for Aristotle, the mind is initially a *tabula rasa* which is informed by sense impressions alone; particular psychological processes convert the latter, through various kinds of abstraction, into knowledge. Saint Augustine, by contrast, held that sense impressions generate knowledge by virtue of "divine illumination." His precise doctrine on this point is never explicitly set out in any satisfactory way,[22] but its broad outlines indicate that he regarded sensory input as "triggering," so to speak, the appropriate acquisition of knowledge direct from God. Like Anselm after him, Augustine identified Truth with God.[23] Gilson has suggested, in perhaps the most coherent interpretation, that the saint did not believe that ideas themselves entered the mind through the divine light but that divine illumination simply enabled apprehension of the *truth* concerning created things; it guaranteed the mind's judgment of a thing presented to it by the senses.[24] Thus no direct access

20. Fonseca, *Commentariorum . . . tomi,* 1:809–10.

21. For a good standard account, see Weinberg, *Short History,* chap. 1, "St. Augustine"; for additional references, see subsequent notes. On the forms, see particularly Augustine's *De diversibus quaestionibus* Q. XLVI.

22. As remarked by Marrone (*William of Auvergne,* p. 11), who observes that Augustine's lack of clarity probably springs from the saint's central concern with theological matters rather than the details of philosophical problems.

23. See Weinberg, *Short History,* chap. 1; Serene, "Demonstrative Science," pp. 498–500; Nash, *Light of the Mind,* esp. chap. 7, examining various views of Augustine's doctrine of illumination; Terry L. Miethe, "Augustine and Sense Knowledge," in *Augustinian Bibliography, 1970–1980* (Westport, Conn., 1982), pp. 171–83. For another recent treatment, see Bruce Bubacz, *St. Augustine's Theory of Knowledge* (New York, 1981), esp. chap. 6. The disagreement in these treatments over the details of Augustine's ideas on this matter bears out Marrone's observation (n. 22, above).

24. Étienne Gilson, *Introduction à l'étude de Saint Augustin* (Paris, 1929), pp. 112–25. Gilson's argument has not been universally accepted; see, e.g., the objections raised in Nash, *Light of the Mind,* pp. 98–101. Gilson's account remains, however, typically lucid,

to forms in the Platonic manner was implied. "The intellectual mind," wrote Augustine, "is so formed in its nature as to see those things, which by the disposition of the Creator are subjoined to things intelligible in a natural order, by a sort of incorporeal light of a unique kind; as the eye of the flesh sees things adjacent to itself in this bodily light, of which light it is made to be receptive, and adapted to it."[25] This is what Augustine elsewhere calls the "inner light of truth which illumines the inner man."[26]

Fonseca tried to maintain that Augustine's doctrine did not really differ from Aquinas's, and his justification would presumably have been Aquinas's own use of the concept of "illumination." Significant differences between the two, however, betray the extent to which Augustine needed to be accommodated into the Thomistic framework. John Morris, in an examination of Descartes's "natural light," has analyzed to that end Aquinas's use of the related terms "intelligible light" and "natural light."[27] He identifies two distinct meanings: the first (and most common) applies to the process whereby the agent intellect forms an idea of a sensed object; it refers to the purely psychological faculty performing the intellectual abstraction.[28] The second concerns the mind's knowledge of its own contents: if it believes something to be true, then it knows that it has that belief regardless of the belief's actual truth-value, and it does so by virtue of the "natural light."[29] Neither of these corresponds to Augustine's "divine" or "inner light," although the second meaning overlaps somewhat with Augustine's when the latter is applied to intellectual truths rather than to truths of cognition, as we shall see later. Relics of Christian neo-Platonic and Augustinian theological traditions in Aquinas, expressed in the doctrines of divine ideas and his own version of illumination, enabled Fonseca to appropriate useful elements of Augustinianism without creating an obvious clash with official Thomism, but Abercrombie's observation of the flexibility of late scholastic, especially Jesuit, philosophy is clearly borne out.

---

erudite, and persuasive, and whether or not it represents accurately the whole picture, it is probably the most satisfactory treatment of Augustine's doctrine. It accords well with the apparent readings of Mersenne and of the Jesuit authors quoted.

25. Augustine *De trinitate* 12.15, trans. A. W. Haddan, in Whitney J. Oates, ed., *Basic Writings of Saint Augustine* (New York, 1948), 2:824.

26. Augustine *De magistro* 40, trans. John H. S. Burleigh, in Burleigh, ed., *Augustine: Earlier Writings* (Philadelphia, 1953), p. 96.

27. John Morris, "Descartes' Natural Light," *Journal of the History of Philosophy* 11 (1973), 169–87, esp. 170–71; see also Owens, "Faith, Ideas," pp. 452–54, "Aquinas and the Rejection of Illumination."

28. Morris, "Descartes' Natural Light," p. 170.

29. Ibid., p. 171.

Fonseca concludes his discussion by showing how the Augustinian conception of illumination fitted into the standard scholastic-Aristotelian account of cognition. Augustine, he says, in quoting the fourth Psalm, "did not signify by these words that every truth that is necessary for seeking salvation can be known by us by that imparting of divine light which shines in our mind. Thus it happens that since we investigate the reasons of things known naturally through principles, and through the conformity of them with such reasons, we understand truths that we are able to know naturally, and consequently through conformity with the eternal reasons which are in the divine mind."[30] Fonseca thus legitimates his employment of Augustine's authority in the prior discussion by presenting it as equivalent in its essentials to the Thomistic view: truths acquired by abstraction via the senses correspond to the prototypical ideas in the mind of God, but the only causal link is through things themselves. Augustine argued for a more direct connection between God's mind and ours.

Abercrombie emphasized the continuing presence within late scholasticism of an Augustinian and Scotist tradition that stretched the maxim "nihil in intellectu quod non prius in sensu."[31] Both he and Gilson make much of Suarez's account of the relation between the "phantasm"—the image of an object received by the senses—and the conception of the object formed in the intellect. Since the form created in the intellect is immaterial and the phantasm (at least in part) material, there arises the problem of explaining the causal relation between them; this is, of course, an aspect of the question considered in the previous chapter concerning "truths of cognition" and the mutual relations of object, objective concept, and formal concept. Suarez's solution arose from his views on the principle of individuation. For the Thomist that principle was simply that matter which, together with the universal substantial form, constituted the individual object; for Suarez it was the *proper existence* of the particular object taken as a whole.[32] As a consequence, a universal form could not be abstracted from an individual, because it was literally inseparable from the very idea of that individual. Instead, the concept of it was *occasioned* by the phantasm. Suarez said that the function of the phantasm was "to present the subject matter and, as it were, a pattern [*exemplar*], to the intellect."[33] Illumination enabled the pattern's rec-

30. Fonseca, *Commentariorum . . . tomi*, 1:810.
31. See also Gilson, *Études*, p. 30.
32. On Aquinas, see Weinberg, *Short History*, p. 204; on Suarez, see (apart from Abercrombie) Copleston, *History of Philosophy*, pp. 360–61. For a full treatment, see Gracia, *Suarez*.
33. Quoted in Abercrombie, *Saint Augustine*, pp. 81–82; Gilson, *Études*, p. 30.

ognition. As Abercrombie remarks, "Suarez is already committed to some form of innatism."[34]

Although both Abercrombie and Gilson discuss this and similar material in establishing the existence of "some form of innatism" that subverted Aristotelian and Thomistic teaching in the period just before the work of Descartes, neither examines in any detail just what that form was. It cannot have been Platonic innatism. No scholastic, including the Jesuits of the late sixteenth and early seventeenth centuries, believed in Platonic forms or in the acquisition of knowledge as a kind of remembering any more than did Augustine. In his commentary on the *Metaphysics* Fonseca rejected the idea of knowledge as reminiscence with the aid of a quotation from Book 12 of Augustine's *De trinitate*,[35] while Mersenne himself, discussing Platonic forms, adopted the saint's position there expressed when he commented that "true Catholic philosophers allow no other ideas than the divine, which produce all things to the likeness of the exemplary cause."[36] What, then, did Augustine or the Jesuit metaphysicians believe that the mind possessed as part of its intrinsic nature—what, precisely, *was* innate? In Augustine's case, the answer would seem to be the faculty to receive the divine illumination by which correct judgments of truth could be made. A similar answer may be appropriate for the Jesuits.

Hans Aarsleff has observed that differences between Descartes's and Locke's assessments of "innate ideas" can be seen as reducing almost to differences in terminology.[37] Quoting from Descartes's "Notes Directed against a Certain Program," Aarsleff shows Descartes clarifying his notion of innateness. "I never," said Descartes, "wrote or concluded that the mind required innate ideas which were in some sort different from its faculty of thinking; but when I observed the existence in me of certain thoughts which proceeded, not from extraneous objects nor from the determination of my will, but solely from the faculty of thinking which is within me, then, that I might distinguish the ideas or notions (which are the forms of these thoughts) from other thoughts *adventitious* or *factitious*, I termed the former 'innate.'"[38] Aarsleff proceeds to point out that Locke did not disagree: "I never," Locke protested, "deny'd a power to be innate, but that which I deny'd was that any Ideas or connections of Ideas was innate."[39] For both Descartes and Locke, the one commonly labeled

---

34. Abercrombie, *Saint Augustine*, p. 82.
35. Fonseca, *Commentariorum . . . tomi*, 1:88. See also Weinberg, *Short History*, p. 41.
36. Mersenne, *Quaestiones*, col. 1164.
37. Hans Aarsleff, "The Tradition of Condillac," in *From Locke to Saussure* (Minneapolis, 1982), pp. 172–75.
38. Quoted in ibid., p. 173.
39. Quoted in ibid., p. 174.

"rationalist" and the other "empiricist," what is innate is the power of reasoning. Descartes's principles are not known in themselves but are infallibly derived from the process of right reasoning.[40]

Suarez's "form of innatism" similarly involves a faculty rather than a collection of inborn, preexisting ideas. Its operation employs something resembling Augustinian illumination as the means of our apprehension of truths from God: the innate faculty makes that process possible. The kinship between Suarez's and Augustine's views comes out most strongly in the case of intellectual, or nonsensory, truths for which, in fact, Augustine's doctrine of illumination seems centrally to have been designed. Jesuit uses of what one might call, by analogy with Anselm's, "ontological proofs" for the existence of God display a strong sense of reason as something deriving from a higher source: Gilson has noted Suarez's argument that the existence of God is necessarily entailed by a proper understanding of the very statement "Deus est."[41] Aquinas ruled out any such proof, but his own "natural light" served to account for our intuitive recognition of metaphysical and mathematical truths in a manner more compatible with Augustine's treatment of the same issue, as Fonseca appears to have recognized. That Aquinas felt the need to *explain* why such truths as "the whole is greater than its proper part" are self-evident perhaps ultimately derives from the non-Aristotelian theological tradition owing to Augustine, which still informed his thought; the idea of explaining self-evidence did not arise in Aristotle's approach to these matters. However, Augustine wanted a guarantee for the mind's perception of truth when considering that kind of statement. What renders the perception reliable? "The certain truths of the sciences are analogous to the objects which the sun's rays make visible, such as the earth and earthly things," Reason tells Augustine in the *Soliloquies*. "And it is God Himself who illumines all. I, Reason, am in minds as the power of looking is in the eyes."[42] The immediately preceding discussion, concerning mathematics, shows what sorts of sciences Augustine intended. The doctrine of illumination applied above all to those truths known in and of themselves, especially the truths of mathematics. Jesuit "innatism" linked the self-evidence of God's existence, the identification of Truth with God, and the divine illuminato-

40. Ibid., pp. 174–75. Robert McRae, "Innate Ideas," in R. J. Butler, ed., *Cartesian Studies* (Oxford, 1972), pp. 32–54, reaches similar conclusions regarding Descartes— "there is no room here for any conception of ideas as part of the original equipment of the mind" (p. 54); "it is the faculty of judging which is innate to the mind" (p. 53)— although, curiously, differing markedly on the correct interpretation of the passage quoted by Aarsleff (pp. 50–52).

41. Gilson, *Études*, p. 31.

42. Augustine *Soliloquia* I.12, trans. John H. S. Burleigh, in Burleigh, *Augustine*, p. 30.

ry source of known truths—paradigmatically intellectual truths—to create a philosophical and theological resource that could perform argumentative tasks denied to strict Thomism yet could also, if necessary, be presented so as to appear compatible with Thomistic orthodoxy.[43]

II

Given this background, it is not surprising that Mersenne too found Augustinian doctrine of great value, possessing as it did both the sanction of the saint's authority and the sanction of orthodox school use. At the same time, he found himself unwilling at a properly theological level to endorse those of Augustine's teachings most exercised by Protestants. Henri Gouhier has described Mersenne's discussion of free will and predestination contained in a letter to the Protestant André Rivet in 1640, where he takes to task both Saint Augustine and Saint Paul.[44] Mersenne is appalled at the apparently arbitrary allocation of grace upheld by these great authorities and rejects Jansen for the same reason; such a doctrine can only, he says, engender despair. Gouhier observes that whenever Mersenne went further than a sort of Erasmian position stressing a Christian life and good works, he tended towards the Jesuit Molinist view on predestination.[45] Although Gouhier presents no evidence for this claim, it seems to be supported by examples like Mersenne's analogy between free will and playing the organ: just as the notes of an organ are already laid out in the shapes and sizes of its pipes, so God knows what an individual would be disposed to do in any particular circumstance; however, the organ still requires that the player depress a key for a given note to sound, and so also an individual must exercise his free will in performing an action.[46] This encapsulates quite neatly Molina's solution to the problem of reconciling God's omniscience with human free will, and Mersenne alludes to Molinism directly in *Traité*

43. It is interesting to note that Locke's rejection of "innate ideas" was attacked in some quarters in the seventeenth century as being "irreligious." See John W. Yolton, *John Locke and the Way of Ideas* (Oxford, 1956), p. 60.

44. Gouhier, *Cartésianisme*, pp. 24–25; Mersenne to Rivet, 10 November 1640, Mersenne *Correspondance*, 10:217.

45. Gouhier, *Cartésianisme*, p. 22; on Molinism, see, e.g., Copleston, *History of Philosophy*, pp. 342–44.

46. Mersenne, *Traité*, p. 65. Mersenne also seems to allude to Molinist doctrine in *L'usage de la raison*, p. 30, referring to "hypothetical necessity."

de l'harmonie universelle.[47] Abercrombie argues that Molina actually preserved the essentials of Augustine's view;[48] however that may be, Mersenne clearly had reservations about the strict Augustinian teaching as employed by the Protestants.

Augustine provided a perfectly safe authority in other theological areas, however, and Mersenne clearly found him an attractive model of Christian piety. In his 1636 work *Harmonie universelle,* he makes the following recommendation: "When preachers wish to elevate their minds to something great and sublime, to dispose themselves to speak to hearers who ordinarily engage in very elevated thought, or to console themselves, I advise them to read the 2nd and 3rd book *De libero arbitrio,* those *De vera religione, De ordine,* and *De beata vita;* the 3rd, 52nd, 56th, 57th, 85th, 151st letter of St. Augustine, and several others which each can choose and read at his leisure, for example the 12th, where he teaches how one ought to pray."[49] Mersenne names no one other than Augustine. Furthermore, in 1642, again writing to Rivet, he remarks that Augustine "is the greatest Christian of all those who have followed the Apostles"; he cites in particular Augustine's commentaries on the Psalms, which Mersenne says he has just re-read.[50] When, on another properly theological issue, Mersenne criticized Descartes in 1640 for the apparent suggestion in the *Meditations* that God was not ineffable (Descartes denied the charge), Mersenne quoted Augustine as his authority: "Deus ineffabilis est."[51]

For Augustine to serve as a philosophical authority, it was important to preserve him as theologically acceptable. "Philosophical" arguments in this period typically carried theological implications, and Mersenne's employment of them for apologetic purposes frequently sharpened that evaluative dimension. Mersenne's views on what should and should not be stressed in Augustinian theology thus re-

47. Mersenne, *Traité,* p. 62. In 1638 Mersenne referred in a letter to a new edition of Augustine containing a study by Bellarmine, which argued that Augustine's writings on predestination and grace were not authentic—Mersenne was in good company in his distrust of these favorite Protestant doctrines: see Mersenne *Correspondance,* 7:214, 219–20n. In a letter to Rivet, 12 November 1639, Mersenne shows some impatience with Molinism and intellectual discussions of grace generally: see ibid., 8:597–99.

48. Abercrombie, *Saint Augustine,* p. 81.

49. Mersenne, *Harmonie universelle,* "De l'utilité de l'harmonie," p. 14.

50. Mersenne to Rivet, 8 February 1642, Mersenne *Correspondance,* 11:39. Nineteen years earlier, speaking in *L'usage de la raison,* p. 50, of models of great philosophical and theological writing, Mersenne had referred to "a doctrine as solid as that of Saint Thomas, or as subtle as that of Saint Augustine, or Aristotle."

51. See Gouhier, *Cartésianisme,* pp. 20–21. Mersenne's use of Augustine's doctrines on evil for apologetic purposes have been noted by Gérard Ferreyrolles, "L'influence de la conception augustinienne de l'histoire au XVIIᵉ siècle," *XVIIᵉ siècle* 34 (1982), 233.

flect a selective use of doctrinal resources, a use aimed at particular ends: Augustine, undeniably one of the principal Fathers of the Church, could never be abandoned to Protestantism, and so Catholic apologists in this period worked hard at elucidating his "true" teachings. In Mersenne's case such an achievement offered additional rewards because it made easier the exploitation of Augustine's arguments and authority in particular philosophical areas, bolstering the legitimation from existing scholastic practice.

We saw in Chapter 3 how Augustine's *Contra Academicos* provided the Renaissance with an important source of information on ancient scepticism, and how the three sources of certainty there defended (mathematics, syllogistic logic, and normal sense perception) found their way into standard rebuttals of scepticism, Academic and Pyrrhonian, including Mersenne's *La verité des sciences*. Mersenne's debts in *La verité* to that Augustinian work are not made explicit, but direct as well as mediated borrowing did occur. For example, the sceptical claim that the variability of the senses renders them incapable of providing us with reliable knowledge finds rebuttal in *Contra Academicos* by an argument evidently familiar to Jesuit philosophers.[52] The senses may be variable, it runs, but one can still be sure that something *appears* to oneself to be a certain way, whether or not the appearance represents the truth concerning the object.

> Then there is no deception, for I do not see how even an Academic can refute a man who says: "I know that this appears white to me. I know that I am delighted by what I am hearing. I know that this smells pleasant to me. I know that this tastes sweet to me. I know that this feels cold to me." Tell me, rather, whether the oleaster leaves—for which a goat has such a persistent appetite—are bitter *per se*. O, shameless man! Is not the goat more moderate? I know not how the oleaster leaves may be for flocks and herds; as to myself, they are bitter.[53]

When Mersenne employs a version of this argument in *La verité*, he betrays his source by his choice of example. The Christian Philosopher recounts the great differences in apprehension of the same taste or smell or appearance among different men and different animals.[54] He goes further than Augustine in disposing of the apparent problem these facts cause, maintaining that at least in principle one could determine the different dispositions of the sensory organs corre-

---

52. See, e.g., nn. 46 and 47 in Chapter 3, above.
53. Augustine *Contra Academicos* 11.26, trans. Denis J. Kavanagh, in Ludwig Schopp, ed., *Writings of Saint Augustine* (New York, 1948), 1:198.
54. Mersenne, *La verité*, pp. 15–18.

sponding to the various apprehensions and thereby account for them. His argumentative tack is very similar, however, and he uses a single example by way of illustration: "At least one knows that the objects of the senses appear differently according to the diverse dispositions of the organ: hence, we seek why flavor is agreeable to one and disagreeable to another, as why gorse is sweet to a goat, and bitter to a man."[55] Oleaster, it should be noted, is not indigenous to France.

Such direct textual borrowings are not, of course, as significant as the adoption of crucial doctrines themselves, prominent among them that of "divine illumination." Mersenne invokes illumination in *La verité* as part of the Christian Philosopher's reply to the Sceptic's persistent arguments for the unreliability of the senses. The doctrine he presents derives from Augustine's account of sensory cognition.

> You believe perhaps that it cannot happen that the understanding not be deceived in its operation, and in its conceptions and ideas, when the senses have been mistaken in the discovery of the exterior object; but things happen quite otherwise than you think, for it [i.e., the understanding] supplements the failings of the exterior, and even interior, senses, which it does by a spiritual and universal light that it has of its own nature from the commencement of its creation, which the Royal Prophet perhaps wished to signify when he said, *Signatum est super nos lumen vultus tui Domine* [The light of your face has been marked upon us, O Lord].[56]

Illumination for Mersenne, as for Augustine, did not involve direct access to the divine ideas; we cannot penetrate the divine essence itself.[57] "This natural light of the mind [continued the Christian Philosopher] is perfected and set in action [*mis en acte*] by means of meditation, study, experience, and the sciences, which nevertheless will never be fulfilled [*accomplie*] until we enjoy eternal glory, and the supernatural light carries the small ray of our natural light to the knowledge of the divine essence; it's this to which the same prophet leads us when he says *in lumine tuo videbimus lumen* [in your light we will see the light]."[58] In similar vein nine years later, Mersenne described our inability to penetrate the essences of things "until it pleases God to deliver us from this misery, and unshackle our eyes by the light that he reserves to his true worshippers."[59]

55. Ibid., p. 19.
56. Ibid., p. 193.
57. For Augustine on this point, see, e.g., Weinberg, *Short History*, p. 41; and Gilson, *Augustin*, pp. 112–25.
58. Mersenne, *La verité*, pp. 193–94.
59. Mersenne, *Questions theologiques*, p. 11.

Mersenne's understanding of the doctrine of illumination (which, as we have said, had its Thomistic version as well) comes out more clearly still in a discussion in *Quaestiones in Genesim* about "common notions" and the existence of God. Mersenne sets out to explain what he means by "our innate notions of divine knowledge" (a thoroughly un-Thomistic idea), and "what that natural light is by which we are said to know certain principles, as much practical as speculative." He describes this light, and these notions, as a "power" implanted by God: "When, therefore, the intellect apprehends the limits of some truth, and by this comprehends without any labor or ratiocination, then that power by which it knows a truth, e.g., 'the whole is greater than its part'; 'the same thing cannot at once be and not be,' etc., is that natural light."[60]

The same applies to moral principles, also upheld on this basis by Augustine in *Contra Academicos* and reiterated by Mersenne in *La verité des sciences*.[61] By its self-reflexive nature, the divinely imparted light in turn tells us that there is indeed a God, and Mersenne concludes by harking back to the line from the psalm quoted by Augustine: "Therefore that power or aptitude of the rational faculty is well called the light of the face of God (because the divine light shines over us to the benefit of these faculties), and is considered to be the imparting of this divine light."[62] Bérulle frequently used Augustine's metaphor of God as a source of supernatural rays, the Word being a sort of intellectual sun whereby truths emanate from God like sunbeams; Mersenne too echoed it on many occasions.[63] The divine essence, he wrote in *Traité de l'harmonie universelle,* is like "an eternal and infinite sun, which darts an infinity of rays on which all our perfections depend."[64] One of those rays is the goodness of God; another is "eternal truth, whence proceed all our truths and our sciences."[65]

As observed earlier, Augustinian "divine illumination" connected closely with claims for the apodeictic nature of the very notion of God, as with Suarez's analysis of "Deus est." Mersenne's *Quaestiones in Gene-*

---

60. Mersenne, *Quaestiones,* col. 278.
61. See Chapter 3, above.
62. Mersenne, *Quaestiones,* col. 278.
63. Abercrombie, *Saint Augustine,* pp. 72–74. Marion, *Sur la théologie,* pp. 144–45, gathers examples from Mersenne.
64. Mersenne, *Traité,* p. 59.
65. Ibid., p. 60. This image remained a constant theme in Mersenne's writings: in the posthumous *L'optique et la catoptrique du Reverend Pere Mersenne Minime* (Paris, 1651), p. 8, he remarks that "it is allowable to think that God is to our understandings what the sun is to our eyes: and there is in a sense no [*il n'y a quasi point de*] consideration about light and rays that cannot be accommodated to the means that God makes use of to draw us to him."

sim contains the same juxtaposition of doctrines, centered on the implicit idea of an innate faculty enabling the receipt of illumination. He approvingly presents Anselm's ontological proof, showing that the concept of "God" necessarily entails that of "existence,"[66] and then moves on to related forms of argument: "For, taking away the first good, which is God, nothing is able to be conceived to be good, to which the former can be reduced, which Saint Augustine says in *De trinitate* Book 8, chapter 3. Take away the latter and the former good, and consider simply, if you can, and you will have God. Neither, certainly, is it wonderful if God be known to exist through himself [*per se*], since the predicate is included in the subject and is utterly the same as the subject."[67] That is, the goodness of everything depends on the goodness of God, and goodness itself, considered simply, is identical with God; therefore, God exists.

Mersenne had already set out the basis for his argument at the start of the whole discussion.

> God is the way by which everything is known, as Saint Augustine discusses in *De trinitate*, usually in this way, that light is the way by which we perceive all colors, as [God] is the cause of knowing everything; it is not possible to hide knowing, since what has been known stands open in the light, since we see everything by virtue of it. Saint Augustine adds that the unshakable form and form of stable truth which is God, just like an incorruptible light, fills most sincerely the vision of the rational mind, through which truth is seen and thought.[68]

The importance of God as ontological guarantor of truth thus plays a central part both as a defense of true knowledge and as a demonstration of God's very existence.

When Mersenne chose two of the thirty-six proofs for the existence of God from *Quaestiones* for inclusion in *L'impieté des deistes*—presumably for their especial persuasiveness—he picked Anselm's and one of Augustine's.[69] The latter works by showing that truth is eternal; it asks, was there any time before which truth was not, and will there be any time after which it will cease to be? In the first case, the argument runs, there would still remain the truth that no truth existed, and this is impossible; the same goes, *mutatis mutandis*, for the second case. Hence, truth is eternal. Truth is then identified with God, since only

---

66. Noted in Gilson, *Études*, pp. 41–42.
67. Mersenne, *Quaestiones*, col. 40. As Lenoble remarks (*Mersenne*, p. 252), this is an Augustinian doctrine explicitly rejected by Aquinas.
68. Mersenne, *Quaestiones*, col. 39.
69. Mersenne, *L'impieté*, 1:111–16.

He can be genuinely eternal and unchanging, and the proof is complete.[70] Thus the resource of Augustinian doctrine once again allowed Mersenne to deploy an argument incompatible with Thomism but bearing all the hallmarks of the highest authority. He had every reason to use that authority to the full. Not only did it serve to validate the reliability of the senses and of intellectual truths, and to prove God's existence; it also provided grounds for believing in the mathematical structure of Creation and an incentive to search for physical reflections of the abstract intellectual harmonies found in number and proportion. Augustine's authority safeguarded such a project theologically, and his arguments justified it rationally; Mersenne drew on each of these in pushing forward his own agenda for natural philosophy.

III

Claude Bredeau—a frequent correspondent of Mersenne in the 1620s and apparently an acquaintance dating from Mersenne's time at the Minim convent at Nevers in the 1610s—was a lawyer by profession, and his letters display considerable erudition in the classics and theology.[71] Like most letters sent to Mersenne, they usually consist of answers to a series of questions, and in one of them, from 1626, Bredeau responds to a remark concerning the utility of mathematics for theology.[72] He embarks on a discussion of his own conviction that "God made use of the number six to create this world";[73] after recalling the six days of Creation, he observes that while Philo considered four to be the number of "firmity and perpetuity," Augustine "makes six to be perfect, in the eleventh book of the *City of God*, chapter 30, at the end of which he adds: *Nec frustra in laudibus Dei dictum est: Omnia in mensura et numero et pondere disposuisti* [Neither has it in vain been said in praise of God: you have disposed everything in measure and number and weight], by which what else does he say, if not that God has made everything by arithmetic and geometry?"[74]

Bredeau goes on to say that Augustine "shows sufficiently that the

---

70. Ibid., 1:112–14. On Augustine's use of this proof, see Lloyd Gerson, "Augustine's Neoplatonic Argument for the Existence of God," *Thomist* 45 (1981), 571–84; Gerson in fact claims that Augustine is not being self-consistent. Perhaps Mersenne never noticed.

71. See De Waard's note in Mersenne *Correspondance*, 1:1–2.

72. Bredeau to Mersenne, 23 February 1626, in ibid., pp. 380–400.

73. Ibid., p. 390.

74. Ibid., p. 391.

theologian must know the sciences" by a statement in the same part of the *City of God*: "Unde ratio mundi contemnenda non est, quae in multis sanctarum Scripturarum locis, quam magni aestimanda sit, elucet diligenter intuentibus"; that is, "Whence the reckoning of the world [i.e., arithmetic] should not be despised; how highly it should be regarded in many places of sacred scripture is made evident, with diligence, by inquirers."[75]

The aspects of Augustine's thought presented here by Bredeau found particular favor with Mersenne: the value of learning (especially mathematical learning) to piety, and God's having "made everything by arithmetic and geometry." As to the first, Mersenne specifically cites Augustine in one of his many homilies on the subject, this time in *Harmonie universelle*. All things lead back to Christ, he says, including the sciences, inasmuch as everything we do is "the expression of the character that God has impressed in us. I add only that the great science of Saint Augustine did not diminish his devotion, and that the reading of his third letter, which he sent to Volusian, where he shows that charity comprehends the sciences, with several others of his letters and treatises, such as those on free will, the true religion, the quantity of the soul, etc., show evidently how much it profited him."[76] A page or two later he declares that "Saint Augustine shows evidently the utility of geometry in his book on the quantity of the soul" because he uses examples from that science when arguing that the rational soul is indivisible and immaterial.[77] This constant theme in Mersenne's writings, which we have seen sounded in passages on the utility of mathematics for theology in *La verité des sciences*,[78] provided the major justification for his *Synopsis mathematica* of 1626. The dedicatory letter prefacing a part of that compilation explains the work's value as an aid to piety, with Augustine as the principal support.[79]

As to the second of Bredeau's Augustinian motifs, God's use of mathematics in creating the world, it is worth remembering the phrase that appears in the title of no less than four of Mersenne's publications: "universal harmony." When they have not ignored it, historians have usually treated this expression as little more than a

75. Ibid. On the issues this raises, see Ernst Cassirer, "Mathematical Mysticism and Mathematical Science," in Ernan McMullin, ed., *Galileo, Man of Science* (New York, 1967), pp. 338–51, esp. 344–47.
76. Mersenne, *Harmonie universelle*, "De l'utilité," p. 23.
77. Ibid., p. 25.
78. Chapter 3, above.
79. Mersenne *Correspondance*, 1:469. Mersenne also remarks in *Harmonie universelle*, "De l'utilité," p. 15, that the *Synopsis* was printed for the benefit of preachers.

literary conceit.[80] Contrasting Mersenne's *Harmonie universelle* with Giorgi's *De harmonia mundi*, Frances Yates has said that the Minim's *"Universal Harmony* will have nothing to do with the *anima mundi* and nothing to do with Francesco Giorgi, of whom he sternly disapproves. Mathematics replaces numerology in Mersenne's harmonic world; magic is banished; the seventeenth century has arrived."[81] However, the suggestion that an unproblematic "mathematics" replaces a "numerology" requiring comprehension in terms of magical beliefs takes rather too much for granted about the character of mathematical approaches to the study of nature. As has long been recognized,[82] metaphysical assumptions inevitably underlie the upgrading of mathematical sciences in the seventeenth century. There is, furthermore, no one kind of straightforward, "modern" view of mathematics. Mersenne's harmonies therefore demand just as much explanation as Giorgi's. The idea of "universal harmony" in fact encapsulates Mersenne's vision of the philosophical meaning of the mathematical study of nature, and it was a vision crucially informed by Augustinian writings.

The metaphysical label "Platonist" is the one nowadays most often attached to promoters of mathematical natural philosophy during this period. Christopher Clavius cited Plato and Proclus in support of the view that mathematics held a position intermediate between metaphysics and physics, and A. C. Crombie has remarked on such motifs in the writings of other Jesuits of the time as examples of a general Platonist tendency within and outside the order.[83] But the value of such a label as either an explanatory or an elucidatory concept may be questioned on the grounds that it does not address the immediate provenance and precise character of the doctrines concerned. A categorization of metaphysical views of mathematics that divides them all between the fundamental options of "Aristotelian" and "Platonic" can, no doubt, be of considerable philosophical value, but the kind of view put forward by Blancanus, for example, while unquestionably falling

80. This charge cannot be leveled at H. F. Cohen, *Quantifying Music* (Dordrecht, 1984), esp. p. 99, although Cohen does not attempt to relate Mersenne's technical work in music to the concept of "universal harmony"; he treats the latter as a vague but powerful idea motivating Mersenne's musical interests. Lenoble, *Mersenne,* has some rather stern remarks about it on p. 369n.3, and less so on p. 531; nonetheless, he recognizes Mersenne's specificity of meaning.

81. Frances A. Yates, "The Hermetic Tradition in Renaissance Science," in *Collected Essays* (London, 1984), 3:243.

82. In the work of Cassirer, Burtt, and Koyré, above all.

83. A. C. Crombie, "Mathematics and Platonism in the Sixteenth-Century Italian Universities and in Jesuit Educational Policy," in Y. Maeyama and W. G. Saltzer, eds., *Prismata* (Wiesbaden, 1977), pp. 63–94.

on the "Platonic" side of the philosophical dichotomy, rests historically on a particular interpretation of Thomas Aquinas's Christianized (and, to be sure, somewhat Platonized) interpretation of Aristotle. Historical understanding must therefore rest on characterizations of this latter kind, which provide explanations rooted in appropriate intellectual and cultural contexts.

References to Plato, or neo-Platonists, clearly found a conventional place in late scholastic writings, and Mersenne not infrequently mentioned Plato in connection with the latter's praise of geometry or description of God as a geometer.[84] However, Aristotle himself often refers to Plato and by no means always disparagingly. In general, it may be said that the Jesuits were not and could not have been authentic Platonists, any more than they could have been authentic Aristotelians, because—as discussed earlier in this chapter—central Platonic doctrines such as that of reminiscence were un-Christian. By the same token, however, they could adopt Augustine's teachings on some of these issues precisely by virtue of his authoritative status as a Church Father—but which teachings they would adopt or ignore depended on what they wanted to do with them. Exactly the same goes for Mersenne. Mersenne recognized the distinction between Plato's own doctrines on the one hand and neo-Platonism, the core of the Platonic revival in Italy, on the other and rejected the latter as erroneous.[85] Thus, when he adopted or promoted conceptions looking, in a generic sense, similar to those of the neo-Platonists, his sanction came not from Plotinus or Ficino or Proclus but from Saint Augustine.[86] The doctrinal specificities of Augustine's teachings also left their mark, however; though they stemmed from his own acquaintance with neo-Platonism, Augustine's ideas about number and mathematical harmony possessed quite distinct characteristics.

The most extensive account of these matters in Augustine's writings occurs in *De libero arbitrio*, with other important discussions appearing in *De musica* and elsewhere. (All the relevant sources were well known to Mersenne.)[87] In *Contra Academicos* the eternal, unchanging truths of mathematics had provided a bulwark against scepticism because they were supposedly independent of the bodily senses, but Augustine's positive views on man's knowledge of nature centered on the *relation* between such eternal truths—known by virtue of illumination

---

84. See Chapter 4, sec. II, above.

85. See Lenoble, *Mersenne*, pp. 206–7; see also in general E. N. Tigerstedt, *The Decline and Fall of the Neoplatonic Interpretation of Plato* (Helsinki, 1974).

86. This is not to say that he did not cite Proclus on occasion.

87. Mersenne quotes from or cites all of Augustine's major and many minor works throughout his writings.

—and sensory knowledge. That involved a concomitant relation between the structure of the created world and the mind of God. According to Augustine, the "science of numbers," which "does not pertain to bodily sense, but stands sure and unchangeable," acts as a sort of template against which sensory truths are judged.[88] The fact that numbers exist in the mind but that we can apply them to corporeal bodies shows that "wisdom has given numbers even to the smallest and most remote of things, and all bodies have their own numbers. But it has not given to bodies the power to be wise, nor even to all souls, but only to rational souls, in which, as it were, it has taken up its abode from whence it ordereth all things, even the smallest to which it has given numbers."[89] Wisdom (*sapientia*)—that is, intellectual truth deriving from God and comprising mathematical, logical, and also moral truths—"ordereth all things" because it is possessed by the rational souls of men as they judge the world. All things were made through the operation of that prototypical wisdom which is God, and so rational judgment necessarily finds the "numbers" for which it seeks: the creation of things and our apprehension of them each proceeds from identical principles. Augustine in fact tended to use the term "number" to stand for all unquestionable and necessary rules of judgment, all the transcendent or intellectual truths that were the manifestations of wisdom: "Whatever delights you in corporeal objects and entices you by appeal to the bodily senses, you may see is governed by number, and when you ask how that is so, you will return to your mind within, and know that you could neither approve nor disapprove things of sense unless you had within you, as it were, laws of beauty by which you judge all beautiful things which you perceive in the world."[90] The rules of judgment had authentic expression in the physical world because the Creation manifested God's wisdom; God utilized them in making the world, and man, participating in wisdom, therefore judged truly when applying them.

Significantly for our interest in Mersenne, Augustine's most extended discussions of nature, intellectual truths, and cognition concern sounds and music. The clearest example of the rapport between mental judgment and the objects of the senses seemed to him to lie in the hearing of music or verse, where numbers, in the form of rhythms, are apprehended by means of the mind's knowledge of the

88. Augustine *De libero arbitrio* ii.24, trans. John H. S. Burleigh, in Burleigh, *Augustine*, p. 149.
89. Ibid., ii.31 (Burleigh, p. 155).
90. Ibid., ii.41 (Burleigh, p. 161).

intellectual truths of arithmetic.[91] Identifying various ways in which number could be said to be involved in this process, Augustine brings the question down to the existence of "judicial numbers." Corporeal numbers may be said to exist in the object of attention and sensory numbers in the receptive senses, but judicial numbers are those by which reason must ultimately make its judgment. Augustine explains himself by a genetic account: first of all, he says, reason noticed that there is "something in the movements of bodies varying in the brevity and length of time." Next, it proceeded to articulate these time intervals into "different numbers." Finally, it turned its attention "to what the soul of which it is the head would do in the measuring, operating, sensing, and retaining of these things. And it separated all these numbers of the soul from bodies. And it saw itself could not notice, distinguish, or rightly enumerate all these things without certain numbers of its own, and it set them above the others as of an inferior order, by means of a kind of judicial appraisal."[92]

When Mersenne discussed *De musica* at some length in *Harmonie universelle*,[93] he completed his own account of Augustine's argument in the following way: "After having considered judicial numbers, which serve only to judge movements subject to time, he endeavors to elevate himself to other more sublime and more excellent numbers which do not at all depend on intervals of time, and which surpass all the others: it is by their means that we judge that such and such movement is not agreeable, and that we see the cause of the agreement in the equality of the parts of all the rhythmic feet of which we have spoken."[94] These are the "unchangeable and eternal numbers of the soul."

Elsewhere in *Harmonie universelle* Mersenne dealt more broadly with the relationship between sounds, the senses, and knowledge. He explicates it in a discussion almost identical to a treatment of the same issues in Augustine's *De libero arbitrio*. Mersenne begins by observing that the ear itself does not know sounds but acts solely as a means by which sounds can be considered by the mind.[95] Consequently, beasts,

---

91. See Edmund John Dehnert, "Music as Liberal in Augustine and Boethius," in *Arts libéraux et philosophie au moyen âge* (Montreal, 1969), pp. 987–91; Robert J. O'Connell, *Art and the Christian Intelligence in St. Augustine* (Oxford, 1978), pp. 67–68.

92. Augustine *De musica* 6.25; trans. Robert Catesby Taliaferro, in Ludwig Schopp, ed., *Writings of Saint Augustine* (New York, 1947), 2:351.

93. Mersenne, *Harmonie universelle*, "De la Rythmique," pp. 424–30.

94. Ibid., p. 429.

95. Ibid., "De la voix," p. 79. Mersenne maintained strongly that music was first and foremost an intellectual and rational endeavor; he never subscribed to the Aristoxenian

because they lack reason, "don't have knowledge of these sounds, but only the representation, without knowing whether what they apprehend is a sound, or a color, or something else."[96] Although apparently not an uncommon idea (it is mentioned, most notably, by Descartes), this last point and its context clearly come in this instance straight out of *De libero arbitrio*. "Reason," it is written there, "distinguishes the senses which are its servants from the data they collect." Therefore, it cannot be believed that beasts "know that light is not perceived by the ears nor voices by the eyes, for we do not discern these things without rational observation and thought."[97]

Mersenne's discussion continues with the observation that since we can distinguish between and judge the senses, there must be a separate "faculty or power" of knowing.[98] Through it, the mind can consider incorruptible as well as corruptible objects and indeed prefers things that are independent, necessary, and immutable. Thus "it is most certain that the mind has a being [that is] distinct from bodies and matter, and that depends only on that which has given it being: that is, on that which has being of itself [i.e., God], of which it carries the image, as it witnesses by its operations, which hold much of the immutable and the infinite."[99] The mind is therefore able to make "propositions that are eternally true," such as that "all the lines drawn from the center of a circle to its circumference are equal; that the diameter of a square is incommensurable with its side; that the whole is greater than its part, and an infinity of other similar propositions." This is possible only if the mind contains these propositions "formally, or eminently"—that is, innately.[100] Mersenne also included in his list of eternally true propositions the existence of an independent, perfect, self-sufficient, eternal being—thereby reemphasizing the source of the mind's grasp of truth.

In Augustine's prototype of this discussion in *De libero arbitrio*, proving the existence of God had in fact been the primary intention. Following his remarks on the necessity of reason for discriminating between the sensory sources of perceptions, Augustine proceeds to

---

doctrine, revived in the later sixteenth century, that the only proper judge of music was the ear: see *Questions harmoniques*, pp. 226–51. On Aristoxenian ideas, see Claude V. Palisca, "Scientific Empiricism in Musical Thought," in Hedley Howell Rhys, ed., *Seventeenth Century Science and the Arts* (Princeton, 1961), pp. 91–137, esp. 124.

96. Mersenne, *Harmonie universelle*, "De la voix," p. 79.
97. Augustine *De libero arbitrio* II.9 (Burleigh, pp. 140, 139–40).
98. Mersenne, *Harmonie universelle*, "De la voix," pp. 79–80.
99. Ibid., p. 80.
100. Ibid.

argue that since reason judges both the senses and external objects, it must enjoy independence from both. Consequently, he declares, reason is superior to the senses, as the senses are to inanimate objects.[101] This consideration provides the route towards evidence of God: if "by itself alone reason catches sight of that which is eternal and unchangeable, it must confess its own inferiority, and that the eternal and unchangeable is its God."[102] Augustine argues that reason does indeed do this and that therefore the conclusion actually follows. He points out first of all that the perceptions of the bodily senses are unique to each person: "We make them completely ours by consuming them and making them part of ourselves, like food and drink of which you cannot consume the same part as I do," even though the objects of sensation themselves remain the same.[103] The science of numbers, by contrast, really is the same for everyone, precisely because the knowledge it provides is unrelated to the senses.[104] "We must know this," says Augustine, referring to the science of numbers, "by the inner light, of which the bodily sense knows nothing."[105] The same holds for other kinds of unchangeable truths, and so we have now identified the eternal and unchangeable thing superior to reason: it is Truth itself, or "wisdom," identifiable with God.[106]

Mersenne singled out one chapter of Augustine's *De musica* for especial note: "It's necessary to read his eleventh chapter, where he compares the movements of the whole world to a verse, and shows the beauty of divine providence in all things."[107] The very breadth of Augustine's view of reason underlay both its appeal to Mersenne and its value to him as a vehicle for promoting the mathematical study of nature. In discussing Augustine's metaphysics, Mersenne furthered his general project by implicating the mathematical sciences, through number, more deeply in the basic *physical* makeup of the world. However, to grasp the central dynamic of Mersenne's understanding of "universal harmony," the key justification of his search for physical analogues of relations between mathematical entities, we must recall the crucial part played by unity in his image of mathematics and its relation to the world.

---

101. Augustine *De libero arbitrio* ii.9–13 (Burleigh, pp. 141–43). For the sake of clarity, I neglect the intermediate role of the interior sense, present in both Augustine and Mersenne.

102. Ibid. ii.14 (Burleigh, p. 144).

103. Ibid. ii.15–19 (Burleigh, pp. 144–47).

104. Ibid. ii.20 (Burleigh, p. 147).

105. Ibid. ii.23 (Burleigh, p. 149).

106. Ibid. ii.39 (Burleigh, pp. 159–60).

107. Mersenne, *Harmonie universelle*, "De la Rythmique," p. 429.

IV

Unity was the basis of mathematics and could be recognized in individual objects: this provided the ultimate guarantee that mathematics could reliably be used in talking about the world. In *Quaestiones in Genesim* Mersenne illustrates and justifies the contention that unity is a principle underlying everything with a long quotation from Saint Augustine's *De ordine*.[108] He takes up Augustine's words immediately following the latter's remark that "there is in reason nothing more excellent or dominant than numbers . . . reason is nothing other than number."[109] The passage he quotes attempts to show the involvement of the idea of unity in all things; part of it calls to mind Mersenne's position that unity is a quasi-essential property of everything recognized as one.[110] "In order that a stone be a stone, all its parts and its entire nature have been consolidated into one. What about a tree? Is it not true that it would not be a tree if it were not *one*? What about the members and entrails of any animate being, or any of its component parts? Of a certainty, if they undergo a severance of unity, it will no longer be an animal."[111]

Because mathematical truths provided constraints on what could and could not be created which were similar in nature to those imposed by essential propositions, Mersenne's comparisons of God with unity took on a particular significance. The central comparison—as found, for example, in *L'impieté des deistes*—involves the relation between God and His creatures, and addresses the following problem: God is perfectly simple, so how can He produce a diversity of creatures? Mersenne resolves the puzzle by dispelling the appearance of necessary contradiction. Unity too is perfectly simple, yet all other numbers, with their diverse properties (of a number-theoretical kind), are produced from it.[112] In *Quaestiones in Genesim* the same analogy appears, and it becomes clear that here is no mere observation of accidental similarities. Everything in the world, says Mersenne, all diversity, springs from unity, and unity itself comes from God, just as other perfections such as goodness take their origin from His perfection.[113] Creatures are produced from God just as numbers (with

108. Mersenne, *Quaestiones*, col. 798.

109. Augustine *De ordine* ii.48, trans. Robert P. Russell, in Schopp, *Writings*, 1:324.

110. See Chapter 4, sec. V, above.

111. Augustine *De ordine* ii.48 (Russell, p. 325); quoted in Mersenne, *Quaestiones*, col. 798.

112. Mersenne, *L'impieté*, 1:417–25.

113. Mersenne, *Quaestiones*, cols. 795–98. The quotation from Augustine cited above appears at the end of that discussion.

all their intrinsic mathematical properties) are produced from unity, and unity itself is an aspect of God's perfection. The argument derives from Aquinas and was encapsulated in the scholastic maxim quoted by Mersenne: "Essentiae sunt sicut numeri."[114]

Unity was also the ultimate basis of harmony. Mersenne made this crucial claim elsewhere in *Quaestiones* as an underpinning to the argument that since God was the principle of unity, our apprehension of harmony yields indirect evidence for His existence.[115] This time the support came from Augustine's *De trinitate*, the relevant passage concerning the consonance of the ratio 2:1 implanted in us by God.[116] Mersenne's most extended discussion of the theme, however, appeared thirteen years after *Quaestiones*, in his consideration of the relations between unity, music, God, and the world in *Harmonie universelle*—and again, Augustine provided the major authority.

The subject under discussion is whether the unison, a ratio of equality, gives rise to all the other consonances, ratios of inequality. Part of the question's interest lies in the character of the unison itself, since it "represents the virtue and treasures of the divinity, and is similar to the first maxims of ethics which Saint Augustine calls the rules and light of the virtues."[117] Some extensive quotation from Augustine illustrates the latter.[118] Mersenne then proceeds to consider how ratios of inequality could be produced from that of equality. There are problems here, he says, since the only way to do it seems to be to compare and add *several* unities—but there *is* only one kind of unity. In geometry, a point can engender a line if the point moves, "but intellectual unity, and consequently equality, which has unity for its foundation, is immobile, and since God is still more immutable and immobile than unity or equality, it is difficult to understand the way in which He created such different things as those that we see."[119]

A solution to this predicament offered by "those who hold that equality is the principle of inequality" involves the observation that God comprises "two ratios of equality due to the three divine persons that constitute the two ratios"; these ratios form the basis of all the others, "as omnipotence is the cause of all creatures."[120] Mersenne rejects this resort to the Trinity, however. Taken by itself, he con-

---

114. Mersenne, *L'impiété*, 1:425. See Chapter 4, above, for further discussion of this point and its Thomistic pedigree.

115. Mersenne, *Quaestiones*, col. 77.

116. Ibid., cols. 76–77; quotation from Augustine *De trinitate* IV.2.

117. Mersenne, *Harmonie universelle*, "Des consonances," p. 29.

118. Ibid., pp. 29–30.

119. Ibid., p. 31.

120. Ibid., pp. 31–32.

tends, "the ratio of equality is so sterile that it cannot engender any other ratio, even though it is considered in God, if one doesn't suppose as well a power of acting; it is necessary that the divine power have its object, be it actual or possible, before one can consider the ratios which proceed from those of divine equality."[121] He then maintains that even if God were regarded as a single all-powerful being, possible and actual creatures would still possess the same ratios of equality and inequality. These ratios, "born from a natural emanation that accompanies the production of created beings," would exist because it is impossible that creatures be neither equal nor unequal to one another. In any case, he concludes, the equality of the three persons of God is not, properly speaking, an equality at all, but an identity; thus it could not establish ratios of inequality.[122]

This discussion established two central points. First, there are ratios of equality and inequality in the world, and they proceed from God. Second, God unquestionably enshrines the ratio of equality, and there can be no ratios of inequality without a ratio of equality—even if the former cannot be produced from the latter directly. This last caveat, Mersenne notes, means that the other consonances cannot proceed directly from the unison but that it remains their necessary underpinning, "since it is impossible for there to be ratios of inequality if one doesn't suppose that of equality," and, moreover, "there can be no ratio of equality outside of God." The ratio of equality remains the "measure of perfection" of the other ratios.[123] Throughout all of this, Mersenne retains Augustine's identification of "ratio" and "reason." God created the world by "reason" or "wisdom," and reason, according to Augustine, "is nothing other than number." Thus Mersenne could say that "there cannot be any natural being, or being of reason, that does not proceed from and depend on sovereign reason."[124]

These Augustinian doctrines fitted comfortably into the scholastic framework discussed in Chapter 4, which considered Mersenne's orthodox adoption of the thesis that God could create anything that was in itself possible. The possible being of creatures, he said, "is so necessary that it cannot be made impossible, since the liaison of its terms and properties is entirely necessary."[125] For example, because "man is a rational animal" is necessarily the case, owing to the very

121. Ibid., p. 32.
122. Ibid.
123. Ibid., p. 33. In *Questions harmoniques*, p. 251, Mersenne observed that "the theory of sciences and arts, and consequently of music," correspond "in some way to the interior operations of God, and to His divine ideas."
124. Mersenne, *Harmonie universelle*, "Des consonances," p. 32.
125. Mersenne, *Traité*, p. 63.

definition of "man," God could not create a man who was not at the same time a rational animal. Essential definitions, being immutable and necessary, therefore fell into the category of eternally true propositions known by the mind independently of the senses. Augustine's concept of the "wisdom" by which God created the world yielded similar conclusions: where a Thomist scholastic emphasized essential propositions as the determinants of what was possible, Augustine emphasized truths of logic and mathematics. The two positions were complementary. Now Mersenne, in contrast to contemporary scholastic philosophers such as the Jesuits, denied that we can ever hope to know which essences God has in fact created, or could create, because we cannot perceive them. That left logic and mathematics as the only sources of unchanging principles having *practical* value for understanding the contingent universe. As Mersenne remarked, echoing Augustine's quotation from the Book of Wisdom, God has ordered everything by number, measure, and weight;[126] he believed that those principles at least could be recognized in and applied to their physical embodiment.

The consonance between Augustinian "numbers" and the usual scholastic conception of number sprang from similar considerations. Scholastic number presupposed the possible existence of things to be numbered, and so number—and hence mathematical truths—derived from God's power to create things. By the same token, these things, if created, could not violate the truths of mathematics; as Mersenne said, "one never fails to find that two times two men are four men, according to the idea that reason had conceived."[127] Augustinian ideas helped to place this view of mathematics within a broader conception of God's relation to His Creation and of both to the human mind.

Music leads us to the contemplation of divine mysteries, says Mersenne in *Traité de l'harmonie universelle*, citing Augustine,[128] and in Theorem XIV of Book 1 he describes "created music" as "nothing other than the order and harmonic proportion that exists between the parts of the world and each individual in particular."[129] This order, Mersenne explains, is connected to the "possibility" of creatures: that

126. See ibid., p. 23; Augustine *De trinitate* XI.11. Mersenne frequently speaks of "number, measure, and weight," a commonplace adaptable to many different purposes; for another notable example, see *Harmonie universelle*, "Du son," p. 43.

127. Mersenne, *La verité*, p. 277; see Chapter 4, sec. IV, above.

128. Mersenne, *Traité*, p. 251. The Augustinianism of Mersenne's musical aesthetics, with its stress on music as a reflection of the beauty of the order in Creation, is discussed in Joseph G. Weber, "Pascal and Music," *Symposium* 30 (1976), 75–91, esp. 75–79.

129. Mersenne, *Traité*, p. 62.

is, to the necessary relation between their terms and properties. Possible beings, because they are defined by such relations, are therefore "born according to interior consonances, by which all creatures praise the power of the Creator." Consequently, "if we could understand the song of all the birds, the cry of all the animals, the noise of all thunder and winds, and if we considered their differences and their proportions, we would find an admirable harmony; for I don't doubt that the author of nature so well disposed the species of the universe one with another that their relations, their dependences, their movements, and their order praise the Creator, and make natural cadences of a most perfect mode, since God is the concertmaster."[130] Mersenne takes care to indicate that he wishes to discuss mathematical proportions and ratios generally: "I will not speak only of harmonic ratios according to their ordinary signification, for I will make use of geometric and arithmetic proportions when necessary, because the sounds that follow these two ratios are very agreeable, and make a good effect, and the Creator . . . is no less praiseworthy in these two proportions than in that which we call 'harmonic.'"[131] As he had remarked a little earlier, "the relations of creatures to God, and of God to creatures, also contains an intellectual harmony which merits that one speak of it eternally, and construct songs, hymns, canticles, and concerts to render homage to the great Master of Music."[132]

"Universal harmony" was, then, more than just a metaphor. Harmony, or music, represented the highest manifestation of divine wisdom because it consisted of the ordering of numerical ratios; number provided the exemplar of necessary intellectual truths. These, contained in our minds by virtue of that light present as a result of God's creation of our souls in similitude to Him, reflected the divine wisdom manifested in Creation.[133] Even though the natures of things remained ultimately unknowable in this life, they too expressed wisdom because essential definitions could only be necessary truths. Thus, when God "created us conforming to His eternal ideas,"[134] He did not merely follow a Thomistic maxim but manifested an Augustinian employment of "wisdom," an "intellectual harmony" correctly represented by our ideas of music.

Things in the world had been made in conformity with common axioms, logical necessities, and the truths of mathematics, and Mersenne understood this to be so through fundamentally Augustinian

130. Ibid., p. 63.
131. Ibid., pp. 63–64.
132. Ibid., p. 61.
133. Mersenne, *Quaestiones*, col. 278.
134. Mersenne, *Traité*, p. 61.

notions of wisdom; he did not observe the strict Thomistic priority of the senses in all knowledge. Nonetheless, sensory knowledge played an important part in his practical natural philosophy, and he stressed the reliability of observations of phenomenological properties for just that reason. In the absence of a guarantee that the senses could recognize and apply them to actual things in the world, "number, measure, and weight" would have been of no more use than essences. However, as the examples Mersenne borrowed from Augustine showed, and as the foundational status of unity implied, these things were in fact inseparable parts of the way we apprehend the world, as well as necessary parts of its grammar and syntax. Divine wisdom meant for Mersenne that a sort of harmony underlay the natural world, discernible in the mathematical ratios governing it. Identifying those ratios, however, was an empirical task.

V

In the *City of God* Augustine discusses the human body. He does not simply remark on its known or conjectured harmonies but comments on the importance of looking for and discovering them. There is, he says,

> in a man's body such a rhythm, poise, symmetry, and beauty that it is hard to decide whether it was the uses or the beauty of the body that the Creator had most in mind. It is clear that every organ whose function we know adds to the body's beauty, and this beauty would be still more obvious if only we knew the precise proportions by which the parts were fashioned and interrelated. . . . But what I have in mind is the rhythm of relationships, the *harmonia,* as the Greeks would say, whereby the whole body, inside and out, can be looked upon as a kind of organ with a music all its own. The beauty of this music no one has yet discovered, because no one has dared look for it.[135]

Mersenne's agenda for natural philosophy involved precisely this: *looking* for the harmonies and proportions of nature, not assuming them in an a priori way. His well-known dispute with Robert Fludd, first unleashed in *Quaestiones in Genesim,* centered on what he saw as Fludd's failure to base specific claims of universal harmony on proper procedures of investigation. The clearest presentation of Mersenne's

135. Augustine *De civitate Dei* XXII.24, trans. Gerald G. Walsh et al., in Vernon J. Bourke, ed., *Saint Augustine: The City of God* (New York, 1958), p. 528.

position appears in the *Traité de l'harmonie universelle* of 1627, where he considers Fludd's ideas at some length.[136]

Theorem XII of the *Traité*'s Book 2 is headed: "To determine whether the harmony and consonances that Robert Fludd puts in the spiritual, celestial, and elementary worlds are well established."[137] It first sets out the general structure of Fludd's opinions—including the notion of consonances in the universe and between the microcosm and macrocosm—and Fludd's conception of God as a kind of light illuminating His creatures; it then examines the details of Fludd's system.[138] In the midst of a typically thorough discussion of Fludd's ideas about the properties of the planets, their associated human virtues, their relation to musical consonances, and the correspondence between musical notes and the corporeal elements, Mersenne stops to make something quite clear: "So as not to be misunderstood, I find no solidity in all this discourse."[139] The lack of solidity did not derive, however, from the notion itself of harmonies and consonances in the world. Mersenne was, he said, "of the opinion of Kepler, who maintains that all the harmonies of Fludd and the Platonists are only analogies and comparisons which have almost no other foundation than the imagination."[140] But Kepler did not, of course, reject the notion of world harmony any more than did Mersenne. Kepler, in his controversy with Fludd, held that if one wished to claim that particular harmonies exist in the fabric of the world, one would have to demonstrate it observationally; the data must fit the alleged regularity.[141] Mersenne approvingly said of Kepler that he "makes use of the compass," while Fludd uses "furnaces and fire"; that is, Kepler

---

136. On this dispute, see Yates, *Giordano Bruno,* pp. 432–47; William Hine, "The Interaction between Science and Religion in the Circle of Marin Mersenne" (diss., University of Oklahoma, 1967), pp. 159–186; Duncan, "Tyranny of Opinions Undermined," pp. 119–28; Peter J. Ammann, "The Musical Theory and Philosophy of Robert Fludd," *Journal of the Warburg and Courtauld Institutes* 30 (1967), 198–227, esp. 216–19, 226. On Fludd, see Allen G. Debus, *The English Paracelsians* (London, 1965), pp. 105–27; idem, "Robert Fludd," *DSB* 5:47–49, with extensive bibliography. Joscelyn Godwin, *Robert Fludd* (London, 1979), provides reproductions of plates from Fludd's works.

137. Mersenne, *Traité,* p. 415.

138. Ibid., pp. 416–17, 418ff.

139. Ibid., pp. 420–22, quotation on p. 421.

140. Ibid., p. 421. For a discussion of Kepler on these issues, see Field, "Kepler's Rejection of Numerology," pp. 273–96.

141. For a useful summary, see Gerald Holton, "Johannes Kepler's Universe," in Robert Palter, ed., *Toward Modern Science* (New York, 1961), 2:192–216. On the Fludd/Kepler controversy, see also Robert Westman, "Nature, Art, and Psyche," in Vickers, *Occult and Scientific Mentalities,* pp. 177–229.

employed the tool of open demonstration, while Fludd adopted the trappings of alchemical secretism and obscurity.[142]

Mersenne displays his agreement with Kepler's approach in the third section of Theorem xiii in the *Traité*'s Book 2, a section devoted to revealing Fludd's errors;[143] he relies on showing that Fludd's facts were wrong. He starts out with Fludd's diagram of the Divine Monochord, a musical string superimposed on a representation of an Aristotelian geocentric world complete with elemental regions and celestial spheres.[144] He proceeds to demolish Fludd's claim that various celestial intervals in the diagram correspond to the ratios of string lengths associated with musical consonances. Mersenne remarks that "there is no need to show how mistaken he is in his measurements if he believed that it is no farther from the sun to the Empyrean than from the earth to the sun," the distances Fludd used in establishing the octave. "Following the hypotheses of Tycho," the distances are 12,858 and 1,142 earth radii respectively. Perhaps, Mersenne continues charitably, Fludd meant to refer not to the true distances but to changes in air density, "inasmuch as the same strings make their sounds more sharp to the extent that the air is rarer."[145] Then, in order to obtain the required 2:1 ratio, the air should be twice as rarefied at the sun as it is at the surface of the earth. But neither an arithmetical nor a geometrical proportion governing the increase in rarefaction with respect to distance from the earth provides anything near that figure; indeed, no plausible rate of rarefaction comes close.[146] This, together with related considerations, leads Mersenne to conclude that "Fludd's Mundane Harmony has no other foundation than his imagination."[147]

Never one to rest with a single objection, Mersenne goes on to give further, often lengthy criticisms of Fludd's claims. Although some are based on logical considerations, Mersenne's principal arguments continue to revolve around the question of whether alleged consonances and harmonies actually correspond to measurable quantities in the world. He found Fludd's repetition of the old canard about Pythago-

142. Mersenne, *Traité*, p. 352. On the issues this kind of dichotomy raises, see Owen Hannaway, "Laboratory Design and the Aim of Science," *Isis* 77 (1986), 585–610.

143. Mersenne, *Traité*, pp. 442ff.

144. Ibid., p. 443.

145. Ibid., p. 444; Mersenne gives no source here for the idea that pitch is proportional to the rarity of the air; however, *Quaestiones*, col. 1560, suggests that it came from Boethius; the passage would probably be *De institutione musica* v.4, purporting to give Ptolemy's opinion.

146. Mersenne, *Traité*, p. 445.

147. Ibid., p. 446.

ras and the hammers particularly irksome.[148] Stemming from antiquity (Mersenne notes its appearance in Macrobius and Boethius), the story maintained that Pythagoras had discovered the numerical ratios associated with musical consonances after hearing the notes made by a blacksmith's hammers on an anvil. Weighing the hammers, Pythagoras found that the hammer producing the upper note of an octave was half as heavy as that producing the lower, and similarly for the other chief consonances. Mersenne had fulminated against this tale in the preface to the second book of the *Traité,* and also against the related idea that weights hung on the end of a string would produce notes an octave apart if they themselves were in a 2:1 ratio; Vincenzo Galilei had already experimentally investigated and demolished the latter, but it still remained current.[149] Mersenne said that the story of the hammers was "entirely contrary to truth and experience" and rebuked those who sheepishly repeated it for being "so negligent that they haven't made a single experiment to discover the truth and disabuse the world."[150]

Although pronouncing himself "of the opinion of Kepler," Mersenne, while also seeking out mathematical relationships as authentic manifestations of divine wisdom, shows greater circumspection about the chances of success. Nonetheless, he considers seriously the evidence for astronomically grounded harmonies and decides that in some instances it looked quite good. In Theorems VI, VII, and VIII of the *Traité*'s Book 2 he looks at the question of whether the distances of the planets exhibit the same ratios as those of musical consonances and dissonances.[151] He had said in *L'impiété des deistes* that he usually preferred to follow Tycho's figures for astronomical parameters "because he seems to have brought greater care to his observations than his predecessors have done."[152] Here, therefore, Mersenne uses Tycho's figures for the distances of the planets from the earth, giving a fairly detailed account of the parallactic techniques and calculations involved, "so that there was nothing in the system of the world that the perfect musician didn't know."[153] Theorem VII then examines the results to see whether musical ratios can be derived from the relations

148. Ibid., p. 447.
149. Ibid., preface to Book 2, [p. 8]; Mersenne also takes the story to task in *Harmonie universelle,* "De la composition," p. 216, and in *Questions harmoniques,* pp. 166–67. For Galilei, see Stillman Drake, "Renaissance Music and Experimental Science," *Journal of the History of Ideas* 31 (1970), 483–500, esp. 496; see also Chapter 6, below.
150. Mersenne, *Traité,* p. 447.
151. Ibid., pp. 353–83.
152. Mersenne, *L'impiété,* 2:187.
153. Mersenne, *Traité,* pp. 353–65; quotation on p. 363.

between such values as the minimum, maximum, and mean distances of the moon from the earth, or the various parallaxes of the planets. Of course, by strenuous combinations of data, some do indeed appear.[154] However, after recommending the tables of astronomical data in *La verité des sciences* as resources for the discovery of many more such consonances and dissonances—for example, between the diameters of different celestial bodies[155]—Mersenne finishes the section with a practical admission that the observational establishment of cosmic harmonies partly depends on the choice of astronomical system: "Since some people prefer to follow the hypotheses of Copernicus instead of those of Tycho or Ptolemy, I want to add a theorem for the benefit of [*en faveur de*] that opinion, and of the hypotheses of the Copernicans, which are different from those of Tycho, although they agree in several things."[156]

Because Mersenne doubted the certainty of any particular astronomical system (although as time went on he seems to have regarded Copernicanism as increasingly probable),[157] his search for celestial harmony could not always find firm anchorage. Tycho by this time represented conservative orthodoxy, but Copernicus deserved serious consideration; although, as Mersenne observed, the two had much in common, the latter's hypothesis yielded harmonies absent from the former's. Copernicus's system, said Mersenne, would serve to promote admiration among musicians for "the providence of God, who has preserved so beautiful a proportion in the order that He has put in all the parts of the universe that man cannot imagine any excellent thing that does not agree with it with a singular perfection, which witnesses the eminent perfection of the Maker [*Ouvrier*]."[158] This seems to have been Copernicanism's greatest attraction for Mersenne, as indeed it was for Kepler and many others. Three years before, Mersenne had written of the Copernicans: "What pleases me in their opinion is that they seem to be great lovers of proportion, for they wish that the diameter of the mobile bodies [i.e., celestial spheres] be a mean proportional between the diameter of the sun, which they make the motor, and the diameter of the firmament, which is the place [in the Aristotelian sense] of all bodies";[159] he went on to discuss such characteristic themes as the proportions between orbital dimensions. Mersenne ob-

154. Ibid., pp. 366–70.
155. Ibid., p. 370.
156. Ibid., pp. 370–71.
157. See Chapter 3, sec. II, above, and references cited there.
158. Mersenne, *Traité*, p. 371.
159. Mersenne, *L'impieté*, 2:193–94.

viously drew this material from Kepler. Unlike Kepler, however, he resisted the temptation to interpret the proportions as definitive evidence of the truth of Copernicanism.

He takes the same line in the *Traité*. Because "there are those who don't follow Copernicus entirely,"[160] Mersenne gives a diagram not only of Copernicus's system but also of those of Tycho and Longomontanus (the latter identical to Tycho's save for the not insignificant substitution of diurnal terrestrial rotation for a daily revolution of the heavens),[161] then presents Kepler's Copernican calculations of parameters and harmonies.[162] After giving the last of these results, "that the triple octave and the minor seventeenth almost agree with Jupiter and Mars" based on the ratios of minimum and maximum orbital speeds,[163] Mersenne pronounces his verdict on Kepler's work: "Most certainly, although he didn't find everything that he could have desired, and although we don't know sufficiently exactly the distances or movements of the planets, he has blazed the trail [*a fait le chemin*] and has shown many things that hadn't yet been thought of."[164]

Mersenne disapproved of the endeavors of Fludd "and the Platonists" but approved of an empirical search for harmonies based on an Augustinian concept of wisdom. Augustine's categories of "wisdom" and "knowledge," *sapientia* and *scientia*, in fact mirror closely Mersenne's own sharp distinction between certain, intellectual truths and knowledge of the contingent, created world. The "right distinction between wisdom and knowledge," said Augustine, is that "the intellectual cognizance of eternal things belongs to wisdom, but the rational cognizance of temporal things to knowledge."[165] Arguing against the Platonic doctrine of anamnesis, he rhetorically inquired why it is that an uninstructed person can answer appropriate questions concerning "intelligible things" but not concerning "things sensible," apart from those that he has seen in his present body or heard or read from someone else.[166] When we remember (from Chapter 3) that the thrust of argument in Augustine's early *Contra Academicos* played a role in the formation of "Ciceronian probabilism," itself important for understanding Mersenne's "mitigated scepticism," the similarities appear to be related at a deep level of tradition and synthesis.

160. Mersenne, *Traité*, p. 372.
161. Ibid., pp. 373, 374.
162. Ibid., pp. 376–83.
163. Ibid., p. 382.
164. Ibid., pp. 382–83.
165. Augustine *De trinitate* XII.15 (Haddan, p. 825); see Serene, "Demonstrative Science," pp. 499–500.
166. Augustine *De trinitate* XII.15 (Haddan, p. 824).

Mersenne's sceptical attitude towards essentialist knowledge of nature sometimes actually manifested itself as a form of Augustinian down-playing of the significance of natural knowledge, a somewhat ironic state of affairs. He remarks in *Harmonie universelle* on the "labyrinth of ignorance and error where we lose ourselves apparently as many times as we wish to reason"; we will find peace only when we rejoin God, as Augustine says: "Inquietum est cor nostrum Domine, donec quiescat in te." The sciences we have in this life, Mersenne continues, are so imperfect that they cause "more affliction and work than pleasure"; again, as Augustine said, "Qui addit scientiam, addit & laborem."[167] Elsewhere in the work Mersenne quotes from *De beata vita* on the limitations of dialectic itself, inasmuch as "all the wisdom and capacity of human understanding cannot at all reveal to us the light of the first truth."[168] Such locutions served to emphasize God's transcendence; Augustine himself did not consistently misprize natural philosophy but simply wished to keep its importance for the Christian in perspective. Mersenne's "universal harmony" could therefore exploit Augustinian ideas as justifications for his mathematical form of natural knowledge without betraying the spirit of his apparently very congenial source; he commended Augustine, as we have seen, for his conjunction of learning and piety. Mersenne too put strict limits on the potential of natural philosophy and did not much mourn what remained unattainable. Furthermore, he saw his philosophy as a route towards God; his assertion that his *Synopsis mathematica* attempted to provide material for sermons should not be taken lightly, for as he said elsewhere, "everything I do, say and think in all my life" is dedicated to the honor of the Creator.[169]

Augustinian justification of "universal harmony" and of the natural philosophical agenda partly attendant upon it had persuasive power because Augustine, as a preeminent Father of the Church, possessed great authority; furthermore, orthodox school philosophical practice in this period reinforced the prestige of Augustine's teachings through scholastic incorporation of non-Thomistic, Scotist, and Augustinian doctrine received from the medieval tradition. Mersenne therefore derived conviction and propaganda for his views from well-sanctioned quarters, placing him far away from subversive and unorthodox phi-

167. Mersenne, *Harmonie universelle*, "Des consonances," p. 33.
168. Ibid., p. 15. Augustine's attitudes on these matters are examined in David C. Lindberg, "Science and the Early Church," in Lindberg and Numbers, *God and Nature*, pp. 19–48.
169. Mersenne, *Traité*, p. 64. When Mersenne observes at the beginning of *Harmonie universelle* ("Preface au lecteur," final page) that he has "taken the liberty of making some small elevations of the spirit to God in some corollaries," he is indulging in a degree of understatement remarkable in a Frenchman.

losophies that adopted aggressively anti-Aristotelian, neo-Platonic affiliations. Although Saint Augustine himself channeled elements of late-antique neo-Platonic doctrine into medieval Christian thought, the difference between that route to the schools of the early seventeenth century and the Ficinean route to men like Fludd counted almost as much as differences in philosophical content. No doubt Mersenne could still be called a Platonist on the basis of particular doctrinal checklists determining in what the "essence" of Platonism consists, but from a properly historical perspective he can more accurately be labeled, if labels are needed, an Augustinian.

Mersenne's position that mathematical proportions and harmonies must exist in the structure of the created world had practical consequences. "Universal harmony" functioned not merely as a metaphysical ornament to technical work in the mathematical sciences but as a vital heuristic and tacit demonstrative premise in specific pieces of mathematical natural philosophy. For Mersenne, there existed a deep and reciprocal relationship between mechanics and the science of music, and "universal harmony" informed both.

CHAPTER SIX

Mechanics, Music, and Harmony

I

THE PRACTICAL implications of Mersenne's concept of universal harmony emerge clearly from his work in mechanics. By integrating music with a mechanical account of sound, he succeeded in creating a way of treating mechanics itself as an exemplification of the harmonious relationships for which music provided the prototype. Mersenne's formulations of mechanical problems, however, and the way in which he incorporated them into his overall philosophical agenda, need to be understood in relation to his use of specific mechanical traditions and models.

Mersenne's models for mechanics were for the most part either ancient or Italian, provided by the most recent attempts of writers like Guidobaldo del Monte to establish a new Archimedean tradition. The sixteenth-century "renaissance of mathematics" had promoted an image of the nature and history of mechanics resting on the twin pillars of the pseudo-Aristotelian *Questions of Mechanics* and the works of Archimedes.[1] Mersenne knew this tradition well, as he did sixteenth- and seventeenth-century Italian mechanics in general; the *Questions of Mechanics*, or *Mechanica* (to give it one of its contemporary titles), plays a prominent role in his mechanical discussions, especially in his earlier works.

During the sixteenth century this short piece emerged from obscurity and then, in the early seventeenth century, subsided into irrele-

---

1. Rose, *The Italian Renaissance of Mathematics*. See also W. R. Laird, "The Scope of Renaissance Mechanics," *Osiris*, n.s., 2 (1986), 43–68.

vancy.[2] Generally accepted at the time as a genuine Aristotelian work but today regarded as a product of the early peripatetic school, the *Mechanica* enjoyed a temporary importance owing to its credentials and their use in establishing the intellectual and disciplinary legitimacy of mechanics. Guidobaldo and his follower Bernardino Baldi accorded it a seminal position in the historical development of Archimedean mechanics. The two found it a convenient starting point for a heroic history of mechanics despite the fact that it presented, among other things, a physical, dynamic approach to statics quite at odds with Archimedes' own procedures and apparently incapable of assimilation into Guidobaldo's and Baldi's Archimedean revival—the latter stressed the use of mathematically rigorous, properly statical procedures untainted by arguments drawn from dynamical considerations. Guidobaldo claimed that in the *Mechanica* "Aristotle publishes many things highly necessary for the understanding of mechanics." Archimedes, he said, "made more explicit and plain the principles of mechanics" and actually followed Aristotle, in effect mathematizing the latter's principles.[3] Baldi approvingly quoted Guidobaldo's opinion, saying that "Archimedes followed entirely in the footsteps of Aristotle as to the principles, but added to these the exquisite beauty of his proofs."[4] While Baldi's commentary on the *Mechanica*, dating from the 1580s but not published until 1621,[5] denies the actual relevance of the text's principles (since Archimedes had effectively rendered them obsolete), it nonetheless upholds them as necessary prolegomena to the work of Archimedes and his successors. In this way, the Aristotelian cake could be had and eaten at the same time; the sanction of Aristotle's authority upgraded the status of mechanics without compromising its Archimedean techniques.

At the beginning of his *Liber mechanicorum* of 1577, Guidobaldo refers to the *Mechanica*'s central theoretical proposition: "It is certainly true, and freely admitted by anyone who learned it previously from Aristotle, that all mechanical problems and all mechanical theorems are reducible to the wheel and depend therefore on its principle, which is apprehended no less by the senses than by reason. The

2. Paul Lawrence Rose and Stillman Drake, "The Pseudo-Aristotelian *Questions in Mechanics* in Renaissance Culture," *Studies in the Renaissance* 18 (1971), 65–104; Laird, "Renaissance Mechanics," which focuses on the supposedly Aristotelian work and its commentators.

3. Guidobaldo, quoted in Rose, *Italian Renaissance*, p. 234.

4. Quoted in Rose and Drake, "Pseudo-Aristotelian *Questions*," p. 91.

5. See Rose, *Italian Renaissance*, p. 248; also Pierre Duhem, *Les origines de la statique* (Paris, 1905), 2:129–39, although the latter displays Duhem's idiosyncratic preoccupation with Leonardo.

wheel is the device that is best adapted to movement, and the more so the larger it is."[6] He goes on to present a formal statical treatise bearing little resemblance to the work he has just endorsed. Guidobaldo does use the *Mechanica* for polemical purposes, to adduce support for his position on the behavior of balances when tilted from equilibrium, but the actual demonstrative arguments still remain Archimedean.[7] The very admissibility of Aristotelian opinions, however, acted to buttress Guidobaldo's claim that the Archimedean tradition rested on the physical principles of the *Mechanica*.

When Mersenne discussed mechanics in *Quaestiones in Genesim*, using it in one of the thirty-six proofs for the existence of God, the doctrines of the *Mechanica* played an important part.[8] Mersenne's proof of the existence of God from mechanics revolves around the *Mechanica*'s view of the circle as the efficient or even final cause of all mechanics. Mersenne proceeds by comparing God to the circle much as, elsewhere, he compared Him to unity.[9] The author of the pseudo-Aristotelian work had commenced with the lever and balance on the grounds that "practically all the other phenomena of mechanical motion are connected with the lever" and had asserted that "the original cause of all such phenomena is the circle."[10] So Mersenne's proof, repeated in the following year's *L'impieté des deistes*,[11] focuses on such circular attributes as perfect simplicity and the comprehension within that simplicity of all possible angles, which supposedly reflects God's comprehension within Himself of all possible creatures. By an implicit and shaky piece of analogical reasoning, Mersenne suggests that since God is therefore like the circle, He is the necessary original cause of mechanics, which consequently bears witness to His existence. In the course of this quite lengthy discussion, covering eight closely printed columns,[12] Mersenne employs the *Mechanica* as his central and almost exclusive text; at one point he gives as an instance of the circle's causal relationship to mechanics the operation of dental forceps, an example lifted straight from the *Mechanica*.[13] The overall purpose of the argu-

---

6. Guidobaldo del Monte, *Mechanicorum liber* (Pesaro, 1577), abridged translation by Stillman Drake in Drake and I. E. Drabkin, *Mechanics in Sixteenth-Century Italy* (Madison, Wis., 1969), p. 241.

7. Ibid., pp. 284–91.

8. On the thirty-six proofs, see Chapter 3, above.

9. Mersenne, *Quaestiones*, cols. 85–86. On comparisons of God with unity, see Chapter 4, above.

10. Pseudo-Aristotle, *Mechanica*, trans. E. S. Forster, in J. A. Smith and W. D. Ross, eds., *The Works of Aristotle*, vol. 6 (Oxford, 1913), 848ª, 847ᵇ.

11. Mersenne, *L'impieté*, 1:436–38.

12. Mersenne, *Quaestiones*, cols. 83–91.

13. Ibid., col. 87; pseudo-Aristotle, *Mechanica*, 854ª.

ment largely explains his single-mindedness, but his commitment to the doctrines he describes is quite genuine. Although Baldi's commentary had appeared only two years before, Mersenne shows familiarity with it in several references, mostly marginal glosses opposing Baldi's criticisms of the *Mechanica*'s teachings. When describing the circle as composed of contraries (contrary motions, simultaneous concavity and convexity),[14] Mersenne troubles to note Baldi's disagreement with this assertion of the *Mechanica* just so that he can dismiss it. A little later, he says that the properties of the circle as set forth in the *Mechanica* can be upheld despite Baldi's criticisms of Aristotle.[15]

These rejections notwithstanding, Mersenne happily retains one principal feature of Baldi's account of mechanics: all the mechanical laws of Archimedes, Guidobaldo, Baldi, and Blancanus (who had written a short commentary on the *Mechanica*) stem, he suggests, from the principles of Aristotle.[16] His listing of the disciplines in *Quaestiones* contrives actually to incorporate this idea. That part of the table covering mechanical topics, both practical and speculative, gives for the most part the expected authors in each branch, including Vitruvius for architecture, Stevin for scenography, Dürer for "pictura," and Salomon de Caus for hydraulics, as well as Archimedes for "aequiponderans" and Commandino for "centrobarica."[17] To find Guidobaldo, however, one must look at the entry commencing the mechanical items. He appears there, alongside Aristotle, against the label "rationalis."[18] Clearly, Mersenne considered that Aristotle's *Mechanica* provided the conceptual and physical basis for the speculative side of the subject as a whole and that Guidobaldo both recognized and elucidated precisely how Archimedes and his successors exploited it. Guidobaldo's perceived importance on this count may be judged from Baldi's expression of surprise that Archimedes failed to acknowledge his debt to Aristotle.

Mersenne's reasons for accepting this view on the one hand and, on

14. Pseudo-Aristotle, *Mechanica*, 847ᵇ–848ᵃ.
15. Mersenne, *Quaestiones*, cols. 87, 89. The only other commentator on the *Mechanica* whom Mersenne cites in this discussion is "Leonicenus," that is, Niccolò Leonico Tomeo, who translated the work from Greek into Latin in the early sixteenth century: see Rose and Drake, "Pseudo-Aristotelian *Questions*," pp. 78–80; Laird, "Renaissance Mechanics," pp. 48–49. Rose and Drake note that the many reprintings of Leonico's translation lack his commentaries, but Mersenne seems to be referring to a commentary, indicating once again the breadth of his erudition: he must have seen an edition of Leonico's *Opuscula*.
16. Mersenne, *Quaestiones*, col. 91. Blancanus's commentary (see Chapter 4, sec. III, above) appeared in 1615; see Rose and Drake, "Pseudo-Aristotelian Questions," p. 92.
17. Mersenne, *Quaestiones*, cols. 1207–8. On Salomon de Caus, see e.g., Duhem, *Origines*, 1:290–92.
18. Mersenne, *Quaestiones*, cols. 1207–8.

the other, rejecting the idea that the Archimedean approach had fully replaced that of the *Mechanica* seem to derive from the narrowness of the statical approach advocated by Guidobaldo and Baldi: Mersenne wanted to keep open the possibility of moving from statics to the mathematical treatment of motion. Although Guidobaldo emphasized the Aristotelian, *physical* underpinnings of statics, he also made a strict disciplinary distinction between it and the study of motion on the grounds that the first was properly mathematical, whereas the second was really a part of physics.[19] Guidobaldo also shackled his subject by a very literal-minded interpretation of the nature of mechanics as a mathematical science. Recognizing the necessity, in extending statics itself, of a correct mathematical abstraction from physical things as the basis of the mixed science of mechanics, he rejected the usual Archimedean simplification (adopted by Tartaglia and others) of treating as parallel the lines of descent along which the weights on a balance strive to descend. Since we know from physics that heavy bodies tend towards the center of the earth, he argued, those lines must in fact converge; and although the convergence is practically undetectable, mathematical rigor would demand that it be taken into account.[20] Similarly, because the *Mechanica*'s explanation for the law of the lever involved the concept of the possible motion of balance arms actually in equilibrium, Guidobaldo rejected it for Archimedes' entirely static proof. Mersenne never let such considerations get in the way of generating useful results; in any case, as the Christian Philosopher told the Sceptic, mathematical demonstrations remained true in themselves regardless of whether they had actual physical instantiation.[21] The ideas found in the *Mechanica* appeared to Mersenne, as they did to Galileo, important as a way of grounding a mathematical approach to motion, and he seems to have had no doubt about their reliability.

In the *Synopsis mathematica* of 1626, Mersenne set out to present examples of absolutely solid mathematical knowledge, in effect continuing the "proof by ostension" directed against Pyrrhonism in the

---

19. See Rose, *Italian Renaissance*, p. 233. Laird, "Renaissance Mechanics," shows how the *Mechanica* was involved in the establishment, during the sixteenth century, of mechanics as a mixed mathematical (or "intermediate") science on a methodological par with optics, astronomy, and music—something for which Aristotelian sanction could be found other than in the *Mechanica* but which lacked authoritative content before the recovery and dissemination of that text in the early sixteenth century.

20. See his remarks in Drake and Drabkin, *Mechanics*, p. 275; see also Rose, *Italian Renaissance*, p. 233.

21. In Mersenne, *La verité*, p. 275; see also the material from *Questions inouyes* (1634) quoted in Lenoble, *Mersenne*, p. 347; and see Chapter 4, above. Reference to the *Mechanica* itself appears in *La verité*, e.g., on page 754.

previous year's *La verité des sciences*.[22] He proceeded for the most part by listing theorems from various classic works such as those of Euclid, Archimedes, or the more recent Maurolico, neglecting the proofs. Part of Mersenne's purpose, as he averred more than once, was to provide material for use in sermons—a not unusual design: a book of 1622 by Elie Binet, for example, written to assist priests in composing homilies, included a section on mathematics,[23] and Mersenne made frequent theological use of mathematics himself. However, one of the sections of the *Synopsis*, the "Mechanicorum libri," differs somewhat from the rest in that it includes discussion of the topics considered and therefore has room for elaborating on conceptual foundations as well as stating conclusions.[24] His presentation of Simon Stevin's inclined-plane theorem, based on the impossibility of perpetual motion, demonstrates the strictness with which Mersenne pursued his chief aim in the *Synopsis*, to provide uncontroversial, certain knowledge: it appears with the caveat that it is based on an imperfectly established physical principle.[25] His caution does not prevent him, however, from claiming in the preface that virtually all of mechanics could be reduced to the axiom "rotunda machina est moventissima, et quo major, eo moventior" (the round [or circular] machine is the most moved, and the greater it is, the more moved)[26]—the fundamental thesis of the *Mechanica*. In addition, at the end of the second part of the "Mechanicorum libri," Mersenne reviews almost the entire *Mechanica*.[27]

Apart from Stevin's work, the findings of people like Guidobaldo and Commandino fill the bulk of the mechanical books, and so the greatest achievements of sixteenth- and early seventeenth-century mechanics appear within an unquestioned conceptual framework derived from the pseudo-Aristotelian work. Mersenne's understanding

22. Marin Mersenne, *Synopsis mathematica* (Paris, 1626), consists of a number of independent parts, only some of which are found in any given volume; for the complicated bibliographical details, see Lenoble, *Mersenne*, pp. xv–xvii. I have used a film of the Bordeaux copy.

23. Mersenne remarked on this purpose of the *Synopsis* in a dedicatory letter prefixed to that collection (see Mersenne *Correspondance*, 1:469) and in *Harmonie universelle*, "De l'utilité de l'harmonie," p. 16. On Binet, see Alex Keller, "Mathematical Technologies and the Growth of the Idea of Technical Progress in the Sixteenth Century," in Allen G. Debus, ed., *Science, Medicine and Society in the Renaissance* (New York, 1972), 1:15; De Waard gives a list of other mathematical compendia of about the same time: Mersenne *Correspondance*, 2:210.

24. A useful description of the contents of the "Mechanicorum libri" may be found in Mersenne *Correspondance*, 14:686–87. See also Chapter 8, below.

25. Mersenne, *Synopsis*, "Mechanicorum libri." p. 138.

26. Ibid., p. 3.

27. Ibid., pp. 146–68. The material cited here and in nn. 25–26, above, may be conveniently found in Duhem, *Origines*, 1:295–98.

of the discipline of mechanics (at least its speculative side) thus impli-cated as a foundational part of the proper formulation and solution of problems the nonstatical approach apparently validated by Aris-totle.

Mersenne deployed that approach, thereby revealing some of the purposes for which he found it useful, in his *Traité de l'harmonie uni-verselle* of the following year. The second of the work's two books proposes to display the manifold analogies between music and other aspects of the world, from our sensations of flavor and odor to the harmony of the celestial spheres. Its Theorem x shows how "conso-nances are similar to *statics*, and to other parts of mechanics."[28] The theorem's formal statement makes explicit the intended breadth of the comparison: "There is the same ratio of the difference of sounds to the difference of strings considered in their length, as there is of the difference of weights to the difference of their distance from the center of the balance, or the fulcrum of the lever, which the Greeks call *Hypomoclion*; consequently sounds can be compared to weights, to statics, to the equilibrium of planes [*l'Isorropique*], and to moving forces."[29] Owing to the fundamental status of the law of the lever, then, Mersenne could square the whole of statics with his musical paradigm—and not only statics but also "moving forces." The pos-sibility of achieving this desired generality arose from the particular way Mersenne chose to characterize the nature of the balance. After describing the inverse relation between weights and their distances from the fulcrum, he noted that as a consequence "there is the same ratio of the speed that the movement of the lesser weight has to the speed that the movement of the greater has, as there is of the distance of the lesser weight from the center of the balance to the distance of the greater weight from the same center."[30] This is thoroughly un-Archimedean, considering a situation that is by definition statical as if it were in motion. It accords with the approach of the *Mechanica*.

The Archimedean, properly statical treatment of the balance adopted by Guidobaldo ran counter both to the pseudo-Aristotelian view and to the medieval tradition associated with the name of Jor-danus Nemorarius.[31] Both of these used dynamical approaches, and

28. Mersenne, *Traité*, p. 391.
29. Ibid., p. 392.
30. Ibid., pp. 393–94.
31. On the Jordanian tradition, see Maurice Clavelin, *The Natural Philosophy of Ga-lileo*, trans. A. J. Pomerans (Cambridge, Mass., 1974), pp. 148–54; Joseph E. Brown, "The Science of Weights," in David C. Lindberg, ed., *Science in the Middle Ages* (Chicago, 1978), pp. 179–205. For Jordanian texts see Ernest A. Moody and Marshall Clagett, eds., *The Medieval Science of Weights* (Madison, Wis., 1960), pp. 119–227.

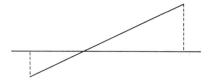

Figure 1

although Guidobaldo and Baldi therefore rejected them, Tartaglia and Cardano had drawn on the Jordanian tradition, and Galileo appears to have exploited the peripatetic source.[32] In practice the two can be regarded as using very similar techniques. The former saw the problem of the balance in terms of what amounted to virtual vertical displacements (Figure 1): should the equilibrated balance tilt from its position of rest, the ratio of the longer arm's vertical displacement to that of the shorter arm would be the same as that of the length of the arms, and hence the inverse of the ratio of respective weights. If equilibrium held for any other relation of weights to arm lengths, the ratio of the displacements would not match that of the weights, and this is taken as impossible. The Jordanian explanation of the equilibrium condition thus works through a fundamentally physical rather than mathematical interpretation involving the tacit assumption that the products of weight and vertical displacement must remain equal on both sides of the balance—an intuition anachronistically comparable to the idea of the "conservation of energy." The peripatetic construal of the situation is in this respect very similar except that instead of concentrating on the potential relative *displacements* of the ends of the balance, it considers their potential relative *speeds,* which of course yield an identical ratio. For the peripatetics, at least in this context, speed is proportional to force—or, rather, force is something understood as productive of constant speed and proportional to it. Thus the relative speeds of the balance arms in the case where they are supposed to move give the relative forces associated with their motion. For equilibrium, then, the weights on the two ends of the balance must exactly counteract those two potential forces: that

32. For a concise summary of sixteenth-century mechanical traditions, including the *Mechanica* and Galileo's use of it, see Stillman Drake, "Physics and Tradition before Galileo," in *Galileo Studies* (Ann Arbor, Mich., 1970), pp. 19–42. On Tartaglia's use of Jordanus, see Winifred L. Wisan, "The New Science of Motion," *Archive for History of Exact Sciences* 13 (1974), 146–48; and Laird, "Renaissance Mechanics," pp. 52–53, with additional references. On Galileo, see also Duhem, *Origines,* 1:297; Clavelin, *Natural Philosophy,* pp. 141ff. On the use of the *Mechanica*'s interpretation of the balance by Cardano, Galileo, and Mersenne, see De Waard's note in Mersenne *Correspondance,* 2:260.

is, their ratio must be the inverse of their respective potential speeds and hence of the lengths of their respective arms.[33]

Mersenne's treatment of the balance in the *Traité*, therefore, in following the *Mechanica*, implies the adoption of an Aristotelian view of force and its relation to speed:

> The reason why weights become lighter or heavier and stronger or weaker according as they are closer to or farther from the center of the balance, or the fulcrum of the lever, is that they have a faster or slower movement, which gives a great virtue to everything that happens in nature. Thence it comes that a hammer blow that we make on a wedge or nail has much greater effect on account of the speed of its movement than if it descended more slowly, or than if we put it gently on the nail without any movement. Now, the movement of weights is so much the faster, as the force by which it is produced is greater: similarly, the weight is so much the heavier to remain in equilibrium with that which moves itself faster, as its movement is slower; such that the lightness of a weight is recompensed by speed as heaviness [*la pesanteur*] is diminished by the slowness of movement. Thus it is that when two different weights are in equilibrium, there is the same ratio of major inequality [i.e., a ratio of which the first term is the larger] between the weights as there is minor inequality between the speeds of their movements, and their distances from the center of the balance.[34]

Mersenne's conceptual union of statics and moving bodies thus rested on a paradigmatic problem solution, the *Mechanica*'s analysis of the balance. As one of his marginal glosses put it, "Quickness or slowness of movement cause of everything that happens with balances."[35]

The eleventh theorem follows up the tenth's rather piecemeal and focused consideration of these matters with a more systematic account: "To determine and explicate what are the principles, and the principal maxims of the science of mechanics."[36] Chiefly devoted to centers of gravity, the chapter cites Pappus and, perhaps more immediately, Commandino, as well as again using material from the *Mechanica*. Mersenne borrows directly the example of how the way a man rises from a chair depends on his center of gravity and on the necessary verticality of the line of direction joining it to the center of the earth (although the *Mechanica*'s author had omitted the last refinement).[37] The theorem ends with a statement of a few propositions

33. See Clavelin, *Natural Philosophy*, pp. 141–43.
34. Mersenne, *Traité*, pp. 395–96.
35. Ibid., p. 399.
36. Ibid., p. 406.
37. Ibid., pp. 406 (citations), 412 (chair); see pseudo-Aristotle, *Mechanica*, 857[b].

taken from that part of Guidobaldo's *Liber mechanicorum* concerning the lever.[38] Mersenne's readiness to combine Guidobaldo's purist Archimedeanism with the impure pseudo-statics of the *Mechanica* underlines his deviation from the former's teachings and his perception of a greater potential fruitfulness in the approach of the latter. For Guidobaldo, the Aristotelian conceptualization of the balance, although somehow a necessary first step, had become obsolete with the advent of Archimedes, who had effectively demonstrated an absolute division between statics and dynamics through his successful mathematization of statics and consequent abandonment of dynamics to physics, the study of motion and change. As Baldi said, Archimedes' work superseded Aristotle's treatment of statics but not his treatment of the mechanics of motion.[39] Mersenne, by contrast, took seriously the peripatetic approach to the balance because he liked its stress on motion, which enabled the extension of mathematical mechanics into areas explicitly forbidden by Guidobaldo. Where Guidobaldo took motion to be by definition physical and hence incapable of assimilation into a mathematical science, Mersenne made no such assumption. If it possessed quantitative properties, then mathematics could speak of it. The comparison between harmony and mechanics drawn in the *Traité* hints at the possibilities that Mersenne envisaged.

Questions theologiques, one of Mersenne's publications of 1634, asserts that the rules governing the balance apply equally to all the "instruments of mechanics" spoken of by Aristotle in the *Mechanica*, as well as by "Balde, Blancan, Monantolius, & Guevare dans leurs Commentaires."[40] These were the four most recent commentaries on the work: Baldi's, 1621; Blancanus's, 1615; Henri de Monantheuil's, 1599 and 1600; and Giovanni di Guevara's, 1627.[41] Mersenne here explains the balance in terms of the "power" (*puissance*) of the weights to go farther (*à faire plus de chemin*) "or to descend faster"; this power is the "cause of their greater weight" at increasing distances from the center.[42] The *Mechanica* thus remained the point of reference for Mersenne's discussions of mechanics in the year that saw the appearance of his book *Les mechaniques de Galilée*, a French paraphrase of Galileo's *Le meccaniche*, which had circulated in manuscript since the

---

38. Mersenne, *Traité*, pp. 414–15; see Guidobaldo, *Mechanicorum liber*, pp. 298–302.
39. Rose, *Italian Renaissance*, p. 249.
40. Mersenne, *Questions theologiques*, p. 38.
41. See Rose and Drake, "Pseudo-Aristotelian *Questions*," pp. 103–4 (with an amendment in Rose, *Italian Renaissance*, p. 175 and note).
42. Mersenne, *Questions theologiques*, p. 38.

beginning of the century.[43] Galileo's treatise, as we shall see later, used certain themes found in the *Mechanica,* and Mersenne not unsuitably adds to his "Preface au lecteur" a "consideration of the two circles which Aristotle has set forth in the twenty-fourth question of his *Mechanics,* because many people find it admirable, all the more in that they don't understand it."[44] Mersenne had also considered this paradox in *Quaestiones in Genesim,* and it enjoyed something of a vogue around this time, but the association of the *Mechanica* with this early Galilean treatise fittingly symbolizes Mersenne's perspective on mechanics.[45] The same purposes for which the *Mechanica* recommended itself to him were also to render attractive some of Galileo's mature innovations.

Rejecting Guidobaldo's restrictive Archimedean ideal of a mathematical mechanics in favor of admitting apparently physical principles relating to motion recalls Mersenne's contention, noted in Chapter 4, that mixed mathematical sciences used physical as well as mathematical assumptions and were to that extent incapable of absolute certainty. It is therefore possible to see Mersenne's implicit rejection of Guidobaldo's desire for mathematical purity in mechanics as reflecting an attitude of disbelief in the possibility of such a thing. If physical assumptions necessarily intruded into mechanics, no rigid barrier prevented the assimilation of principles relating to motion. In this way, Mersenne's mathematical natural philosophy showed signs of moving away from the model of mixed mathematics, which gave it its intellectual credentials, and towards a more general vision of the mathematical exegesis of nature—hence his eventual adoption of Isaac Beeckman's term "physico-mathematics."[46] Mersenne never departed far from the standard model, however, and he did so in this

43. Marin Mersenne, *Les mechaniques de Galilée* (Paris, 1634), for details on which see the introduction to the critical edition by Bernard Rochot (Paris, 1966), and Lenoble, *Mersenne,* pp. xx–xxi. On the dating of Galileo's treatise, see the generally accepted account in Stillman Drake, *Galileo at Work* (Chicago, 1978), pp. 55–56.

44. Mersenne, *Les mechaniques,* p. 17 (page references to this work follow the Rochot edition).

45. See De Waard's note in Mersenne *Correspondance,* 1:13; Baldus and Blancanus are cited in this connection in Mersenne, *Quaestiones,* col. 70. On interest in the paradox, see also Israel E. Drabkin, "Aristotle's Wheel," *Osiris* 9 (1950), 162–98 (Mersenne is discussed on pages 173–76); Pierre Costabel, "La roue d'Aristote et les critiques françaises à l'argument de Galilée," *Revue d'histoire des sciences* 17 (1964), 385–96. For Benedetti's notable treatment of this paradox, see Drake and Drabkin, *Mechanics,* pp. 193–95, with further references in the notes.

46. E.g., in Marin Mersenne, *Cogitata physico-mathematica* (Paris, 1644), which is basically a compendium of mixed mathematical sciences, including local motion; see Chapter 8, below.

case only to the extent that the mechanics of local motion seemed a promising area of extension for such existing mathematical techniques as those of statics or music, and a proving ground for the natural philosophical agenda sanctioned or represented by "universal harmony." In the 1630s Mersenne's pursuit of such a mechanics came to focus on Galileo's work, but in the 1620s the peripatetic approach of the *Mechanica* served as his principal guide to the very Galilean subject of falling bodies.

II

Isaac Beeckman, the Dutch schoolmaster, mechanical philosopher, and mentor of Descartes, recorded in his *Journal* in 1629 a discussion of Mersenne's mechanical ideas. He considered material from the *Traité de l'harmonie universelle* together with a letter from Mersenne known only from the fragment Beeckman chose to quote.[47] After rejecting Mersenne's contention that "quickness or slowness of movement" is the "cause of everything that happens with balances"—this implies, he said, that a heavy body will fall faster *in vacuo* than a light one, given Mersenne's equation of heaviness with speed[48]—Beeckman quotes from Mersenne's letter.[49] In that passage, Mersenne rejects Beeckman's assertion (made in an earlier letter) that bodies accelerate as they fall, and he gives two reasons for so doing. The first is theoretical, based on an analysis of free fall that measures speed against the distance fallen. Mersenne argues that since at every point in its path the relevant parameters governing the body's descent— namely, its weight and its disposition to undergo this kind of natural motion—remain constant, there should be no difference in its behavior between one part of the fall and another. The second reason is that Beeckman's claim lacks empirical support; Mersenne's own experience fails to show that bodies accelerate naturally. In fact, if anything, experience seems to indicate that they slow down somewhat as they fall, presumably due to air resistance, an observation Mersenne appears to have made to his correspondent Robert Cornier the year before.[50] Beeckman, however, regarded these statements only as evi-

---

47. Reprinted in Mersenne *Correspondance*, 2:256–62.
48. Ibid., pp. 256–57.
49. Ibid., p. 257.
50. See ibid., p. 58 and note, with further references.

dence of Mersenne's lack of understanding of the relations between weight and speed.[51]

One could, with Beeckman, regard Mersenne's conceptions of statics and dynamics as confused or misguided, but such a judgment would presuppose the very standards of evaluation that were under dispute. Since there were at this time competing standards—one could choose those of the peripatetic tradition or those of the Archimedean, for instance—an overall approach to mechanics needed to be constructed with reference to criteria of plausibility that had not achieved consensual status. Mersenne chose the *Mechanica* as his authoritative touchstone, and given the necessity of some a priori set of assumptions with which to work, his position cannot be called unreasonable if it enabled him to make sense of his subject matter. However, his other touchstone, experience, held an even higher place in his argumentative repertoire. Isaac Beeckman might say what he liked, but if experience failed to show that falling bodies accelerate, then there was an end of it. In fact, by denying the acceleration of falling bodies, Mersenne also went against commonly accepted scholastic doctrine, although there it acted more as an anomaly than as a functional part of physics; in effect, Mersenne avoided the anomaly by denying it. He had made experiments explicitly to determine this issue, evidently seeing the appeal to experience as a powerful one. Writing to him on 18 December 1629, Descartes mentions a remark by Mersenne (from a letter no longer extant) concerning two "experiences" supposedly indicating that bodies fall at a uniform rate: Mersenne had written that light bodies certainly do so shortly after they commence their descent, "quoad sensum."[52]

This last phrase, which reappears in a letter from Beeckman to Mersenne in 1630, is clearly Mersenne's own. "You say," wrote Beeckman, "that you have experienced that a stone falling from a height of fifty feet is moved with no greater speed in the last twenty-five feet than in the first twenty-five, as far as the senses can judge [*quo ad sensum*]. And you add "quoad sensum" appropriately [*opportune*], for if you will assume a bladder filled with air, the opposite will appear doubtful from a distance to the senses [*sensibiliter*]."[53] Beeckman's apparent sarcasm did not trouble Mersenne. Indeed, Beeckman's devaluation of sensory evidence ran counter to the thrust of Mersenne's whole argument and therefore *could* not be taken seriously. By employing experiments, Mersenne affirmed his position

51. Ibid., p. 257.
52. Ibid., p. 344.
53. Ibid., p. 457.

that appearances provided the only sound basis for contingent knowledge of nature. They could not be transcended to discover essences,
and they could not be accorded necessity; hence Beeckman's causal, a
priori reasons lacked cogency. To the extent that Mersenne sought
mathematical regularities in nature, the idea that falling bodies accelerate uniformly need not have appeared repugnant and in fact
proved later to be highly attractive. But for the moment, Mersenne's
stake in maintaining the reliability of sensory experience, and his
disinclination to compromise the peripatetic conceptual apparatus of
the *Mechanica*, outweighed such considerations.

Mersenne disregarded Beeckman's comments, therefore, and in
1631 he wrote to Jean Rey that while Rey might claim that heavy
bodies travel faster at the end than at the beginning of their fall,
"experience makes me see the contrary: for a cannonball descends as
fast during the first twenty-five feet as during the last twenty-five."[54]
Clearly recounting the same experiment as the one he had reported
to Beeckman but this time neglecting any possible progressive retar-
dation of fall by air resistance,[55] Mersenne thus continued to deny
natural acceleration on empirical grounds. In the same and subsequent letters to Rey he also asserted, "against the common opinion,"
that heavy bodies do not fall at a greater rate than light bodies, something that Rey apparently found hard to swallow.[56] In April 1632
Mersenne attempted to convince him: "Truly, I am astonished at
what you distrust of my experiment [*expérience*] of the equal speed of
an iron bullet and a wooden bullet: for if several persons of quality
who have seen and made the experiment with me were simply to
swear [*signer*] solemnly to you, they would witness it to you authen-
tically."[57] The appeal to empiricism is total. On this occasion Mersenne made no attempt to put forward theoretical arguments, relying
instead on the testimony of "several persons of quality." This kind of
technique for establishing claims in natural philosophy and in the
mathematical sciences, centering on reports of set-piece, preferably
witnessed experiments, had already begun to enter the practice of
Jesuit writers and fitted well Mersenne's ideal of proper scientific
procedure.[58] There can be no doubt, however, that interpretive as-

54. Ibid., 3:188.
55. Cf. note in ibid.
56. Ibid., p. 196n; also ibid., 4:21–23nn.
57. Ibid., 3:274–75.
58. See Dear, "Jesuit Mathematical Science." Mersenne's recourse to empiricism
seldom goes beyond that of such prominent Jesuit writers as Blancanus, Scheiner, and
(later and most notably) Riccioli.

sumptions underlay Mersenne's position on the issue, as his theoretical argument against Beeckman indicated. In the wake of Galileo's work, which provided a previously unavailable alternative to the *Mechanica* tradition, Mersenne quickly reinterpreted his experimental evidence.

In 1633 he issued a pamphlet on falling bodies, supporting the contention that their descent tends to follow the odd-number rule associated with uniform acceleration.[59] Beeckman had tried to persuade Mersenne with the idea of a series of impulses successively impelling the mobile downwards while the mobile continued to retain all of the motion imparted to it by preceding impulses—an explanation of uniform acceleration original with neither Beeckman nor with Benedetti, who had also suggested it.[60] Unconvinced by this as to the truth of the appearances themselves, Mersenne nonetheless now reversed his opinion, despite previous resistance based on sensory experience, which he had presented as the ultimate arbiter. He still shied away from commitment to any particular causal mechanism, however. The pamphlet reviews the various arguments proposed to account for the characteristics of free fall and finds them all unsatisfactory. But Mersenne notes that the hypothesis of a sort of magnetic attraction exerted by the earth might explain the "geometrical proportion" observed in fall: that is, the increase of distance according to the square of the time, "inasmuch as the activity of all sorts of natural agents diminishes itself in a doubled ratio [i.e., square] of spaces."[61] The confusion evident here perhaps arises from a conflation of direct proportionality between speed and distance with that between speed and time, mediated by the Aristotelian relationship of speed to force. In any case, Mersenne concludes that one could certainly invent many other explanations as well without thereby finding the true cause. Consequently, "it suffices to expound [*expliquer*] the phenomena of nature, since the human mind isn't capable of possessing its causes and principles."[62]

Mersenne, to take him at his word, must have decided, on the basis of the lessons of experience, that uniform acceleration does occur in free fall. Until a short time before he wrote his pamphlet, experience

59. For details, see note in Mersenne *Correspondance*, 3:437–39; some of this pamphlet is reprinted as Appendix 3 to ibid., pp. 630–33. See also the discussion in Pierre Boutroux, "Le Père Mersenne et Galilée," *Scientia* 31 (1922), 347–50.

60. See Beeckman's letter to Mersenne, October 1629, in Mersenne *Correspondance*, 2:280–81, and note. On Benedetti, see, e.g., Alexandre Koyré, "Giambattista Benedetti, Critic of Aristotle," in McMullin, *Galileo*, pp. 98–117, esp. 111.

61. Mersenne *Correspondance*, 3:633.

62. Ibid.

had shown no acceleration, but by late 1633 Mersenne had read Galileo's *Dialogue*, and Galileo's statement of the law of fall seems to have convinced him where those of others (notably Beeckman) had not.[63] Part of the reason for Mersenne's sudden conversion may lie in his general admiration for Galileo, dating from the previous decade,[64] but it is quite clear from his writings of 1634 and, especially, 1636 (the *Harmonie universelle*) that the principal factors were Galileo's account of the inclined-plane experiments and the adaptability of Galileo's conception of mechanics to the concerns that Mersenne had previously addressed using the *Mechanica*. Mersenne had known of the astronomical Galileo at least since the early 1620s,[65] but he gives no sign of acquaintance with Galileo's mechanical work in either the *Synopsis mathematica* or the *Traité de l'harmonie universelle*, or in letters of the 1620s.[66] In 1634, however, as we have seen, he published a paraphrase of Galileo's early treatise known as *Le meccaniche*.[67]

Les mechaniques de Galilée, mathematicien & ingenieur du duc de Florence deals with statics and the simple machines, covering the standard topical headings in effect established by Pappus. In a dedicatory letter prefacing the work—addressed to Henri de Reffuge, a member of the *parlement* of Paris—Mersenne discusses his reasons for producing it. Apart from the general motive of publishing a comprehensive work on statics (to which effect he included some material taken from Guidobaldo),[68] he wishes to take the opportunity to present "several rare and novel additions." These "contain new speculations, which can serve to penetrate the secrets of physics, and particularly everything that concerns movements as much natural as violent."[69] Given Mersenne's constantly reiterated convictions about the limits of human knowledge, talk of "penetrating the secrets of physics" smacks of hyperbole, but his reference to the concepts of natural and violent motion betrays the continuing presence of Aristotelian habits of

63. The *Dialogue* is mentioned in the pamphlet; see Rochot's introduction to Mersenne, *Les mechaniques*, pp. 7–8; see also De Waard's note in Mersenne *Correspondance*, 2:261–62.

64. See Lenoble, *Mersenne*, p. 392.

65. Ibid. The 1616 condemnation of Copernicanism is reproduced in Mersenne, *Quaestiones*, col. 904; Mersenne's earliest publication, *L'usage de la raison*, alludes to Galileo's telescopic discoveries (dedication "À Madame la Mareschale de Vitry," [p. 4]).

66. On Mersenne's ignorance of Galileo's mechanics in 1626, see Rochot's note in Mersenne, *Les mechaniques*, p. 13.

67. For details, see Rochot's introduction in ibid.; also De Waard's note in Mersenne *Correspondance*, 4:76–77.

68. Mersenne, *Les mechaniques*, pp. 14–15.

69. Ibid., p. 13. Rochot's note on p. 14, which attempts to equate Mersenne's remarks on the action of simple machines with the principle of inertia, is misleading; it appears to follow Lenoble, *Mersenne*, pp. 357–58.

thought in his mechanics. Mersenne still considered mechanical equilibrium in terms of potential speeds, drawing on the *Mechanica* as his authority, in *Questions theologiques* of the same year. Since Galileo's treatment of equilibrium in *Le meccaniche* (often taken to be an adumbration of the idea of "virtual velocities") also reflected the approach of the *Mechanica*—as has been noted by commentators from Duhem to Clavelin and Drake[70]—Mersenne could quite readily coordinate Galileo's work with the framework he had used hitherto, and that fact facilitated his adoption of Galilean techniques relating to the problem of fall.

An example from Mersenne's 1626 *Synopsis mathematica* brings out the similarities between his approach to mechanics and that of Galileo. Discussing equilibrium on inclined planes, Mersenne first considers Simon Stevin's argument for an inverse proportionality between the length of a plane and the effective weight of the heavy body resting on it, which, for two connected bodies each tending to descend on a different slope, yielded an equilibrium condition requiring the proportion of absolute weights to be the inverse of that of their respective sides (Figure 2). Mersenne then goes on to make an observation manifesting his association of equilibrium and potential speeds:

> But all that [Stevin's argument] seems to depend on the axiom that I touched on above: the speed of descent of one of the weights is to the speed of descent of the other as the length of one of the sides of the triangle is to the length of the other; accordingly, two descents are equal when they correspond to a same diminution of the distance from the center; now, the greater the side of the triangle or, which comes to the same thing, the more the plane is oblique, the longer also is this side; the descent of a heavy body that follows this side is that much slower, and its approach to the center of the universe is that much slower.[71]

Lenoble misunderstood this passage, taking Mersenne to be speaking of relative speeds of fall down inclined planes and claiming that Mersenne therefore anticipated Galileo by several years.[72] Duhem, however, regarded it as a duplication of one of Galileo's arguments in *Le meccaniche* demonstrating the law of inclined planes by means of vir-

70. See n. 32, above.
71. Mersenne, *Synopsis*, "Mechanicorum libri," p. 141; translation compared with Duhem's French in *Origines*, 1:298.
72. Lenoble, *Mersenne*, p. 463. This error is repeated by Rochot in Mersenne, *Les mechaniques*, p. 68n.1, citing Lenoble. Lenoble's remarks about Galileo's discussion of fall along inclined planes in the *Dialogue* also seem confused, as do his comments on Mersenne's treatment of that discussion in *Harmonie universelle*: Lenoble, *Mersenne*, p. 463n.2.

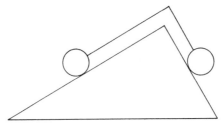

Figure 2

tual velocities.[73] In fact, Duhem was only partially right and for the wrong reasons. There is, as we have said, no evidence that Mersenne knew of Galileo's treatise in 1626. His discussion does closely parallel one in *Le meccaniche* but not the one using "virtual velocities" to demonstrate the inclined-plane law. The true similarity shows a common approach echoing the *Mechanica*.

Mersenne's subject in the quoted passage is the relation of potential vertical movements of the two weights. When speaking of the descent of either, Mersenne specifies its "approach to the center of the universe": that is, the vertical component of the motion. Galileo's equivalent discussion in fact *follows* a demonstration of the law of the inclined plane using his concept of *momento* to express the effective weight of a body on an oblique surface.[74] He first asks whether the inclined plane obeys the general rule of mechanical instruments that "whatever is gained in force by their means is lost in time and in speed."[75] It might seem not, he says, elucidating the point with the aid of a figure (see Figure 3): E will be moved exactly the same distance in the same time along AC as F moves down along CB. Already Galileo is emulating the technique of the *Mechanica*: having specified for his thought experiment the equilibrium condition that the ratio of weights F and E equals that of lengths BC and CA, he imagines what would happen were that equilibrium to be disturbed. He proceeds to bring the inclined plane back into the fold of law-abiding mechanical instruments with a refinement of his analysis: despite first appearances, "it should be noticed that although the movable body E will have passed over all the line AC in the same time that the other heavy body F will have fallen through an equal interval, nevertheless the

73. Duhem, *Origines*, 1:298–99.

74. For an analysis of that demonstration, see Clavelin, *Natural Philosophy*, pp. 165–68. Galileo used the word *momento* in a number of different ways.

75. Galileo Galilei, *On Motion and On Mechanics*, trans. I. E. Drabkin and Stillman Drake (Madison, Wis., 1960), p. 176.

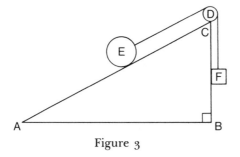

Figure 3

heavy body E will not have been removed from the common center of heavy things more than the distance along the perpendicular CB, while the heavy body F descending perpendicularly will have dropped by a space equal to the whole line AC."[76] Galileo, treating the inclined plane as a mechanical instrument like a pulley, produces a description identical to Mersenne's in the *Synopsis. Contra* Duhem, neither of the two in these parallel passages attempt to demonstrate the law of the inclined plane; they have moved on from that to deal with the relative vertical movements of two weights already assumed to be in equilibrium. Their apparently independent considerations of the relative speeds of descent and ascent of mechanically linked weights match exactly the *Mechanica*'s technique of comparing the relative speeds of the mechanically linked weights at each end of a balance.

Galileo gives a version of the *Mechanica*'s treatment of the balance following a properly statical proof akin to that of Archimedes.[77] He reproduces the pseudo-Aristotelian argument quite faithfully although less qualitatively, explaining how greater speed compensates for lesser weight, so that speed can increase *momento*; the discussion strongly recalls Mersenne's in the *Traité*. Galileo introduces it rather tentatively: "It seems to me that we should not pass by in silence another agreement and probability by which the same truth [i.e., the law of the lever] may reasonably be confirmed to us."[78] When Mersenne produced his own version of this in *Les mechaniques de Galilée*, he chose a more direct form of expression: "It is still necessary to note another property which confirms the preceding truth."[79] Galileo's mature ideas, for which *Le meccaniche* represents an important developmental stage, became accessible to Mersenne via their conjunction

76. Ibid., p. 177.
77. Ibid., pp. 155–57.
78. Ibid., p. 155.
79. Mersenne, *Les mechaniques*, pp. 32–33.

with the doctrines of the *Mechanica,* which Mersenne had already taken up for his own purposes.

Mersenne's attitude towards Galileo's experiments on falling bodies nevertheless displays instructive contrasts with that of Galileo himself. In *Questions theologiques* Mersenne addressed the topic briefly, and while accepting the Galilean definition of naturally accelerated motion, he treated it as if it were of trivial importance. The real task, he said, lay in determining at what point and in what respects particular falling bodies cease to follow this proportion.[80] Where for Galileo the mathematical regularity of uniform acceleration represented a sort of unadulterated paradigm of free fall from which actual cases deviated according to accidental circumstances, for Mersenne it was simply an empirical regularity holding for the most part but not always. Mersenne wanted to find mathematical structures instantiated in nature, but his complaint against Robert Fludd that such things should be sought out through scrupulous observation and measurement, not imposed according to a preconceived plan, was a genuine expression of the form he considered appropriate for mathematical natural philosophy. That form determined the layout of Mersenne's pamphlet of 1633, which records his experiments to measure the time of fall of balls dropped vertically from various heights; the figures he gives fit uniform acceleration very well.[81] The striking feature of the experimental reports, however, characteristic also of similar material in *Harmonie universelle,* is that they give precise measurements and parameters.[82] Galileo had little interest in absolute rates of fall and concerned himself with proportions between magnitudes, but Mersenne, while similarly on the lookout for proportions, did care about absolute values. The reasons seem connected as much with evaluating the reliability of experimental reports as with ascertaining quantitative truths about nature. In the pamphlet Mersenne discusses the figures Galileo had mentioned in the *Dialogue* and the units he had used; he decides that Galileo's experiments are not to be trusted because the values claimed differ so markedly from his own.[83] This is hardly surprising when one considers that Galileo's numbers serve no more

---

80. Mersenne, *Questions theologiques,* p. 17.
81. See note in Mersenne *Correspondance,* 3:438.
82. E.g., in *Harmonie universelle,* "Du mouvement des corps," pp. 86–88.
83. Mersenne *Correspondance,* 3:438–39. *Harmonie universelle* repeats his criticisms of Galileo's claimed experimental results. See Alexandre Koyré, "Experiment in Measurement," pp. 89–117. Mersenne's "replications" were actually somewhat different from Galileo's reported in the *Dialogue;* Mersenne may have changed his evaluation of Galileo's empirical claims after seeing *Two New Sciences:* Thomas B. Settle, "Galilean Science: Essays in the Mechanics and Dynamics of the *Discorsi*" (diss., Cornell University, 1966), pp. 68–81.

than an illustrative function in his accounts. The contrast with Mersenne, who displays tables showing distances fallen with respect to time, could hardly be greater.[84]

Mersenne's view of motion and mechanics, as inaugurated in the pamphlet, remained largely constant until 1644, when a change occurred (which is considered in Chapter 8). The picture of mechanics in the five works of 1634—the *Questions theologiques, Questions harmoniques, Questions inouyes, Preludes de l'harmonie universelle,* and *Les mechaniques de Galilée*[85]—and above all in the great *Harmonie universelle,* which came off the presses in 1636–37, preserves the form adopted in 1633. Final acceptance that falling bodies tend to undergo uniform acceleration, empiricism, scepticism about causal explanations of fall, and the shadow of Galileo provide the main ingredients. Mersenne briefly considers fall in *Les mechaniques,* restricting himself to a seven-page presentation of Galileo's statements and claims—taken from the beginning and end of the *Dialogue*—concerning motion on inclined planes.[86] In *Harmonie universelle,* as in the pamphlet, however, the same points receive extended critical appraisal principally based on Mersenne's own experiments: the best-known example is probably Mersenne's examination of Galileo's crucial claim that falling bodies acquire the same final speed for the same vertical distance of fall, regardless of path.[87] Alexandre Koyré has remarked also on Mersenne's repetition here and elsewhere of his demonstration that the path of a body permitted to fall freely to the center of the earth would not, contrary to Galileo's statement, be a semicircle; Koyré observes that Mersenne seems inordinately proud of his achievement.[88] Most of Mersenne's criticism focuses on experiments, however, and one of its most notable features is his mistrust of Galileo's experimental assertions. Nonetheless, he does not seem disposed to undermine Galileo's basic conceptual approach; indeed, Mersenne's great interest in discussing Galileo's work stemmed precisely from that approach. Mersenne certainly wanted to put concrete observation at the heart of his natural philosophy; *expérience* remained for him the only legitimate source of natural philosophy's content. But correlation with metaphysical and mathematical doctrines provided its form and established its meaning.

84. See the table in Mersenne *Correspondance,* 3:438.
85. Precise dates are given in ibid., pp. 440–41.
86. Mersenne, *Les mechaniques,* pp. 67–74. For the Galilean passages, see Galileo, *Dialogue Concerning the Two Chief World Systems,* trans. Stillman Drake, 2d ed. (Berkeley, Calif., 1967), pp. 22–28, 450–51.
87. Mersenne, *Harmonie universelle,* "Du mouvement des corps."
88. Alexandre Koyré, "A Documentary History of the Problem of Fall from Kepler to Newton," *Transactions of the American Philosophical Society* 45 (1955), 337.

Guidobaldo del Monte had made a rigid distinction between statics and mechanical motion, while Simon Stevin rejected the *Mechanica*'s interpretation of the balance because he considered it preposterous to explain a statical situation by talking about speeds.[89] Mersenne's interest in the *Mechanica*, before he became acquainted with Galileo's ideas, rested on its potential to overcome this division and bring both the large existing body of work on statics and the investigation of such dynamical matters as percussion and fall into a unified perspective. Galileo improved on the tradition of the *Mechanica* by developing that potential with the idea, presented first in *Le meccaniche*, that a sphere resting on a smooth surface required only an infinitesimal force— that is, a force smaller than any designated—to set it in motion. Contrary to the teaching of Pappus and, following him, Guidobaldo, this novel conceptualization effectively demolished the barrier between statics and dynamics by introducing a bridge between mechanical force and motive force: it could be used to show that only an infinitesimal difference existed between the force needed to maintain equilibrium and that required to initiate motion, and to argue that the two quantities should therefore be regarded, in functional definition and in magnitude, as identical.[90] Mersenne recognized in the work of Galileo new and attractive possibilities in mechanics because they stemmed from a reading of the *Mechanica* similar to his own. He protested, however, that his eventual conversion to acceptance of the odd-number rule governing free fall resulted from the inclined-plane experiments,[91] and the refinement of experimental technique that these represented no doubt played its part in allowing Mersenne to give *expérience* its proper place in the conceptual scheme and hence to legitimate Galileo's mathematical treatment of motion.

Richard Westfall has rightly observed that Mersenne's discussions of Galileo's work and of inclined planes in *Harmonie universelle* all involve a concept of equilibrium in which speeds balance weights.[92] This is, of course, in keeping both with the *Mechanica*'s physical view of mechanics and with Galileo's idea of *momento* in *Le meccaniche*. Westfall also notes, however, that Mersenne inverts the concept for bodies descending along inclined planes. Mersenne regards that proportion of a body's weight supported by the plane as counterbalancing the

89. Duhem, *Origines*, 1:266–67.

90. Mersenne discusses this question, giving Galileo's solution without acknowledgment, in *Questions inouyes*, pp. 15–16. For Guidobaldo's approach, see Drake and Drabkin, *Mechanics*, pp. 320–21, 325; see also Rose, *Italian Renaissance*, p. 233.

91. E.g., Mersenne, *Harmonie universelle*, "Du mouvement des corps," p. 86.

92. Richard S. Westfall, *Force in Newton's Physics* (London, 1971), pp. 115–17.

total, or absolute, weight.[93] The body's speed of descent is then given by the residual motive weight acting down the plane, and Mersenne clearly sees it as analogous to the potential speeds of the ends of a conventional balance. He thus uses the correlation of speed and weight established by the statical situation to derive a rule applicable to dynamics. The unification of techniques had the advantage of allowing an easier integration of mechanics as a whole into the scheme of "universal harmony."

III

Mersenne accomplished the harmonization of mechanics through the mechanization of music. Not merely for him another of the quadrivial disciplines, music was central to Mersenne's mathematical endeavors because it provided the paradigm of harmony by which the rest could be developed and judged. Mersenne wrote more on music than on any other single subject, starting with the search for its psychological powers derived from the humanist project to restore ancient music.[94] Even after rejecting the humanist path, he continued to pursue the notion of a "musique accentuelle" directed towards similar ends, and in *Harmonie universelle,* building on material presented in *La verité des sciences,* he discusses combinatorics and its role in determining the most beautiful melody possible, again attempting to bring the effects of music under disciplinary control.[95] He also, especially in *Harmonie universelle,* considered tuning systems and described specific instruments.

These obviously "musical" interests cannot, however, be separated from those appearing to us as having more to do with the "physics of sound." Although it is easy, and perhaps for certain purposes justified, to see some of Mersenne's investigations as forming a distinct area of study corresponding to the later subdiscipline of "acoustics," there is in fact a firm integration between this and the other parts of his musical work.[96] He intended *Harmonie universelle* as a compen-

93. Mersenne, *Harmonie universelle,* "Du mouvement des corps," p. 124.
94. See Chapter 2, above.
95. See Chapter 7, below. See also, and more generally, Alistair C. Crombie, "Mathematics, Music and Medical Science," in *Actes du XIIᵉ Congrès International d'Histoire des Sciences, Paris 1968* (Paris, 1971), 1B:295–310; idem, "Experimental Science and the Rational Artist in Early Modern Europe," *Daedalus* 115 (1986), 49–74, esp. 63–67; Cohen, *Quantifying Music,* 112–14.
96. Sigalia Dostrovsky, "Early Vibration Theory," *Archive for History of Exact Sciences* 14 (1975), 169–218, does tend to make a separation between the two, concentrating on

dium of all those things the "perfect musician" should know, and to that end he included not only the descriptions of musical instruments, scales, and the art of composition, but also exhaustive treatments of the physical nature of sound, the behaviors of vibrating strings and organ pipes, and the mechanics of movement. Mersenne was certainly not merely taking the opportunity to publish material unrelated to music while putting a properly musical treatise through the press; the full plan of the imperfectly realized *Traité de l'harmonie universelle* had also provided for coverage of those topics.[97] The various elements were unified by the overall theme of "universal harmony," which related the evident conjunction of experience and number found in music with the structure of the created world as a whole. Since harmony represented the divine wisdom ordering Creation, a full understanding of it, which Mersenne took to be the goal of the "perfect musician," necessarily involved discovering how it came to be instantiated in musical sounds.

Time, as Augustine had stressed, played an essential role in our apprehension of the numbers in music. Change and motion, intimately related to time, characterized the physical world, and so musical harmony participated in "universal harmony" through the motion of sound. Mersenne treated sound as a disturbance in a medium, a quasi-mechanization by no means original but which he exploited to establish an identity: sound became movement and, reciprocally, movement became sound.[98] Thus, "all movements that occur in the air, in water, or elsewhere, can be called sounds, inasmuch as they lack only a sufficiently delicate and subtle ear to hear them; and the same thing can be said of the noise of thunder and of cannon with respect to a deaf person who doesn't perceive these great noises."[99] The first

---

"acoustics." See also Frederick Vinton Hunt, *Origins in Acoustics* (New Haven, Conn., 1978), pp. 82–100; Hunt emphasizes Mersenne's experiments to determine the speed of sound. As a classical mathematical science, music formed a natural focus of study for those interested in such other sciences as mechanics: for a survey, see Armand Machabey, Sr., "Quelques savants-musiciens de l'époque de Mersenne," *Revue d'histoire des sciences* 11 (1958), 193–206.

97. Mersenne, *Traité*, "Sommaire des seize livres de la musique" (following "Preface au lecteur").

98. For the background to this contention, see Alan E. Shapiro, "Kinematic Optics," *Archive for History of Exact Sciences* 11 (1973), 135–41; and Frederick Bill Hyde, "The Position of Marin Mersenne in the History of Music" (diss., Yale University, 1954), chap. 6. Aristotle had associated sound with disturbance in the air but did not *identify* the two; the mathematical acoustical treatise by the Jesuit Josephus Blancanus adopts exactly the same position, guided by the Aristotelian disciplinary division between mathematical sciences and physics: Josephus Blancanus, "Echometria," in *Sphaera mundi* (Bologna, 1620), pp. 415–43.

99. Mersenne, *Harmonie universelle*, "Du son," p. 2.

book of *Harmonie universelle,* on "the nature and properties of sound," therefore spent its eighty-four pages dealing entirely with sound's physical—or, more properly, mechanical—characteristics. The order found in music was a mechanical order governing the motion of the producers of musical sounds as well as all other corporeal bodies in the universe.

Mersenne could not interpret music in mechanical terms at the expense of harmony, however; music, not mechanics, preeminently instantiated the mathematical relationships that he hoped to find throughout Creation. Harmony had to be extended to mechanics even while bringing music within the ambit of mechanical analysis. This meant that, for Mersenne, the criterion for a successful mechanical interpretation of music was that it incorporate the simple numerical Pythagorean ratios to express musical consonances. In fact, an even more basic incentive underlay the whole attempt: the validity of those ratios in music itself had recently come into question, and the precise nature of the threat shows how Mersenne's mechanics of sound constituted an attempted answer.

During the sixteenth century, in the face of changes in musical practice which had occurred since the High Middle Ages, musical theorists began to confront the need for alterations in the standard Pythagorean account of consonance. Known throughout the Middle Ages primarily by means of Boethius's *De institutione musica,*[100] this scheme recognized as consonant only the octave (2:1), the fifth (3:2), and the fourth (4:3), and its explanation of their consonance relied purely on numerical formalism. The standard medieval didactic device of the monochord illustrated the relevance of the ratios to sounds by employing a movable bridge to divide its single string into the respective lengths appropriate to the musical intervals. In the wake of the development of polyphony, however, with its routine employment of major and minor thirds and sixths as consonances, the Pythagorean theory ceased to represent musical practice adequately, and its modification became a principal goal for theorists.[101] Assigning appropriate ratios to the new consonances, accomplished by analogy to the procedure yielding the old consonances, appears to have presented no great difficulty.

The fifth could be seen as resulting from the division of the octave

---

100. Claude V. Palisca, "The Science of Sound and Musical Practice," in Shirley and Hoeniger, *Science and the Arts,* p. 60.

101. Cohen, *Quantifying Music,* pp. 1–7; Palisca, "Scientific Empiricism," pp. 101–3. The development of polyphony in the fifteenth and sixteenth centuries is discussed in Edward E. Lowinsky, "Music in the Culture of the Renaissance," *Journal of the History of Ideas* 15 (1954), 530–33.

into proportionate parts. The octave of a note given by a particular string would be produced by halving that string's length, as shown in Figure 4, where the ratio 2:1 appears as AB:AO; the ratio 3:2 for the fifth is then similarly interpreted in the diagram as AB:AF, AF sounding a note a fifth above that sounded by AB. The fourth is the complementary interval to the fifth, completing the rise to the octave; it thus corresponds to the string-length ratio AF:AO, which is 4:3. The traditional Pythagorean consonances therefore depended on the placement of F: that is, on the length AF with respect to AB and AO. Hence arose the concept of harmonic proportion: AF is called the "harmonic mean" of AB and AO, defined by the fact that the ratio of the difference between AB and AF to that between AF and AO equals the ratio of AB to AO. Since the essence of the Pythagorean approach lay in numbers rather than in geometrical magnitudes, a more characteristic way of describing a fifth as a harmonic mean was by using numerical series, so that the sequence "keynote, fifth, octave" would typically appear as "6, 4, 3." The interval of the fourth then appears as that between 4 and 3, yielding its ratio, just as the fifth is that between 6 and 4, equal to the ratio 3:2. This numerological version represented for Pythagorean theorists the authentic account of musical consonance, and its exemplification on the monochord acted only as an illustration. Consonances were consonances precisely *because* they corresponded, in some transcendental way, to ratios of small whole numbers. Nonetheless, the use of the monochord remained the sole technique by which the intersection of ratios and musical intervals could be realized; without it, the ratios would have been meaningless.

The newly accepted consonances, the thirds and sixths, appeared simply by dividing the fifth in the same harmonic proportion as produced the fifth itself when applied to the octave. Thus AT, in Figure 5, the harmonic mean between AB and AF, is given by the condition that TB : FT equals AB : AF—that is, length FT must be two-thirds of length TB. Since FB is itself one-third of the total string length AB, simple arithmetic shows that TB is one-fifth the total string length, or AT four-fifths that length. So the musical interval between the notes produced by AB and AT corresponds to a string-length ratio of $1:\frac{4}{5}$, which is 5:4, the major third. Just as the fourth was the residual interval between the fifth and the octave, so the residual interval between the major third and the fifth (the difference between the notes from string AT and string AF) is a ratio of 6:5, the minor third. The respective complementary intervals between the major and minor thirds and the octave—namely, the minor and major sixths— turned out to have ratios of 8:5 and 5:3.

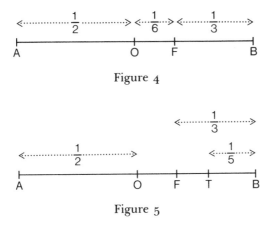

Figure 4

Figure 5

These ratios displayed empirical correspondence to the intervals newly employed as consonances. Their apparently neat incorporation into the existing model of theoretical analysis, however, created more problems than it solved. For example, if the fifth could be divided harmonically to produce consonant intervals, why could not the fourth, which yielded ratios of 7 : 6 and 8 : 7? These were analogous to the thirds created from the fifth but were nonetheless classed firmly as dissonances. The most important attempt in the sixteenth century to justify the inclusion of the thirds and sixths within the charmed circle of consonance avoided this problem by reemphasizing the numerological basis of musical theory implicit in the older Pythagorean scheme. Gioseffo Zarlino, in his *Istitutioni harmoniche* of 1558, argued that consonances correspond to the various ratios of the first six integers, a numerical range he called the *senario*. This restriction of consonant ratios arose because, Zarlino observed, six is the first perfect number (a number equal to the sum of its factors).[102] Zarlino thus renovated musical theory by reinforcing its reliance on the assumption of a transcendental relationship between music and numbers.

The identification of particular numerical ratios with particular consonances, although illustrated by means of string lengths, had never conventionally been restricted to them. Because numbers rather than whatever they counted stood at the heart of scientific

102. My understanding of the technical issues discussed in this and the previous paragraph is heavily indebted to Cohen, *Quantifying Music*, esp. pp. 4–5, 34–43; for more on Zarlino, see also Palisca, "Scientific Empiricism." Zarlino incorporated the ratio 8:5, representing the minor sixth, into the *senario* by saying that it should properly be regarded as deriving from 4:5 and 2:1; for this and another attempt at removing the anomaly, see Cohen, *Quantifying Music*, p. 6.

music, it was commonly assumed, but not considered worth examining, that the Pythagorean ratios applied as much to the tensions of musical strings as to their lengths: that doubling the tension (by doubling the weight used to extend the string) while keeping the sounding length constant would raise the pitch by an octave. As we saw in the last chapter, however, Vincenzo Galilei reported that his experimental trials showed this assumption to be false: during his controversy with his former teacher Zarlino he claimed that, for equal lengths, tensions must vary as the inverse *squares* of the Pythagorean ratios to produce the corresponding consonances.[103] For an octave, therefore, the tension should be quadrupled, not doubled, and the ratio would be not 2 : 1 but 1 : 4.

Stillman Drake sees the value of Galilei's work in terms of the removal of "number mysticism" from music and its replacement by "the direct study of the actual application of number to the material instruments of music."[104] Certainly, Galilei intended to explode Zarlino's *senario* and the fingerprinting of consonances by the Pythagorean ratios. But equally, he seems to have remained committed to the relevance of ratios to consonances. D. P. Walker, besides pointing out Galilei's inconsistencies and polemical opportunism in the debates with Zarlino,[105] observes that Galilei—after arguing that tension ratios have an inverse-square relationship to the direct Pythagorean ratios applicable to string lengths—proceeds to maintain that the relationship of organ pipes to the ratios is cubic with respect to their lengths. Empirically, says Walker, this is wildly erroneous.[106] (Drake does not mention the matter at all.) Although it does not show that he failed to perform real experiments, Walker's observation does indicate that Galilei had neither abandoned the use of ratios in the theory of music nor retained them on purely empirical grounds. Galilei claimed that his acceptance of the superiority of "just" consonances, those according exactly with the accepted numerical ratios of string

103. Ibid., p. 82; Palisca, "Scientific Empiricism," pp. 127–28; Drake, "Renaissance Music," pp. 483–500, esp. 495–97 (a modified version of which appears as "Vincenzo Galilei and Galileo" in Drake, *Galileo Studies*, pp. 43–62). Strictly speaking, the mathematical operation should be described as doubling and inverting the corresponding ratios: see Michael S. Mahoney, "Mathematics," in Lindberg, *Science in the Middle Ages*, pp. 145–78, esp. 162–68, for a very clear account of medieval ratio theory; and for its career, Edith Sylla, "Compounding Ratios," in Everett Mendelsohn, ed., *Transformation and Tradition in the Sciences* (Cambridge, 1984), pp. 11–43.

104. Drake, "Renaissance Music," p. 497.

105. D. P. Walker, *Studies in Musical Science in the Late Renaissance* (London, 1978), pp. 17, 20–22.

106. Ibid., p. 24.

lengths, rested on empirical grounds alone, but the case of the organ pipes suggests that he in fact considered ratios to have some kind of theoretical value; he appears to have wished to relate them to the audible phenomena of music through their identification with the physical dimensions of sound producers.[107] But he saw no grounds—or, at least, he underlined the lack of justificatory criteria as a polemical weapon against Zarlino—for privileging string lengths rather than string tensions, or the length of pipes, as the quantities appropriate to manifest the true musical ratios. Thus Galilei demonstrated that the whole idea of particular ratios representing particular musical intervals and serving as sufficient explanations of consonance or dissonance lacked clarity.

The breadth of options open to Galilei and others underlines the significance of his continued adherence to just consonances. The problems introduced by the admission of thirds and sixths to the status of consonances went far beyond the arbitrary justification of the *senario*; they involved the practical problems of tuning. Deriving consonances from the division of the monochord into small-number ratios failed, for mathematical reasons, to provide a straightforward division of the octave into a diatonic scale. The Pythagorean scale, constructed around the fourth and fifth, yielded ratios for thirds and sixths which deviated from the "just" values calculated in the manner described above, and the deviation—the "syntonic comma" of ratio $81 : 80$—was clearly audible. It arose from the derivation of the size of the whole tone from the difference between the fifth and the fourth, a ratio of $9 : 8$, and its combination with the ratios of those consonances to yield in addition a value for the semitone and hence a complete diatonic scale. Attempts in the sixteenth century to create a scale in which all consonances—fifths, fourths, thirds, and sixths—were just had therefore to vary slightly the size of the tone depending on its position. The most popular solution, adopted by Zarlino, enjoyed the advantage of ancient precedent in that it appeared as one way of dividing the octave in Ptolemy's *Harmonica* (showing also that not everyone in antiquity had rejected the consonance of thirds and sixths). Known as "syntonic diatonic," or simply "just intonation," this tuning system used two different tones, called major and minor, of ratios $9 : 8$ and $10 : 9$. It maximized the number of just consonances in the scale, and although it did not succeed in making all possible consonant intervals correspond perfectly to the desired ratios, it did quite a good job of reconciling modern practice with the essence of musical Pythagoreanism and

---

107. Cf. Palisca, "Scientific Empiricism," p. 130.

displaced the Pythagorean system itself during the course of the century.[108]

The imperfections of just intonation, however, still left a significant problem. Benedetti showed that if singers always observed the mathematically correct ratios, the inevitable result over the course of a melody involving particular, common progressions would be a shift in the overall pitch, as syntonic commas worked their way in.[109] No fully adequate solution appeared possible, and there were practical reasons why theorists could not easily brush the difficulty under the carpet. Although musical instruments like the human voice, with a continuum from which to choose notes, naturally made slight adjustments to avoid any shift in pitch, the late-medieval emergence of recorders, fretted viols, and organs—as well as the use of fretted lutes—presented an unavoidable problem because they had to be tuned to give a fixed, discrete set of notes; no slight accommodations during the course of performance were possible. Just intonation resulted in frequent "off" notes; practicing musicians therefore routinely resorted to the expedient of some form of temperament. A tempered scale divided the octave in such a way that most or all consonances deviated almost imperceptibly from their just values, but no consonant interval deviated so far that it offended the ear. In effect, temperament spread the inequalities of the syntonic comma (and some other mismatches similarly resulting from incommensurabilities between the various consonances) across the notes of the scale so that they never intruded too obviously at any given point.[110] Many systems were proposed and practiced, but Simon Stevin's advocacy of equal temperament in the early years of the seventeenth century, although not itself influential, represents an approach to the whole matter worth noting precisely because it was an option that others such as Galilei could have chosen but never did. It involved the rejection of the very concept of "just" consonance.

Equal temperament produced an octave divided into twelve equal semitones. As a result, no consonance (except, of course, the octave itself) remained just. It was conventionally associated with the name of Aristoxenus, an older contemporary of Plato who held that the ear alone properly judged consonance and that Pythagorean musical ideas therefore had no legitimacy; musicians found it especially suited to the tuning of fretted instruments. Stevin's argument in its favor,

108. Cohen, *Quantifying Music*, pp. 34–41; Walker, *Studies*, p. 8; Palisca, "Scientific Empiricism," pp. 113–14.

109. Ibid., pp. 114–18.

110. Drake, "Renaissance Music," p. 490; Walker, *Studies*, pp. 9–10; Cohen, *Quantifying Music*, pp. 41–43.

however, was based on the grounds not that it best accorded with the judgment of the ear but that the mathematical division which produced it was a more rational division of the octave than were the cobbled-together scales incorporating just consonances. Each semitone was now a twelfth of the octave's 2 : 1 ratio or, in more modern terminology, the twelfth root of one-half, and Stevin maintained that the consonant intervals defined by this system were the *true* consonances; they did not approximate the just consonances, but supplanted them.[111]

Stevin's argument is, in principle, unanswerable: although the trained ear can certainly distinguish between just consonances and their tempered counterparts, nothing more determinate than a delicate aesthetic judgment can ultimately resolve the question of which, on a purely auditory basis, should be preferred. Evidently, more than the constraints of practice—which actually embarrassed it—motivated attempts to retain the ideal of just consonance. Those attempts needed to be especially vigorous if they were to meet the challenge of Galilei's undermining of a neat, invariable relationship between the simple number ratios and all physical variables of sound producers. Without some sort of underlying identity between the neo-Pythagorean ratios and their musical intervals, the mathematical construal of harmony became empirically meaningless.

The importance of all this for Mersenne's enterprise was enormous. The previous chapter showed that he regarded music as, first and foremost, an intellectual discipline. Musical practice endeavored above all to realize the ideal construct represented by musical theory.[112] In *Preludes de l'harmonie universelle* (1634) Mersenne devotes twenty pages to a consideration of whether the ear or the understanding is the proper judge of music, coming down firmly on the side of the understanding.[113] His arguments center on the inexactitude of the senses, which reason alone can rectify. Although a circle drawn freehand may appear perfect to the eye, a truly perfect circle conceived by reason shows that the former is really imperfect. So also, he says, the ear hears as perfect certain consonances that only approach perfection, "but it is constrained to confess their imperfection when reason gives the perfect [consonances]."[114] The ear is simply not sen-

---

111. Cohen, *Quantifying Music*, pp. 48–69. See also Walker, *Studies*, p. 5.
112. Connected with this was the additional issue of the causes of music's effects on its hearers; Mersenne found himself unable to account for the crucial physiological basis of music's effects. See Crombie, "Mathematics, Music"; Crombie, "Experimental Science"; and Cohen, *Quantifying Music*, p. 110.
113. Mersenne, *Les preludes de l'harmonie universelle* (Paris, 1634), pp. 144–64.
114. Ibid., p. 159.

sitive enough to judge tiny differences; the impressions of the senses must be judged by reason.[115] Mersenne saw the task of the musician as a search for mathematical regularities in the world, comparable with the astronomer's "saving the phenomena": the musician's office is to "conserve or find the reasons [ratios? *raisons*], which accord with the hearing, following the apprehension [*sentiment*] of the majority of men; as that of the astronomer is to conserve or to establish hypotheses of the celestial movements, after having observed all the phenomena that ordinarily appear."[116]

In similar vein, Mersenne asserts that in music, reason "seeks the causes of movement and sound" and, again, that it considers the "causes and nature" of sound.[117] He fails to specify exactly what kinds of causes he means, but one may conjecture with some confidence that they would be formal and efficient causes: that is, number ratios and the mechanics of sound production—the latter presumably covering the "nature" of sound. Mersenne describes reason as performing a fairly complex job of processing the raw material of heard sounds: "It regulates [*regle*] them, and rejects those that are contrary to reason, and that offend it, and admits those that follow the harmonic ratio."[118] This seems like a circular procedure: reason rejecting sounds as consonances on mathematical grounds and thereby showing how true consonances fulfill certain mathematical criteria. But it is fairer, perhaps, to describe Mersenne's methodological idealization as intellectual "bootstrapping," relying on basic principles of reason to structure experience. Reason, he says, "seeks the causes for which certain intervals are suitable [*convenables*] to it, that is, more agreeable than others; which it does so perfectly that it obliges itself [*il se necessite luy-mesme*] to avow that its discourse is true [*veritable*]: as when it says that whatever is more simple, and better ordered, is easier to understand than whatever is composite and confused."[119] And this is true of all the sciences, "for it is incumbent upon learned men who employ their life and their study in contemplation to show that the works of nature are well-ordered, and that there is nothing that is confused or happens by chance, particularly in what concerns vision or hearing, which approach reason more than the other senses and which serve us for learning the sciences and for praising, con-

115. Ibid., pp. 159–62.
116. Ibid., p. 162.
117. Ibid., p. 158.
118. Ibid., p. 164.
119. Ibid.

templating, and admiring the works of God, and the excellence and grandeur of the maker [*l'ouvrier*]."[120]

Mersenne's valuation of the theoretical side of music as an exemplification of universal harmony did not blind him to the exigencies of musical practice, however, and he had too great an interest in the construction and tuning of musical instruments to disregard the importance of temperament. Of equal temperament, he observed that "the lute, the viol, and other similar instruments preserve this division in their temperament, so that one can say that all the makers of these instruments are disciples of Aristoxenus."[121] Unlike Aristoxenus and Stevin, however, Mersenne treated tempered consonances as mere approximations to the true consonances. Discussing the intervals resulting from the tempered scale employed for organs,[122] he confessed that "the temperament that is used to produce these consonances cannot content those who wish to hear the perfection of proportions in accords and harmony."[123] Just consonances were the real thing: particular ratios of small numbers really did define consonant intervals independently of the ear, which helped to confirm them but did not serve to establish them. Mersenne admitted that much of the agreeableness of particular harmonies depended "on custom, preoccupation, the capacity of the ear, and the imagination," but having said so, he found no contradiction in immediately returning to a mathematical determination of the "excellence" and "power" of the twelfth vis-à-vis the octave.[124] Music was not the province of the vagaries and uncertainties of human aesthetic judgment; it was properly a contemplative study leading to the comprehension of prototypes— meaning mathematical prototypes—in the divine mind.[125]

Mersenne therefore sought to retain the musical relevance of the ratios established and justified by Zarlino, because the theory of music that expressed and exemplified universal harmony incorporated them at its heart. The *senario*, however, faced both the embarrassment

120. Ibid., p. 163.
121. Mersenne, *Harmonie universelle*, "Des instrumens," p. 60; on Mersenne and temperament, see Hyde, "Mersenne in the History of Music," chap. 10, pp. 304–464; also Cohen, *Quantifying Music*, pp. 111–12.
122. Usually, in this period, a mean tone system rather than equal temperament: see Cohen, *Quantifying Music*, p. 43.
123. Mersenne, *Harmonie universelle*, "Des orgues," p. 351. Mersenne recognized that human singing did not follow the exact proportions either: Mersenne *Correspondance*, 2:275. For an examination from a musicologist's perspective, see Albion Gruber, "Mersenne and Evolving Tonal Theory," *Journal of Music Theory* 14 (1970), 36–67.
124. Mersenne, *Harmonie universelle*, "Des consonances," p. 66, also 89.
125. Mersenne, *Les preludes*, p. 172.

of Galilei's findings and the threat of being rendered irrelevant by the widespread use of temperament. Benedetti had adumbrated a solution to the difficulty (in a letter, published in 1585 but written two decades earlier), which gave a physical interpretation to the ratios associated with musical consonance.[126] It had long been accepted that a note's pitch increased with frequency of vibration and that the shorter a string, *ceteris paribus*, the more rapidly it vibrated. Benedetti asserted that for a given tension, strings vibrate at a frequency inversely proportional to their lengths. Each stroke of the vibration produces a pulse which is transmitted through the air; consonances arise when the pulses from two strings coincide regularly and often. Thus when the lengths of two strings are in a ratio of 2 : 1, each pulse sent out by the longer string coincides with every second pulse from the shorter. The octave can then be interpreted as a frequency ratio of 1 : 2 rather than as a transcendental ratio of 2 : 1 instantiated in string lengths. In the case of the fifth, coincidence of pulses occurs once every second cycle of the longer string and once every third cycle of the shorter, a frequency ratio of 2 : 3. Benedetti drew up a table assigning to each consonance its own number, corresponding to the product of the relative length of a string and its relative frequency with respect to the other string of the consonant pair. The shorter of the two string lengths sounding a fifth, for example, has a length that is two to the longer's three and a frequency that is three to the longer's two. So the characteristic number for this consonance is six, the product of two and three (for the shorter string) or three and two (for the longer).

H. F. Cohen has observed that the table shows a continued fascination with the formal properties of numbers; Benedetti's purpose in laying it out seems to have been to exhibit that successive numbers in the list are themselves in ratios corresponding to the traditional number ratios of the consonances.[127] Rather than dismissing the "numerological" interpretation of those ratios in favor of a physical correlation with the physics of sound production, he found a new way of exhibiting their immanence, not only in consonances themselves but also in the mutual relations of consonances. Nonetheless, the interpretation of consonance as relying on the coincidence of pulses opened up the possibility of shifting the foundations of acoustical

126. Palisca, "Scientific Empiricism," pp. 104–10; Cohen, *Quantifying Music*, pp. 75–78; see also Palisca, "The Science of Sound," p. 67.
127. Cohen, *Quantifying Music*, pp. 76–77 (differing from Palisca's interpretation).

harmony from numerical formalism to mechanics.[128] That Benedetti appears to have seen his idea as a way of exploring the role of number in music at a deeper level, however, signals a parallel implication: the coincidence theory might serve as a means of shifting to mechanics the foundations of numerical formalism itself.

By the 1630s, and probably independently of Benedetti's work, the use of vibrations and the coincidence of pulses as the basis of musical harmony had found its way into the writings of Beeckman, Galileo, Descartes, and Mersenne.[129] D. P. Walker's observation that the coincidence theory was "compatible" with the arithmetical theories of the Pythagoreans and Zarlino hints at the implications for number harmony.[130] By lending physical intelligibility to numerical ratios previously regarded as abstract formal causes, the theory absorbed the techniques and arithmetical assumptions of its predecessor. Anyone who lacked an interest in retaining Pythagorean ratios and harmonic proportion had no reason to adopt it; Simon Stevin, for instance, could have found no more merit in the vibrational approach than in the Pythagorean. Mersenne, however, committed to just consonances and the mathematical apparatus of harmony, incorporated it into a renovation of the theory of music that had answers to Galilei and firm arguments against regarding temperament as anything other than a means of approximation.

The force of Galilei's objections derived from the lack of grounds for treating string lengths as any more intimately related to the nature of sound than string tension (or the length of pipes). Since string lengths, contrary to Pythagorean legend, seemed to provide the only direct manifestation of the simple ratios, retention of the latter's preeminence became problematic. No doubt the difficulty might partly have been circumvented by noting that in Galilei's own account the relationships of the other variables relied on compounds of the string-length ratios. But with no explanation of what that meant, the theoretical structure would have remained unsatisfactory. Mersenne found in the coincidence theory a basis for treating one particular

---

128. Given Cohen's convincing reading of the evidence, Palisca seems to be mistaken in imputing awareness of this possible implication to Benedetti himself.

129. Cohen, *Quantifying Music*, chap. 2 and, on Beeckman, pp. 116–61, esp. 127–29. Cohen characterizes Beeckman's "regularity" theory as slightly different from Benedetti's, Galileo's, Descartes's and Mersenne's "coincidence" theories: his focused on regularities in "sound-silence" patterns rather than frequency of coincidence of pulses; it translated readily into a coincidence theory, however, and the similarities seem more important than the differences.

130. Walker, *Studies*, p. 13.

physical parameter of sound production, frequency of vibration, as privileged and prior to all others. This parameter had the great advantage of yielding ratios effectively identical to the traditional ones. The attractions of the coincidence theory were therefore considerable, but if it were to do its job of underpinning the theory of music in a properly scientific way, it needed independent support. To make the new conception of consonance plausible, Mersenne attempted a demonstration of the central proposition that the frequency of a string's vibration was inversely proportional to its length.

Benedetti had attempted no proof at all. The doctrine that longer strings vibrate more slowly and emit lower notes dated from antiquity, and Benedetti's assumption of strict inverse proportionality clearly derived from that commonplace; moreover, as he merely threw out the idea in a letter, a rigorous formulation ought not to be expected. In *Quaestiones in Genesim* Mersenne had devoted a column or so to the matter, principally referring to Boethius, but did not go beyond stressing the reliance of pitch on the "velocity" of strings (and the size of pipes, especially the trachea) and observing that, "caeteris paribus," the longer the string, the lower the note.[131] He made no attempt in *Quaestiones* to establish any strict proportional relationship,[132] and there is no reason why he should have done so: he learned of the coincidence theory only in 1629, from Isaac Beeckman; before that date, little of importance rested on the relationship of frequency to length.[133]

Beeckman had invented a demonstration of the required frequency-to-length relationship in 1614 or 1615, recording it in his *Journal*.[134] He sent a version of it to Mersenne fifteen years later,[135] and it appears, unattributed, as one of the fundamental theorems in *Harmo-*

---

131. Mersenne, *Quaestiones*, col. 1559; see also De Waard's note in Mersenne *Correspondance*, 1:136n.1.

132. Contrary to De Waard's implication in Mersenne *Correspondance*, 1:136n.1.

133. With one minor exception: in *Traité*, pp. 394–95, Mersenne's comparison of the speeds of weights on the ends of a balance with the speeds of vibrating strings does imply a strict inverse proportionality of length to frequency; there is no attempt at a demonstration of this assumption, however.

134. Reprinted in Mersenne *Correspondance*, 2:234–35. See Dostrovsky, "Early Vibration Theory," pp. 184–85; Cohen, *Quantifying Music*, pp. 123–24, and 197–200 on Mersenne's indebtedness to Beeckman. For Beeckman's work on vibrating strings and his version of the coincidence theory, see (apart from Cohen's extensive treatment) Klaas van Berkel, "Beeckman, Descartes et 'la philosophie physico-mathématique,'" *Archives de philosophie* 46 (1983), esp. 624–26, emphasizing music theory as the central feature and exemplar of Beeckman's "physico-mathematics"; Frédéric de Buzon, "Descartes, Beeckman et l'acoustique," *Archives de philosophie* 44 (1981), Bulletin cartésien X, pp. 1–8; idem, "Science de la nature et théorie musicale chez Isaac Beeckman (1588–1637)," *Revue d'histoire des sciences* 38 (1985), 97–120.

135. Mersenne *Correspondance*, 2:231.

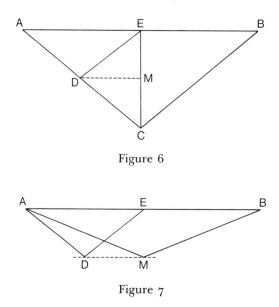

Figure 6

Figure 7

nie universelle: "the ratio of the number of returns of all kinds of strings is the inverse of their lengths."[136] Mersenne there describes the movement of a displaced string as a kind of violent motion comparable to the throwing of a stone, and the demonstration of the theorem relies on an idealized model in which the initial force acting on the string at the moment of its release directly determines the string's subsequent speed.

Consider two strings AB and AE of equal tension (Figure 6). If AB is pulled sideways so that its center is now at C, and AE is similarly displaced by stretching to D, the tensions on the two strings, now ACB and ADE, remain equal because they form similar triangles. The forces tending to return them to their initial undisplaced states are taken to be directly proportional to the string tensions, so that they too are equal; hence, the argument runs, the speeds of the two strings upon release will also be equal. Since point D is displaced only half as far as point C but returns with the same speed, the shorter string must perform its oscillations about centerline AE in half the time required by the longer string about AB; the frequency of vibration is therefore in inverse proportion to string length. Mersenne confirms the conclusion by considering a case in which string AB is displaced only half its previous distance, to point M (see Figure 7), giving it the same initial

136. Mersenne, *Harmonie universelle*, "Des mouvemens des chordes," pp. 157–58.

amplitude as AE. Then, he says, the tension on AMB is only half that on ADE, "as it is easy to conclude by the proportion of triangles." Hence, its starting speed at M is only half that of AE starting at D, and the relative frequencies remain unaltered.[137]

Mersenne's presentation of Beeckman's proof elaborates it considerably and draws in assumptions and implications lacking in the original. The proof therefore takes on a form in *Harmonie universelle* that must be regarded as Mersenne's own. Page upon page of similar analyses follow, investigating variant cases and examining changes in speed during the course of an oscillation, and the techniques applied derive from those used in the original proof. Thus Mersenne maintained his Aristotelian equation of force and speed: the force tending to return a string to its position of rest is directly proportional to the displacement; therefore, so too is the speed of the string upon release. Moreover, Mersenne's subsequent consideration of a string's variation in speed after release confirms that this relation between force and speed holds generally, not merely at the string's initial release. Still adhering to the conceptualizations informing his discussions of the balance in *Traité de l'harmonie universelle*, Mersenne did not see the initial displacement alone as directly determining the subsequent speed of the string.[138] Instead, he envisaged a linear deceleration as it moved towards its central position of equilibrium, because the force impelling it back would itself decrease linearly. He compares the motion to that of a violently propelled missile: "Missiles that are moved violently go so much more slowly as they are farther from their origin, that is, from the force by which they have been thrown," just as the displaced string slows in proportion to its displacement. As the force decreases, so too does the speed.[139]

In remaining true to the mechanical assumptions of the peripatetic tradition, however (and this despite the important role of Galileo's work elsewhere in *Harmonie universelle*), Mersenne created problems for himself. His idealized model of the behavior of vibrating strings failed to explain why, as is patently and by definition the case, such strings move back and forth rather than coming to rest immediately.

137. Ibid.; note that my labeling of the diagrams differs from Mersenne's for the sake of clarity.

138. Beeckman made the tacit assumption that the string continued throughout its passage with the same speed as it had on release.

139. Mersenne, *Harmonie universelle*, "Des mouvemens des chordes," p. 158. Although Mersenne never committed himself as to why a missile continues to move after its release by the mover, the evidence here suggests that he thought in terms of a self-dissipating impetus—despite his apparent acceptance at various times of Galileo's quasi-inertial ideas, first in the *Les mechaniques* version of *Le meccaniche*. For one treatment (among many) of the impetus theory, see Clavelin, *Natural Philosophy*, pp. 91–99.

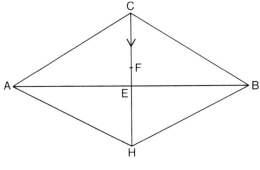

Figure 8

If the speed of a string were truly proportional to its displacement, it should slow in a linear fashion upon release, reaching a velocity of zero at the central position of equilibrium.

Mersenne addresses the problem after considering the phenomenon of the decay of oscillation. It appears, he says, that the string undergoes natural motion towards its "center," the position of equilibrium, and then violent motion away from that center as a result of the "impression" it has by that time acquired. He admits, however, that this interpretation presents certain difficulties. The first is that it requires the string to accelerate in proceeding from the extreme to the central position. The second "consists in knowing why the string does not stop in [the center], since it seems that it has no other design than to return to its center."[140] The first point confronts two kinds of objections, since "experience and reason"—the one term referring to Mersenne's experiments with thousand-foot ropes and the other to the sort of analysis described above—

> make me conclude that point C of the string [see Figure 8] goes always diminishing its speed from C as far as H, for since it only returns because of the violence that stretches it, it ought to return so much the faster the more it is stretched: which I demonstrate in this way. When one draws it only as far as F, or to whatever point one wishes between F and E, it takes as long a time to perform its oscillation [*tour*] as when it is drawn as far as C, or farther, which cannot happen without its going so much the more slowly as it is drawn less and consequently less subjected to violence [*violentée*]: now, this violence is so much the less as the point C approaches E, in which it is no longer subjected to violence, whence it follows that it ought to go less fast in proportion as it advances towards E,

140. Mersenne, *Harmonie universelle*, "Des mouvemens des chordes," p. 161.

at which it would rest if the air which surrounds ACB didn't push it still towards H.[141]

Mersenne simply denies that the string accelerates towards the equilibrium position.[142] Instead, he reiterates that speed is proportional to displacement and suggests a way out of the apparent dilemma he has created: the string, he now proposes, continues on past the center because of air disturbance. He expands on the idea in a separate Proposition "to explain why the string which returns from the place to which it is drawn passes several times through its center without stopping there." As Mersenne remarks, "we seek a very obscure reason for a very evident effect." Indeed, he continues, "it seems to me that to give the reason for this phenomenon it would be necessary to know [cognoistre] the different plays of the air, and the different impressions that it makes on the string it repulses."[143] The air, he decides, adds a new force to that which returns the string to its center.[144] He is unable to be more precise.

Mersenne effectively admits his ultimate inability to accomplish a satisfactory theoretical account of vibrating strings when, after giving this sketchy explanation of perhaps the most basic aspect of vibration, he canvasses a couple of incompatible alternatives. "One can also say that whatever has once started to move, with whatever movement it be, would move eternally if not for the resistance of the air"; perhaps, then, in the absence of air resistance, not only would the string continue to vibrate, but there would be no decay in amplitude. Or else, Mersenne continues, since the string actually does move in the air, one can "imagine" that it moves back and forth for as long a time as it would continue moving if projected freely in a straight line so as to receive the same initial "impression." These remarks, little more than afterthoughts, clearly go against the whole thrust of Mersenne's previous analyses, and he seems in consequence to have thought it wise to emphasize again what he considered to be the most important point: "One should not, however, neglect the reason arising from the effort

141. Ibid., p. 162. It is important to use Mersenne's own corrected copy of *Harmonie universelle* (the one reproduced in facsimile; see Bibliography) throughout this proposition because of systematic labeling errors in the original text. The similarities between Mersenne's and Aristotle's explanations of the air's role in the motion of projectiles are especially striking because the latter's had been explicitly applied to vibrating strings by Jesuit philosophers: see Wallace, *Galileo and His Sources*, p. 192.

142. Mersenne never himself calls it an "equilibrium position"; he always calls it a "center," explicitly by analogy with a gravitational center.

143. Mersenne, *Harmonie universelle*, "Des mouvemens des chordes," p. 165.

144. Ibid., pp. 165–66.

which each part of the string makes to regain its place and situation, which serves it like gravity [*pesanteur*] to weights, to return to its center E."[145]

Mersenne's examination of the mechanics of vibrating strings—built on analogies with the behavior of weights, considered along lines laid down in the *Mechanica*—failed to support adequately the contention that frequency and string length were inversely proportional. Mersenne nonetheless accepted its truth; he even used it to determine the absolute frequencies of particular notes by extrapolating from very long strings, the oscillations of which could be counted, to very short strings of the same tension.[146] Beeckman's putative demonstration helped to render the relationship more plausible but clearly did not provide the reason for Mersenne's initial acceptance of it. A similar state of affairs holds in the case of Mersenne's acceptance of and argument for the isochronism of vibrating strings. Following a suggestion from Descartes, Mersenne maintained that since the note produced by a string remains of the same pitch even while the amplitude of vibration decays, the frequency evidently stays constant. However, this presupposes that pitch is indeed a direct function of frequency, a claim itself resting on a tacit acceptance of the isochronism of vibrating strings.[147] No mystery attaches to Mersenne's position, of course: he assumed without rigorous proof those things necessary to establish the coincidence theory of consonance because that theory offered the best grounds on which to defend the traditional mathematical basis of harmony.

After a long discussion of the octave in *Harmonie universelle*'s book "Des consonances," Mersenne gets down to business with Proposition XVI, which discusses in conventional terms the division of the monochord to produce the fourth, the fifth, and their concomitant Pythagorean intervals.[148] The succeeding proposition, however, addresses the physical nature of the fifth.

> This consonance, which the Greeks call *Diapente* because of the five sounds [i.e., notes] that it contains, is composed of two movements, of which one hits [*bat*] the air twice while the other hits it three times: thence it is that the string that is so divided that it leaves three parts on one side and two on the other produces the fifth, inasmuch as the side of three parts hits the air twice while the other, which only has two parts,

145. Ibid., p. 166.
146. See Dostrovsky, "Early Vibration Theory," pp. 197–98; and Hunt, *Origins in Acoustics*, pp. 90–94.
147. See Dostrovsky, "Early Vibration Theory," p. 185, for Mersenne's argument.
148. Mersenne, *Harmonie universelle*, "Des consonances," p. 60.

hits it three times, since the number of strokes [*battemens*] is reciprocal to the length of strings, as I have demonstrated elsewhere.[149]

Even had he possessed a less problematic demonstration of the crucial frequency/length relationship, Mersenne would still have had no physiological grounds for supposing that the regular concurrence of sound pulses would produce the sensation of consonance. In fact, the structure of his commitment coordinates around the original Pythagorean ratios themselves. If one were already disposed to regard as significant those string-length ratios that correlated so neatly with consonant intervals (as Stevin and others were not), one might tend to identify ratio and consonance, taking the ratio to express something essential about the consonance. Then, even if the ear found perfectly pleasing a fifth with a ratio slightly different from 3 : 2, the harmony of the precise ratio would be regarded as more exact. Mersenne adhered to just such a position, and by developing a version of Beeckman's coincidence theory, itself based on a mechanical conception of consonance (justified by the classical association of sound with disturbances in the air), he found a way of squaring Galilei's findings with Zarlino's consonant ratios.[150] Rather than being transcendental ratios instantiated in all variables of sound production, they became ratios of vibrational frequencies standing at the heart of a new musical, or acoustical, program of mechanistic research. This program, pursued in *Harmonie universelle*, aimed at discovering how vibrational frequency itself related to the physical variables of sound production and how those relationships thereby embodied the mathematical harmonies expressed in sound. The periodic coincidence of pulses surely caused the sensation of consonance, therefore; that way, music remained mathematical—or, in Augustine's sense, rational— and at the same time provided a technical means of displaying the harmonies that governed all bodies in motion and at rest.

Vibrational frequency was inversely, not directly, proportional to string length, and its use consequently resulted in an inversion of ratios: the fifth, for instance, became associated with a 2 : 3 ratio of frequencies instead of a 3 : 2 ratio instantiated in string lengths. Because Mersenne adopted the vibrational coincidence theory as a way of retaining the Pythagorean ratios in music, however, he played down the importance of the change.

149. Ibid. See also Palisca, "Scientific Empiricism," pp. 110–12.
150. We saw in Chapter 5, above, how Mersenne used Galilei's findings on the relation between pitch and string tension to argue against Fludd in *Traité*. He had already referred to Galilei's work in *La verité*, pp. 617–18. Galilei's continued use of numerical ratios clearly had value for Mersenne.

It's necessary to remark once and for all that it makes no difference whatever whether the smaller or greater term of the ratios to express the consonances goes first; that is, it is as true [*veritable*] to say that the ratio of the octave is subduple [i.e., 1 : 2], and that that of the fifth is subsesquialterate [2 : 3],[151] as to say that the former is duple and the latter sesquialterate, although this second way favors the length or thickness [*grosseur*][152] of strings. . . . But if one considers the vibrations of strings, the greater [i.e., longer string] ought to be signified by the lesser number, since it vibrates more slowly, and consequently the ratio of the octave will be subduple when one starts with the large string, *although one can always retain the duple ratio for greater ease, and to accommodate oneself to ordinary usage, and to the positions of the ancients.* [My emphasis][153]

Proposition XIII of the "livre des dissonances" proclaimed that "there is no difficulty in the theory of music, and all the consonances, dissonances, songs, and concerts are made solely by the addition or subtraction of strokes [*battemens*] of air."[154] In reducing the theory of music to mechanics, Mersenne succeeded in retaining the traditional Pythagorean analysis and overcoming the "difficulties" that had threatened it.

Sigalia Dostrovsky has described Mersenne's exposition in *Harmonie universelle* of what have become known as "Mersenne's Laws" governing the frequency of vibrating strings. She remarks that Mersenne investigated and refined these relationships by experiment but did not himself originate them; she then examines a peculiarity of the rule on string tension. Mersenne says that to tune identical strings an octave apart, the ratio of tensions, or affixed weights, should be 4 : 1, "inasmuch as the weights are in a doubled ratio [i.e., square] of the harmonic intervals."[155] However, he immediately proceeds to warn that in order to make the interval accurate, the ratio should in practice be $4\frac{1}{4}$: 1. As Dostrovsky observes, this correction, apparently intended to apply generally, is clearly empirical. "It is interesting," she continues, "that Mersenne divided his empirical result into two components: a 'law' (rule 1) and a 'correction' (rule 2). What he chose to call the law happens to have been correct, but one wonders how he knew. Was it physical intuition or a Pythagorean confidence in the

---

151. See Mersenne's explication of these terms for ratios in *La verité*, pp. 320–24.
152. Dostrovsky, "Early Vibration Theory," p. 186, explicates Mersenne's use of this word.
153. Mersenne, *Harmonie universelle*, "Des consonances," p. 61.
154. Ibid., "Des dissonances," p. 137.
155. Dostrovsky, "Early Vibration Theory," pp. 185–87, here referring to Mersenne, *Harmonie universelle*, "Des instrumens," pp. 123–26, quotation on p. 123.

importance of small whole numbers?"[156] We can now answer that question. It was the latter.

IV

Mersenne used mechanics to explain musical harmony. In so doing, however, he necessarily presupposed that at a deeper level, harmony was immanent in mechanics itself, as indeed in all of Creation. He had already exercised that presupposition in *Traité de l'harmonie universelle*, prior to his acquaintance with the possibility of a mechanical "saving of the phenomena" in music. Book 2 of the *Traité* attempts to illustrate the ways in which "consonances are found in all the parts of this universe."[157] Mersenne draws parallels between musical consonance and such diverse things as odors and geometry;[158] his discussion of the balance, touched on previously, takes place as part of a demonstration that "there is the same ratio of the difference of sounds to the difference of strings considered in their length, as there is of the difference of weights to the difference of their distance from the center of the balance, or the fulcrum of the lever . . . consequently, sounds can be compared to weights, to statics, to the equilibrium of planes [*l'Isorropique*], and to moving forces."[159] Just as a weight becomes more heavy or more powerful the farther it is from the center of a balance, so a uniform string gives forth a lower note the longer it is. Conversely, the sharper the note, the shorter the string and the faster its movement in proportion as the string shortens.[160] "It's therefore necessary to conclude that just as there is the same ratio of the lesser and greater weights to their greater and lesser distance from the center of the balance, and of these weights and these distances to the speed of their movements, there is also the same ratio of the length of strings to the lowness or height [i.e., pitch] of sounds,

---

156. Dostrovsky, "Early Vibration Theory," p. 187. Mersenne himself never makes any terminological distinction between the "law" and the "correction"; indeed, he never uses the term "law" (*loi*) for any physical rule, employing instead the word "rule" (*règle*). For the most recent treatment of "laws of nature" from the Middle Ages to the Scientific Revolution, see Jane E. Ruby, "The Origins of Scientific 'Law,'" *Journal of the History of Ideas* 47 (1986), 341–59; see also John R. Milton, "The Origin and Development of the Concept of the 'Laws of Nature,'" *Archives européennes de sociologie* 22 (1981), 173–95. Dostrovsky's reading remains correct in spirit, however.

157. Mersenne, *Traité*, "Preface" to Book 2, [p. 1]; "Epistre" to Book 2, [p. 4].

158. Some of these parallels, including the comparison with odors, are found in Boethius, *De institutione musica*.

159. Mersenne, *Traité*, p. 392.

160. Ibid., p. 394.

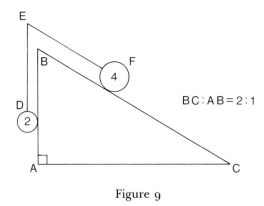

Figure 9

and of the movement of the [weights] with the movement of the [strings]."[161]

Three vital elements of Mersenne's approach to musical and mechanical problems appear here: the *Mechanica*'s interpretation of the balance; the assumption without proof of the inverse proportionality between frequency and string length that later became crucial for Mersenne's adoption of the coincidence theory; and an attempt to construe a paradigmatic mechanical situation as structurally equivalent to the production of musical notes. Beeckman's ideas about the nature of consonance were about to fall on very well-prepared ground.

Mersenne continues with a comparison between the law of the balance and man's relationship to God, then goes on to consider equilibrium on inclined planes. He manages to find a fairly ingenious musical interpretation. The equilibrium of weights has no parallel equilibrium of sounds in the ratio of the attached weights providing the tension; however, he explains, "if we extend two strings, equal in all respects, on two supports [*chevalets*], and one be drawn by a weight of four pounds on the oblique side of a triangle such as ABC, and the other perpendicularly by a weight of two pounds [see Figure 9], these two strings would produce unison, which we can call the *equilibrium of sounds*."[162]

Finally, Mersenne returns to the balance. Following the discussion examined earlier about the effect of a weight's distance from the center on its "force," and of concomitant changes in its "velocity,"[163] he outlines another correlation with the ratios of music. Referring to

161. Ibid., p. 395.
162. Ibid., pp. 397–98. Note that ED and EF are assumed to be of equal length here.
163. Ibid., pp. 398–400.

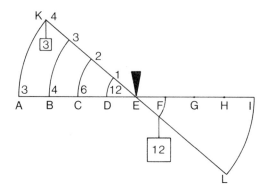

Figure 10

Figure 10, he considers "these four numbers 12, 6, 4, 3," which of course correspond to the weights required to counterbalance the twelve units suspended from F at successive multiples of distance EF along the arm EA. The numbers, says Mersenne, "give us the principal consonances of music." Thus "12 and 6 make the octave, 12 and 3 the double-octave [i.e., the fifteenth], 12 and 4 the twelfth, 6 and 4 the fifth, and 4 and 3 the fourth."[164]

Music represented for Mersenne the most striking evidence of a mathematically and logically ordered universe, and in showing how mechanics participated in its formal structure, he related the behavior of heavy bodies to "universal harmony." In *Harmonie universelle* he attempted to save that evidence—both from the sorts of difficulties exploited in La Mothe Le Vayer's *Discours sceptique sur la musique*[165] and from the implications of Galilei's work—by effectively reversing the logical priorities: he used mechanics to guarantee that music embodied rational harmonies in a way similar to that in which, in the *Traité*, he had used music to reveal the harmonies hidden in mechanics.

Nonetheless, music itself remained the touchstone of "universal harmony." Having finally accepted the doctrine of uniform acceleration in free fall, Mersenne brought out the attractions of its formal

164. Ibid., p. 400.
165. Mersenne prints this, with his rebuttal, in *Questions harmoniques*, pp. 84–165, although he does not use the coincidence theory in his rebuttal (it does appear, in a different context, on page 19). On this subject generally, see Duncan, "Tyranny of Opinions Undermined," chap. 4, "Scepticism and Musical Science," pp. 265–332. La Mothe Le Vayer emphasizes Aristoxenian kinds of arguments, and so Mersenne stresses music as an intellectual science.

characteristics through the presentation of a proposition designed to calculate "from what places weights ought to fall to make such harmonic proportions, and such accords and discords, as one would wish, when they encounter each other."[166] Mersenne employs the supposition that, all other things being equal, a falling body produces sound in the ambient air of a pitch proportional to the body's speed, so that an octave corresponds to a doubling of the speed of fall. On this basis, he determines the various heights from which bodies would have to be dropped, together with the time intervals necessary between releases, for the bodies to come together at the precise moment at which the notes associated with each would combine harmoniously.[167] Mersenne thus endeavors to match the proportions of free fall with those of musical harmony, and he displays both kinds together in detailed diagrams and tables.[168] Evidently, free fall exhibited "universal harmony" only so far as it conformed to the pattern presented by music, and Mersenne painstakingly elucidated the relationship, much as he had done for the balance nine years before. He did not merely exploit the theorems of others, however. "Universal harmony" directed his own production of technical mechanical results.

In his research, correspondence, and writing on the behavior of vibrating strings, dating chiefly from the late 1620s until the appearance of *Harmonie universelle*, Mersenne kept in mind an apparently close mechanical analogue: the pendulum.[169] In 1618 Isaac Beeckman had contemplated the similarity of pendulums and musical strings, and the juxtaposition of the two appears frequently in letters to or from Mersenne in 1629 and the early 1630s.[170] This is true particularly of letters from Descartes, which, because they take the form of answers to Mersenne's endless questions, treat the two phenomena together even though Descartes himself apparently considered them to be quite different. His objections sprang from his apprehension that a different kind of force operated in each case. On

166. Mersenne, *Harmonie universelle*, "Des dissonances," p. 134.
167. Ibid., pp. 134–37.
168. Ibid., p. 136. This was less trivial or contrived than it may seem: the calculated heights of fall and time intervals required to produce consonance display ratios akin to those of music not simply because Mersenne has arranged them that way but because the odd-number rule yields them. Other rules governing fall would not necessarily do so.
169. For his work on vibrating strings, see Dostrovsky, "Early Vibration Theory," pp. 185–98; Hyde, "Mersenne in the History of Music," chap. 9, pp. 275–303; Pierre Costabel, "Annexe V" to René Descartes, *Règles*, trans. Jean-Luc Marion (The Hague, 1977), pp. 319–22. There is a short discussion in Lenoble, *Mersenne*, pp. 482–86; relevant letters are noted in Mersenne *Correspondance*, 4:17, 427.
170. For Beeckman, see Mersenne *Correspondance*, 2:210–11nn; and for letters juxtaposing pendulums and vibrating strings, see, e.g., ibid., pp. 205–6, 317–19, 346.

one occasion he denied the isochrony of the pendulum, in contrast to vibrating strings, because the weight of a pendulum bob remains constant, whereas the force acting on a plucked string varies with amplitude.[171] Mersenne, however, tended to accept Beeckman's (and, later, Galileo's) assertion that the period of a pendulum was independent of amplitude and hence that pendulums were isochronous.[172] On another occasion, Descartes answered a question about the possibility of a *media quies*, or point of rest, between the outward and inward phases of motion of a vibrating string or between the upward and downward swings of a pendulum;[173] he protested Mersenne's bracketing together of the two because "the oscillations [*tours et retours*] of a string attached by both ends is one thing, and those of a string attached only by one end, having a weight at the other end, is another."[174] This terminology seems be Mersenne's own, and it reappears in *Harmonie universelle*'s "Livre premier des instruments."

Addressing the problem of determining how long a string continues to vibrate, Mersenne proceeds naturally from musical strings to pendulums. The previous proposition had discussed the proportion of diminution of amplitude in a vibrating string, but the present question, says Mersenne, "is much more difficult . . . inasmuch as one cannot perceive [*on ne peut remarquer*] the last vibration or oscillation [*tremblement ou retour*] of strings, whether they have one of their ends held or whether they are attached by both ends." Mersenne therefore approximates, noting that although in the former case the oscillations occur much more slowly than in the latter, they also last longer, so that, "perhaps," the final number of oscillations will be the same for each.

> Whence one can conjecture that there is the same ratio of speed of oscillations of the string fixed by both ends to that of the oscillations of the other, as there is of the duration of oscillations of the latter to the duration of oscillations of the former, which will happen if, being held by both ends, it makes 90 oscillations in the space of a second, and if, being held only by one end, its oscillations last 90 times as long as those

171. Ibid., p. 346.
172. See notes in ibid., p. 321, and 4:451.
173. This was a classical question usually posed with respect to bodies thrown upwards, which slow and then commence to fall. Mersenne addresses it in regard to vibrating strings in *Harmonie universelle*, "Des mouvemens des chordes," pp. 163–65. Beeckman's ideas required a *media quies* at extreme positions of a vibrating string: see Cohen, *Quantifying Music*, pp. 128–29.
174. Mersenne *Correspondance*, 5:126.

of the other. The same thing must be said of each oscillation of one compared with the other, and consequently the table in the preceding Proposition can serve equally the one and the other string.[175]

(The table to which Mersenne refers details the decay of amplitude of a vibrating string—that is, one "held by both ends"—calculated from the starting point of empirical data.)[176] Unlike Descartes, Mersenne saw the two cases as modes of the same basic phenomenon: an oscillating string. Descartes considered that the difference in force characteristics argued against any profound similarity, but Mersenne, who knew that the weight of the bob had no effect on a pendulum's period,[177] saw a difference only in the precise contrivance of the string's points of anchorage.

We have seen the crucial importance to Mersenne of the claim that the frequency and length of musical strings were inversely proportional. In the early 1630s no such proportionality had been established for the pendulum. In 1632 Galileo went no further in the *Dialogue* than to make a vague observation that the period decreased with increasing length, while Descartes, analyzing the situation as a variant of free fall, arrived at idiosyncratic conclusions owing to his rejection of the odd-number rule.[178] Mersenne was the first to state that the period of a pendulum is proportional to the square-root of its length. Alistair Crombie has noted that this rule first appears, without proof or elaboration, in one of Mersenne's "Additions" to *Les mechaniques de Galilée*, in 1634,[179] and the full exposition presented in various parts of *Harmonie universelle* two years later still predates any other publication of the relationship.[180] Mersenne's quite thorough explica-

175. Mersenne, *Harmonie universelle*, "Des instrumens," Proposition XVIII (the first page of which is shown as 45, but the pagination is in disarray).

176. Ibid., facing page to beginning of Prop.XVIII.

177. See, e.g., ibid., final paragraph of Prop.XVIII.

178. For the state of the question at the time, see notes in Mersenne *Correspondance*, 2:321 and 4:444–46. For Descartes and free fall, see Alexandre Koyré, *Galileo Studies*, trans. John Mepham (Atlantic Highlands, N.J., 1978), pp. 79–94; Koyré's account is called into question on good grounds, however, in Stillman Drake, "Free Fall from Albert of Saxony to Honoré Fabri," *Studies in History and Philosophy of Science* 5 (1975), esp. 357–60. For a case of an apparent exception to Descartes's rejection of Galileo's rule, see Antonio Nardi, "Descartes 'presque galiléen,'" *Revue d'histoire des sciences* 39 (1986), 3–16. See also Chapter 8, below.

179. Crombie, "Mathematics, Music," pp. 299–300; also Alistair C. Crombie, "Mersenne, Marin," in *DSB*, 9:319. Mersenne's statement is in *Les mechaniques*, p. 70 (note misprint giving time ratio as 4:1, an error also found in the original); Rochot did not comment on the significance of this passage in his notes.

180. See note in Mersenne *Correspondance*, 2:321. Piero E. Ariotti, "Aspects of the Conception and Development of the Pendulum in the 17th Century," *Archive for History of Exact Sciences* 8 (1972), 329–410, deals significantly with Mersenne only on pages 378–79, regarding isochrony.

tion, in contrast to his approach to free fall, involves little empirical justification, and it displays links with the analogous rule for musical strings.[181] Since he made no categorical distinction between vibrating strings and swinging pendulums, and since musical harmony integrated with mechanics and thereby with "universal harmony," he apparently saw the pendulum as a natural extension or additional manifestation of the mechanical principles underlying music.

Mersenne's demonstration relied on treating the downward swing of the bob as a case of free fall (see Figure 11). Galileo had compared the arc described by a pendulum to an infinite succession of inclined planes: Mersenne asserted that because bodies descend along all planes of whatever inclination according to the odd-number rule governing free fall, the vertical component of a pendulum bob's descent must increase in the same way. Hence the vertical distance fallen, as in ordinary free fall, is proportional to the square of the time, and so the time of a half-swing is proportional to the square root of the initial height of release. For any given angle of release, that height is itself directly proportional to the string length, from which it follows that the period is proportional to the square root of the length.[182]

When discussing the behavior of vibrating strings, Mersenne described their tendency to return to the "center" when displaced as being "like gravity to weights."[183] In neither case did he think that he could explain the true physical causes at work, but he conceptualized the formal mechanical situations according to the same basic model. The pendulum—a string held at one end—manifested a particular kind of free fall, the appropriate analysis for which isolated the vertical component of motion and treated it as uniform acceleration downwards. The movement of a vibrating string—a string held at both ends—was also a kind of "natural" motion towards a center, ideally represented by speed decreasing uniformly in proportion to decreasing distance from the central position, although actually occurring as deceleration towards a point somewhat beyond it. The oscillatory motion in both cases resulted from a thwarting of the ten-

181. See esp. Mersenne, *Harmonie universelle*, "Du mouvement des corps," pp. 131–35. A full and reliable account is given as Appendix 3 in Mersenne *Correspondance*, 4:444–55. It draws on the *Harmonie universelle* and its contemporary Latin counterpart, Marin Mersenne, *Harmonicorum libri XII* (Paris, 1648), which is a later edition of the work originally issued in two parts. For a comparison of the two editions, see Lenoble, *Mersenne*, p. xxii.

182. There may be a curious connection between Mersenne's derivation using Galileo's law of fall and the origins of that law itself: David K. Hill, "Galileo's Work on 116v," *Isis* 77 (1986), 283–91, esp. 289–90, suggests that Galileo may have derived the relation $v \propto \sqrt{s}$ from his law of chords, itself related to analysis of pendulum motion.

183. See above, text to n. 145.

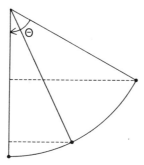

Figure 11

dency towards the center, owing to the inelastic properties of the string restraining the pendulum bob's further descent and making it swing upwards, or to the disturbance of the air reinforcing the musical string's impetus and making it carry on past its center. The structural similarities stem from Mersenne's still very Aristotelian mechanics, wherein (as the pamphlet of 1633 speculated) falling bodies must be impelled by a force varying in such a way as to produce uniform acceleration, speed being directly proportional to force, and variation of speed with time being caused by variation of force with distance. On the basis of these conflations, the change in speed of the vibrating string, as the force impelling it to the center decreased linearly, exactly mirrored the change in the unconstrained vertical speed of the pendulum bob as the force generating free fall accelerated it.[184]

Mersenne investigated vibrating strings in the first place because they produced musical sounds. Beeckman's analysis, and his own elaboration of it, provided a mechanistic grounding for Pythagorean harmony. The techniques serving to mechanize music, since they were designed to retain its existing mathematical character, necessarily served also to establish harmony in mechanics itself. Mersenne's derivation of the pendulum rule exemplifies his search for "universal harmony" and shows how his belief that Creation embodied a rational order implied more than simple encouragement towards mathematical natural philosophy; it also involved the construction and ap-

---

184. Clearly, the discontinuities of motion involved in both cases never appeared to Mersenne as a problem; there were no reasons why they should have. If one thinks both of models of reflection in optics and analogous treatments of bodies rebounding from solid surfaces (seen together in, e.g., Descartes's *Dioptrique*), one realizes that discontinuities of motion were routinely implicated in the mathematical sciences of the period. On this point, see also Drake, "Free Fall," which explicitly discusses discontinuous accounts of the mechanism of natural acceleration.

plication of specific mathematical and mechanical procedures. Musical strings, pendulums, harmony, and mechanics were inextricably connected in Mersenne's work. At the beginning of *Harmonie universelle,* following the index, appear three pages that Mersenne filled with small print at the last moment when he discovered that the printer had left some empty space.[185] They contain material taken from a version of parts of Galileo's *Two New Sciences,* which Mersenne had seen in manuscript not long before.[186] Two of these pages describe Galileo's account of how pendulums can be used to illustrate the periodic coincidence of oscillations characterizing musical consonances, a topic found in the "First Day" of Galileo's discourses; Mersenne specifies string lengths suitable for revealing them easily to the eye.[187] Thus, from his hasty perusal of Galileo's new treatise, Mersenne picked out as especially valuable an analogy between pendulums and musical strings that showed, in effect, how both embody harmony. The remaining page of this addition details, as a complement, Galileo's laws of local motion.

The teachings of Saint Augustine sanctioned Mersenne's attempts to find manifestations of "wisdom," number and harmony, in the physical world. Mersenne wished on that basis to extend the scope of the mathematical sciences, to exploit their usefulness and their solidity, and to uncover causes in physical phenomena to the extent that mathematics could provide them. He adopted Beeckman's term "physico-mathematics" not because he accepted Beeckman's own approach (which in large measure he did not) but because it expressed neatly his own ambitions for a mathematical and empirical approach to nature. Mersenne persisted, despite Galileo, to effect the crucial junction between statics and dynamics, force and speed, using concepts from the peripatetic tradition. With the *Mechanica*'s model problem solutions linking statics to the study of local motion, and with Beeckman's coincidence theory, mathematical regularities could be constructed that connected the science of mechanics (taken as the

185. As mentioned on the first page of the three.

186. See Crombie, "Mersenne," p. 319. For a discussion of Mersenne's acquaintance with the *Two New Sciences* during the final stages of composition of the *Harmonie universelle,* see Marin Mersenne, *Les nouvelles pensées de Galilée* (Paris, 1638/39), introduction to the critical edition by Pierre Costabel and Michel-Pierre Lerner (Paris, 1973), pp. 20–28.

187. On Galileo and the musical material of the *Two New Sciences,* see Walker, *Studies,* pp. 27–33; and Cohen, *Quantifying Music,* pp. 85–92, in which the interesting error involved in the comparison is noted on pp. 91–92, drawn from notes to the critical edition of Mersenne, *Nouvelles pensées.* On this point, see also William R. Shea, "Marin Mersenne: Galileo's 'traduttore-traditore'," *Annali dell'Istituto e Museo di Storia della Scienza di Firenze* 2 (1977), fasc. 1, p. 69.

union of statics and local motion) to the science of music in such a way as to yield results in areas previously the province of physics alone. Without "universal harmony," however, the project lacked any conviction, being no more plausible than scholastic physics without access to essences.

CHAPTER SEVEN

Philosophical Systems, Essentialism, and the Language of Philosophy

I

SEVENTEENTH-CENTURY criticism of scholastic approaches to learning often centered on the scholastic use of Aristotelian doctrines concerning epistemology and cognition.[1] Questioning scholastic-Aristotelian accounts of the psychology of perception, however, not only carried epistemological implications but also entailed a reassessment of the nature and function of language. Scholastic Latin provided a form of discourse tailored to the expression of its own world view; scholastic logic had rested on linguistic foundations, and correct procedures of reasoning themselves relied on views of the structure and nature of grammar and the signification of words.[2] Furthermore, the status of names, which classified individuals in the world into groups and enabled general statements to be made about them (that is, enabled the enunciation of knowledge claims), rested on the way in which universals could be predicated of things. Those who rejected scholastic-Aristotelian epistemology and physics therefore needed to redefine the role of language in natural philosophy. The seventeenth century saw many attempts at creating new ways of conforming language to natural knowledge, manifested in projects for "philosophical" languages.[3]

1. For an excellent summary of Aristotle's epistemology, see Gaukroger, *Explanatory Structures*, pp. 90–96.
2. Terrence Heath, "Logical Grammar," esp. pp. 41–46; L. Jardine, *Bacon*, pp. 4, 20.
3. See esp. M. M. Slaughter, *Universal Languages and Scientific Taxonomy in the Seventeenth Century* (Cambridge, 1982), which considers the relation between ideas on language and essentialist scientific taxonomy, with particular emphasis on botanical classification.

Mersenne's concentration on mathematical sciences did not exempt him from consideration of these matters, if only for the simple reason that mathematical formulations required linguistic structures to act as correspondence rules connecting them to things in the world. His concern with cognition and the kind of knowledge that could successfully be sought about nature thus drew him into discussions of the place of language in natural philosophy and the character of language itself. Once again, Mersenne's position drew heavily on school doctrines; paradoxically, however, his differences with such seventeenth-century antischolastic systematists as Descartes and Bacon emerged not from that fact but from a crucial departure from essentialist ambitions shared equally by those systematists and scholastic-Aristotelians. The importance of language to Cabbalists, hermeticists, and other dangerously unorthodox philosophers—represented above all for Mersenne by Robert Fludd—provided additional reason to confront questions of the proper place of language in philosophy.

The table of disciplines in *Quaestiones in Genesim* lists as the appropriate grammatical authors those who had produced the standard textbooks of the time, covering Latin, Greek, and Hebrew.[4] Mersenne had described grammar as being concerned with "speaking and writing well,"[5] indicating a conception of the subject that fits perfectly his choice of authors. Latin, the most important of the three languages, is represented by Despauterius, whose textbook was the most widely used in France during the sixteenth and early seventeenth centuries. Designed to teach correct Latin—that is, Latin according to classical usage—the work prepared pupils to tackle the best Roman orators, historians, and poets. Mersenne probably studied it, and its approach conformed to the humanist educational program.[6]

The scholastic predecessors of Despauterius had directed gram-

---

4. Mersenne, *Quaestiones*, cols. 1209–10; the authors are "Despauterius, Clenardus, Pagninus." For a discussion of their books, see Louis Kukenheim, *Contributions à l'histoire de la grammaire grecque, latine et hebraïque à l'époque de la renaissance* (Leiden, 1951), pp. 83–84, 137 (Despauterius); 39, 43, 135 (Clenardus); 119–20, 126, 140 (Pagninus). On Clenardus and Greek grammars in general, see also W. Keith Percival, "The Grammatical Tradition and the Rise of the Vernaculars," in Thomas A. Sebeok, ed., *Historiography of Linguistics* (The Hague, 1975), pp. 245–47 and, on Despauterius, p. 240. For a discussion of humanist grammars as a preparation for rhetoric training, see Heath, "Logical Grammar," esp. p. 39.

5. Mersenne, *Quaestiones*, col. 1206.

6. The book was the standard text in French Jesuit colleges: Rochemonteix, *Un collège de Jésuites*, 3:12–17; although Mersenne probably received his elementary grammar training at Le Mans before going to La Flèche (see Chapter 2, above), the continuity of his education and the general use of Despauterius, together with Mersenne's own citation of him, leaves little room for doubt as to the orientation of Mersenne's view of grammar. For further information on Despauterius's textbook, see G. A. Padley, *Grammatical Theory in Western Europe, 1500–1700: The Latin Tradition* (Cambridge, 1976), chap. 1.

matical training towards different pedagogical ends. Instead of preparing the pupil for rhetoric, they gently introduced him to philosophy; grammatical categories were explained not simply by their correct usage but by a formal description in Aristotelian philosophical terms.[7] The chief medieval grammar, Alexander of Villa Dei's *Doctrinale*, for example, described the use of the genitive in the phrase "epistola Pauli" as one of cause and effect: "Paulus" takes the genitive case because Paul is the efficient cause of the letter.[8] In this way, explication of a grammatical point also provided a small lesson in philosophy; the scholastics were interested in Latin as a language of philosophical analysis rather than of elegant style or cultural expression. The differing aims of humanist educators led them to sever this close connection between grammar and Aristotelian philosophy. Their approach nonetheless carried certain significant, though largely tacit, assumptions.

Humanist grammarians followed the lead of their classical predecessors, particularly Donatus and Priscian, while also interpreting their sources in a way that reflected the humanist regard for classical writings as repositories of ancient wisdom. Like Priscian, they divided words into two basic classes, nouns and verbs, on the grounds that the world consists of *things* and *actions*. Since actions could be either active or passive, verbs themselves had to be further subdivided. Humanist grammars thus considered words in their relation to the world: that is, with respect to the things and the modes of existence that they signified. Meaning was paramount; the signification of words, not their morphological structure, determined their classification.[9] In medieval grammar, by contrast, words had two roles, one lexical and one grammatical; the first concerned signification, and the second a word's function in a sentence. Thus *hominis*, like *homo*, signified a "man" but unlike *homo* it also *consignified* the genitive case (or, more accurately, those things for which the genitive stood).[10] Similarly, according to a medieval and Aristotelian definition, a verb signified action and consignified tense. Humanist grammarians abandoned the notion of consignification and used only that of signification.[11]

For pedagogical more than for philosophical reasons, even the precise meaning of "signification" tended to become obscured in the textbooks of the humanists. Scholastic-Aristotelian doctrine held that

---

7. Heath, "Logical Grammar," pp. 11–16; G. L. Bursill-Hall, "The Middle Ages," in Sebeok, *Historiography of Linguistics*, pp. 179–230, esp. 180–81.

8. Heath, "Logical Grammar," p. 12.

9. Padley, *Grammatical Theory: Latin Tradition*, pp. 29–57, esp. 45–46, 56; see also pp. 77–96: Ramus was something of an exception to this last generalization.

10. See ibid., p. 56; the example is my own.

11. Ibid., p. 38.

words directly signify notions in the mind, relating to things themselves only indirectly through those notions. The humanist emphasis on semantic criteria, however, encouraged the treatment of words as *names* for *things*. In grammars not designed as prolegomena to philosophy, questions of reference could go by the board: it is easy to see how, when the goal is simply to teach the art of writing and speaking well, "the noun is the name of a thing" has greater pedagogical force than complex explanations of signification.[12] Logic texts were more careful, as we shall see below, but humanists took grammar itself to reflect the categories of the world. Lorenzo Valla, for example, had wanted philosophical truth to reside in Latin as used by the Roman authors.[13]

Nonetheless, in certain important respects the humanist view of language closely resembled the scholastic. The humanists classified logic as a *scientia sermocinalis*, a discipline concerned with language, because they saw language as the proper vehicle of reason.[14] Scholastic doctrine, too, maintained that reason resides in language and that language manifests reason. At this fundamental level, therefore, the two approaches admitted of some sort of accommodation. J. C. Scaliger's *De causis linguae Latinae* (1540), an influential work known to Mersenne, provides a striking example.[15] A polemical treatise discussing the proper treatment of grammar, *De causis* adopts, in addition to its humanistic regard for usage in determining grammatical canons, an analytical approach which has been compared to that of the medieval *modistae*.[16] Using Aristotelian terminology, Scaliger based grammatical rules on an examination of the nature of grammatical classes, and analyzed phrases and sentences to reveal the "real" structure often hidden by actual locutions (the concept of "ellipsis" best known for its use by the grammarians of Port-Royal).[17] All

---

12. Ibid., pp. 38, 56.

13. Paul Oskar Kristeller, "The Renaissance," in *Renaissance Thought and Its Sources*, ed. Michael Mooney (New York, 1979), p. 250. For a discussion of the extent to which Valla adhered to the criterion of classical usage, see Percival, "Grammatical Tradition," pp. 254–56.

14. E. J. Ashworth, *Language and Logic*, pp. 32–33; Mersenne brackets logic as a *scientia sermocinalis* in the table in *Quaestiones*, cols. 1209–10.

15. I have used a later edition, J. C. Scaliger, *De causis linguae Latinae libri tredecim* (n.p., 1580). Mersenne refers to the work in *Harmonie universelle*, "De la voix," p. 77. On Scaliger's book, see Jean Stéfanini, "Jules César Scaliger et son *De causis linguae Latinae*," in Herman Parret, ed., *History of Linguistic Thought and Contemporary Linguistics* (Berlin, 1976), pp. 317–30.

16. E.g., by Vivian Salmon, "Pre-Cartesian Linguistics," *Journal of Linguistics* 5 (1969), 170.

17. For examples, see Stéfanini, "Scaliger," p. 326. Manuel Breva-Claramonte, *Sanctius' Theory of Language* (Amsterdam, 1983), pp. 62–72, discusses Scaliger. Perhaps the most notable of early emphases on the importance of ellipsis is Thomas Linacre, *De*

this presupposed an identification of the grammatical dimension of language with reason, something traditionally assumed even in the prototypical grammars of Romans like Varro; as Scaliger said, speech should reflect the order of concepts in the mind.[18] He followed Aristotle in regarding words themselves as purely arbitrary signifiers, contrasting this position with that of Plato and the Pythagoreans, who supposedly took them to be in some way natural.[19] The grammar and syntax that structured words, however, had fundamentally philosophical foundations.

By the early seventeenth century, "philosophical grammar" of this kind had become a fairly standard genre, its sixteenth-century antecedents including, apart from Scaliger's treatise, a work by Francisco Sanchez, or Sanctius, called *Minerva seu de causis linguae Latinae* (1587).[20] Sanctius adopted an approach similar to Scaliger's but without the emphasis on Aristotelian terminology, and that set the subsequent pattern. In the seventeenth century, Vossius, who drew on Scaliger, produced a philosophical grammar (as did Campanella and Caramuel y Lobkowitz, among others); Vossius's book at least was certainly known to Mersenne. The most famous example, the Port-Royal grammar of 1660, thus fitted into a well-established tradition.[21] These newer forms of grammatical analysis complemented, in a sense, the humanists' rather pragmatic style of teaching grammar but

emendata structura (1524): see G. A. Padley, *Grammatical Theory in Western Europe, 1500–1700: Trends in Vernacular Grammar I* (Cambridge, 1985), pp. 233–39.

18. See, in general, Padley, *Grammatical Theory: Trends*, pp. 269–82; for the reference to Varro, see Breva-Claramonte, *Sanctius' Theory of Language*, pp. 28–31; for Scaliger, see Padley, *Grammatical Theory: Latin Tradition*, p. 63.

19. J. C. Scaliger, *De causis*, Cap. LXVII, pp. 142–143. Plato's *Cratylus*, the central text for interpretation of Plato's views on language, is discussed in Brian Vickers, "Analogy versus Identity," in Vickers, *Occult and Scientific Mentalities in the Renaissance*, pp. 97–100, where Vickers sees Plato as arguing in favor of conventionalism, contrary to popular Renaissance interpretations. Breva-Claramonte, *Sanctius' Theory of Language*, pp. 21–26, discusses the possible interpretation of the *Cratylus* as holding that language was at first natural but became conventional through corruption and change (an interpretation perhaps adopted by Epicurus and apparently held by Sanctius).

20. An earlier version, which remained little known, appeared in 1562: see Manuel Breva-Claramonte, "Sanctius' *Minerva* of 1562 and the Evolution of His Linguistic Theory," *Historiographia Linguistica* 2 (1975), 49–66; also Breva-Claramonte, *Sanctius' Theory of Language*. For another discussion of Sanctius, see Padley, *Grammatical Theory: Latin Tradition*, pp. 97–110.

21. See, in general, Salmon, "Pre-Cartesian Linguistics," pp. 172–74; Padley, *Grammatical Theory: Latin Tradition*, pp. 160–84; Robin Lakoff, "Review of *Grammaire générale et raisonée*," *Language* 45 (1969), 343–64; Herbert E. Brekle, "The Seventeenth Century," in Sebeok, *Historiography of Linguistics*, pp. 277–382, esp. pp. 330–33. Vossius is referred to in Mersenne, *Harmonie universelle*, "De la voix," p. 77; for Mersenne's relations with Campanella, see Lenoble, *Mersenne*, pp. 40–43, 154–55.

at the same time remained largely compatible with the interpretation of language employed in scholastic-Aristotelian philosophy and logic.

Whether or not adopting an Aristotelian approach, and whether or not presenting a simplified account for the purposes of elementary schooling, writers on grammar all agreed that it was something given in nature, that it reflected modes of thought which in turn reflected modes of existence. Such a view represented absolute orthodoxy.[22] Apart from Despauterius, Mersenne would have read such remarks as these in his schoolbooks: Soarez, on rhetoric, wrote that "discourse is as it were a certain image of reason"; Fonseca regarded dialectic as a study that treated not only "external discourse, but also internal"— the latter, referred to as "orationes mentis," clearly identifying speech and reason.[23] When Mersenne came to describe grammar in *La vérité des sciences,* he gave an account apparently drawn directly from school teaching on the subject, emphasizing the correlation of grammatical categories with modes of existence in the world. The Christian Philosopher tells the Sceptic that "the Art of Grammar isn't founded in air but in the nature of things," despite the fact that we cannot know essences.

> For although our words [*dictions*], which it [grammar] teaches, don't represent the essence of things, nonetheless they make us remember what we have penetrated in each thing by the force of the mind, and although we cannot found names on essence, we found them on effects, on action, on resemblance, and on the other accidents; whence it comes about that verbs signify action when they are *active,* and the *passives* [signify] passion; *participles* signify essence or existence; *pronouns,* persons, and what appertains to them. *Adverbs* [signify] the determinations of actions; *prepositions,* the relations things have with each other; *interjections* signify the passions, and the patient; and *conjunctions,* the conjunction or separation of each thing compared with another.[24]

In saying that words "make us remember what we have penetrated in each thing by the force of the mind," Mersenne means that words signify concepts which derive from the world itself. The passage as a whole makes it clear that orthodox accounts of the nature of grammar suited Mersenne because they conformed perfectly to his position on what could and could not be known about nature. Man could know the actions, appearances, and phenomenal interactions of bodies, but

22. See Breva-Claramonte, *Sanctius' Theory of Language,* chap. 2; Padley, *Grammatical Theory: Trends,* chap. 4.
23. Soarez, *De arte,* p. 13; Fonseca, *Institutiones,* p. 15. On both of these books, see Chapter 2, above.
24. Mersenne, *La vérité,* pp. 72–73.

access to their true essences belonged to God alone. Language exactly measured the difference between the two kinds of knowledge because grammatical structure already expressed knowable things. A statement's underlying grammatical form constituted a logically analyzable proposition; as Fonseca implied, the rules of grammar reflected the nature of reasoning; reasoning, working on sensory data, could express true things about the world. Language therefore provided an ideal vehicle of knowledge. Essential knowledge remained unattainable, however, just as words themselves could never grasp essences. The structure and operations of language captured the structure and operations of the visible world, but the lexical content of language—words—failed to capture the true contents of the world: that is, the essences instantiated within it.

II

While logicians argued over how words signified,[25] other scholars in this period concentrated on words themselves, using them to consider the evolution and interrelationships of languages and treating as unproblematic their reference to things and actions. J. C. Scaliger's illustrious son Joseph examined the languages of Europe in precisely this way, isolating eleven groups—four major and seven minor—and accounting for them with the idea of "parent" languages. The four major groups, he said, had each descended from a different "matrix" or "womb" language; these he labeled "Godt," "Deus," "θεος," and "Boge." Languages belonging to the same modern group displayed their affiliation through similarities between their respective words for the same things—such as God. Thus French, Spanish, and Italian, among others, all descended from the matrix language "Deus," and many common words in each language bore obvious phonological resemblances to their counterparts in the others.[26]

Scaliger's approach displays clearly how the "comparative lin-

25. On this issue, see E. J. Ashworth, *Language and Logic*, pp. 42–45; but see also esp. idem, "Do Words Signify Ideas or Things?" *Journal of the History of Philosophy* 19 (1981), 299–326, in which the author argues convincingly that the contemporary use of the term "signification" should *not* be taken as synonymous with "reference"; instead, "signify" meant "make known" or "make manifest." That is the sense in which I have used it in my discussion and in which Mersenne seems to have used it.

26. Joseph Scaliger, "Diatriba de Europaeorum linguis," in *Opuscula* (Paris, 1610), pp. 119–22. For a discussion of Scaliger's work in this field, see Daniel Droixhe, *La linguistique et l'appel de l'histoire (1600–1800)* (Geneva, 1978), pp. 60–76. J. C. Scaliger discusses consonant mutations from Greek to Latin in *De causis*, Cap. xxviii, p. 66.

guistics" of the period focused on words, not grammatical and syntactic structure, and how it could disregard as irrelevant any questions of the nature of signification and reference. Reference, grammar, and syntax could be taken in their essentials as common to all languages because they were conventionally regarded as invariant aspects of reason with a fixed relationship to the world; they therefore had no role to play in tracing ancestries. For this reason Scaliger regarded his matrix languages as entirely unrelated to one another. The assumptions behind his approach were typical: although in the seventeenth century the theory of the "Scythian" language postulated a common ancestor for most of the members of the modern Indo-European group, it too rested entirely on similarities between words.[27]

Such theories had general currency right from the beginning of the century. Claude Duret's *Thresor de l'histoire des langues de cest univers* (with an approbation dated 1607), a work known to Mersenne, provides a summary of contemporary ideas about language and languages.[28] Duret discusses Scaliger's four main European groups and adds non-European families—among them a group of languages later in the century dubbed "Semitic," between which a connection had been increasingly claimed throughout preceding decades and for which Hebrew was the "Mere et Genetrice."[29] Duret explains the process whereby languages change and branch; he points out how, in traveling from region to region throughout the world, "we find a great difference or dissemblance in the same and similar languages . . . on account of the diverse accents, mutations, additions, and detractions of certain of their letters."[30] The concept of a "mutation" of letters occurring naturally over time, and in due course engendering many languages from a common parent, formed the basis of contemporary comparative linguistics.

But another major resource both informed and motivated these discussions: the Book of Genesis. Duret headed his chapter on the matrix languages "Into how many kinds and manners of languages the Hebrew tongue was altered and changed after the confusion of

27. George J. Metcalf, "The Indo-European Hypothesis in the Sixteenth and Seventeenth Centuries," in Dell Hymes, ed., *Studies in the History of Linguistics* (Bloomington, Ind., 1974), pp. 233–57; Daniel Droixhe, "Le prototype défiguré: L'idée scythique et la France gauloise (XVIIe–XVIIIe siécles)," in Konrad Koerner, ed., *Progress in Linguistic Historiography* (Amsterdam, 1980), pp. 123–37.

28. Claude Duret, *Thresor de l'histoire des langues de cest univers*, 2d ed. (Yverdon, 1619). The work is referred to in Mersenne, *Quaestiones*, col. 23; see De Waard's note in Mersenne *Correspondance*, 2:329, which also refers to sixteenth-century works on comparative linguistics.

29. Droixhe, *La linguistique*, p. 46.

30. Duret, *Thresor*, p. 269.

the tower of Babel."[31] The two stories to which his title alludes held great importance at this time. The confusion of tongues at Babel provided the starting point for any genetic account of the development of modern languages from their antecedents; the assumption that until that time man spoke Hebrew reflected the most common opinion on the matter and connected directly with the story of Adam naming the animals. The biblical description of how God had brought all the animals before Adam so that he might assign names to them suggested to many people—especially but by no means exclusively Cabbalists—a supernatural origin for the first, original language. If Adam's naming was divinely inspired, then he could be supposed to have given to animals—and, by extension, to all other things—their *proper* names, names expressing their real natures.[32] General opinion held that man continued to use this first language after the Fall until the confusion of tongues occurred. Most of those who engaged in debate on the matter agreed that despite the appearance of many new languages at Babel, the primitive tongue had survived, and they most often identified it with Hebrew.[33] Other languages—Samaritan, and even German or Dutch—also found their supporters, but whatever the choice, its defense usually rested on the contention that it contained more radical words than any other language: the primitive, Adamic language would not have made frequent use of compounds or derived words because it gave each kind of thing a unique, proper name.[34]

The idea that words express the natures of the things they name

31. Ibid., p. 268. Joseph Scaliger's discussion is noteworthy for its lack of interest in the origins of the matrix languages. Scaliger is concerned only with going back as far as purely linguistic evidence seems to allow, not with tracing the present state of affairs from its supposed origin.

32. Paul Cornelius, *Languages in Seventeenth and Early Eighteenth Century Imaginary Voyages* (Geneva, 1965), pp. 5–23, provides a good account. This point serves as a good indication of how languages were identified with their words, especially words of concrete reference, rather than their structures.

33. Ibid. See W. Keith Percival, "The Reception of Hebrew in Sixteenth-Century Europe," *Historiographia linguistica* 11 (1984), 28, which cites Bibliander, *De ratione communi omnium linguarum et literarum* (1548), as saying that all scholars agree on Hebrew as the parent language of all others. See also Karl A. Kottman, "Fray Luis de León and the Universality of Hebrew," *Journal of the History of Philosophy* 13 (1975), 297–310. Williams, *The Common Expositor*, pp. 228–29, provides some of the etymological arguments current in this period for believing in the primitiveness of Hebrew. Duret, *Thresor*, pp. 42–43, presents the standard view.

34. See Cornelius, *Languages*, pp. 20–21. Duret, *Thresor*, p. 822, attacks Goropius for maintaining that Low German was the primitive language. Stevin made claims for Dutch on this basis: Simon Stevin, "Discourse on the Worth of the Dutch Language," in E. J. Dijksterhuis, ed., *The Principal Works of Simon Stevin* (Amsterdam, 1955), 1:58–93.

caused some divergence of interpretation. Medieval and Renaissance pedagogues adhered firmly to the Aristotelian position that words were arbitrarily imposed signs, not natural entities of some kind; this is the doctrinal division that J. C. Scaliger characterized as "Aristotle versus Plato." Writers of textbooks on grammar and logic in the sixteenth and seventeenth centuries invariably adopted the view that words came from custom, not necessity. Fonseca, in Mersenne's college dialectic text, said that words, "by which we speak together, and writing, by which we communicate with those who are absent, are signs *ex instituto*": that is, institutional, conventional.[35] Duret's discussion remains consistent with this orthodox view. Since the Fall, he says, the knowledge of the natural histories of animals contained in Hebrew names has become very obscured, but a few vestiges remain. For example, the stork, "so much praised on account of its charity towards its father and mother," is called *Chasida,* "that is, good-natured, charitable, endowed with piety." Similarly, the three names of the lion, *Ariech, Labi,* and *Laüsch,* relate to other words signifying various attributes of lions, such as ferociousness and solitude.[36] Thus Duret simply shows how Hebrew names can be said to indicate properties of things through their similarity to other Hebrew words.

Adherents to neo-Platonic, hermetic, or Cabbalistic world views all shared the opposing attitude towards words and hence adopted a more radical interpretation of Adam's naming.[37] For them, occult correspondences between things, or between things and Platonic forms, allowed words to possess resemblances to the things they signified—in a manner akin to that in which, for the Paracelsian, the liver-shaped leaf of a plant signified the plant's efficacy in curing disorders of the liver.[38] Cabbalists discovered the hidden resemblances and affinities between things through a system of numerology that assigned numbers to the letters of the Hebrew alphabet; occult connections existed between those things the names of which yielded identical sums.[39]

Mersenne took a dim view of such ideas. He regarded the arguments in favor of occult significations as a misuse of authentic Platonic

35. E. J. Ashworth, "Words," pp. 306–8; Fonseca, *Institutiones,* pp. 19–20.
36. Duret, *Thresor,* pp. 39–40.
37. Vickers, "Analogy versus Identity," uses these attributes as hallmarks of an "occult" mentality; it is questionable, however, whether a discrete "mentality" is the best concept to apply here.
38. Walter Pagel, *Paracelsus* (Basel, 1958), pp. 50–53, 148–49.
39. Gershom Scholem, *Kabbalah* (Jerusalem, 1974), pp. 196–203; Lenoble, *Mersenne,* pp. 96–103.

doctrine and ridiculed the Cabbalistic number games, calling the study of the Cabbala a waste of time.[40] Accordingly, he interpreted the stories in Genesis quite differently. In his early works he did lend some credence to the notion that Adam's prelapsarian language had carried insight into the essences of things. We cannot know essences, he said in *La verité des sciences,* but God could have made words uniquely fit for signifying them and could have given those words to Adam. Thus, "perhaps the names Adam imposed had this privilege," but "since that time names have withdrawn so much from their first origin that we no longer recognize any vestige of it."[41] By the time *Harmonie universelle* appeared in 1636, however, Mersenne had moved away from his previous position of compromise. Possibly influenced by some remarks of Descartes in a letter of 1629, he now denied that words could, even in principle, correspond naturally with essences. Descartes, apparently in response to a query from Mersenne, wrote that involuntary utterances like laughing or crying, which are the same in all languages, might be called "natural" signifiers; nonetheless, "when I see the sky or the earth, that doesn't oblige me to name them in one fashion rather than in another, and I believe that it would be the same even if we had original justice [i.e., before the Fall]."[42] Mersenne echoed the point:

> The sound of words has no such correspondence with things natural, moral, and supernatural that their pronunciation alone could make us understand their nature or their properties, because sounds and movements are not characters attached to the things that they represent ... the names that Adam imposed on animals are in their nature as indifferent to signify stones or trees as animals, as would be agreed if one examined judiciously the Hebrew or Chaldean vocables, which are held to have been pronounced by Adam, since the letters, the syllables, and their pronunciation are indifferent, and signify nothing other than what we wish.[43]

40. Yates, *Giordano Bruno,* pp. 434–35; Lenoble, *Mersenne,* pp. 97, 102n.1. Mersenne called the Cabbala a waste of time in *Quaestiones,* col. 282; this was one of many remarks that raised the ire of Robert Fludd in his *Sophiae cum moria certamen . . .* (Frankfurt, 1629), p. 115.

41. Mersenne, *La verité,* p. 71. On this point generally, see Lenoble, *Mersenne,* p. 514, and Crombie, "Mersenne," esp. pp. 319–20.

42. Descartes to Mersenne, 18 December 1629, in Mersenne *Correspondance,* 2:352. This distinction between the two kinds of utterance was the standard scholastic "natural" versus "ad placitum": see E. J. Ashworth, *Language and Logic,* p. 41.

43. Mersenne, *Harmonie universelle,* "De la voix," p. 65.

Harmonie universelle frequently opposes the idea that words can have natural signification.[44] The reasons for Mersenne's antagonism seem quite clear: the notion deviated from school orthodoxy and formed a part of magical and naturalistic doctrines. As Jacob Boehme soon demonstrated, attributing occult as well as referential signification to words and denying their arbitrary institution connected readily with the most extreme kinds of enthusiasm.[45] Furthermore, since natural signification implied knowledge of essences, it jarred with Mersenne's general epistemological position. In *La verité* the Christian Philosopher replies to the Sceptic's arguments about the uncertainty and unreliability of names by mocking their premises: "As regards the names that we give to things, I agree with you that there are some that are very badly imposed, and I complain particularly about some surnames, which are so dirty, and so improper, that one must redden with shame in pronouncing them, or even in thinking of them."[46] Mersenne thus rejects as meaningless the proposition that sounds can in themselves be more or less fit to express particular ideas. In fact, he says, "names serve us only to comprehend and signify what we want to say, and what we have in the mind."[47] He cites as an example the widely different words in Greek, Latin, and Italian that denote hitting someone. He then asks why, if words can be suitable to their objects, one might not also signify "the song of the partridge by *cacare*, on account of its voice, which imitates this word [*diction*]."[48] The remark, made in French, assumes a knowledge of Latin: *cacare* means "to defecate."

Mersenne's remarks in *Harmonie universelle* about the origin of language interpret the Biblical stories accordingly. Tacitly accepting Hebrew as mankind's first language, he comments on "the simplicity of the first inhabitants of the earth, who, having need of only a small number of things, invented only a small number of words [*vocables*]."[49] J. C. Scaliger had made an identical observation, apparently to illuminate the nature of language itself rather than to shed light on true historical origins: words were human institutions established to

---

44. E.g., ibid., pp. 10–11.
45. On Boehme and words, see Hans Aarsleff, "Leibniz on Locke on Language," in *From Locke to Saussure*, pp. 60–61; Alexandre Koyré, *La philosophie de Jacob Boehme* (Paris, 1929), esp. pp. 457–62.
46. Mersenne, *La verité*, p. 69.
47. Ibid.
48. Ibid., p. 70.
49. Mersenne, *Harmonie universelle*, "De la voix," p. 74.

serve human needs.[50] In both *La verité* and *Harmonie universelle* Mersenne discusses the traditional suggestion that the cultural characteristics of a people, including language, express the temperament (or
balance of bodily humors) appropriate to their geographical location.
Most notably elaborated in the sixteenth century by Jean Bodin, the
theory accounted for the difference between, for example, Germans
and Italians in terms of northern and southern locations with their
respective climatic and astrological peculiarities.[51] Mersenne concludes that "different manners of speaking . . . depend more on institution and custom than on temperament";[52] in either case, however, language (identified with words) remains a part of culture, not a
key to the natures of things, and still conforms to orthodox Aristotelian doctrine.

Mersenne also ruled out a different kind of apparently "natural"
signification. Doing so reduced still further the credibility of essentialist and correspondence theories of language, while sharpening the
scholastic-Aristotelian concept of signification itself. Descartes's letter
of 1629 had referred to sounds such as laughing and crying, or animal noises, as, in a sense, "natural."[53] Mersenne set out to establish
that even such utterances as these bore no necessary relation to the
things they signified. Words, he argued, are more than just utterances: thus, when birds learn to pronounce words, they can have no
understanding of their meaning, uttering them only "when nature
and appearances [*especes,* i.e., sensory input] excite them, and prompt
them to it."[54] Only man can form the voice into a word, since "the

50. Stéfanini, "Scaliger," p. 322. This use of accounts of historical origins parallels
that of the philosophes in the eighteenth century: the point was to illuminate the
present situation by showing how it *could* have come about. On the eighteenth century,
see Aarsleff, "The Tradition of Condillac," pp. 146–209, esp. 161. Mersenne himself
engages in just this kind of argument in *Harmonie universelle,* "De la voix," p. 11.

51. Jean Bodin, *La méthode de l'histoire,* a translation by Pierre Mesnard of *Methodus ad
facilem historiarum cognitionem* [1576] (Algiers, 1941), pp. 69–122; see, e.g., Mersenne,
La verité, p. 71.

52. Mersenne, *Harmonie universelle,* "De la voix," p. 61. Mersenne echoed this opinion in his manuscript continuation of *Quaestiones:* see quotation in Lenoble, *Mersenne,* p.
517n.5.

53. There are similar statements in the "Discours de la méthode," *Oeuvres de Descartes,* 6:58. Language was usually taken to be an attribute unique to man (reflecting its
identification with reason), so this kind of "natural signification" was generally regarded as not being a proper part of true language. Duret (*Thresor,* p. 21), like Aristotle,
held this position. Lenoble (*Mersenne,* pp. 155–56) emphasizes Mersenne's desire to use
language as a demarcation criterion between man and animals so as to counter the
claims of "naturalists" like Pomponazzi.

54. Mersenne, *Harmonie universelle,* "De la voix," p. 52.

word [*parole*] cannot be formed in discourse except by the mind [*esprit*]."[55] Therefore, the jargon of birds "isn't worthy of the name of word [*parole*], if we take it in the same signification as the Latins take *verbum*, which ought to be pronounced with intention to signify by each word the things for which they have been invented."[56] In short, true signification required intentionality. The "different voices that serve to express the passions of the soul . . . are as natural to man as to other animals," but they do not have privileged, or natural, signification of their appropriate passions because, just as with genuine words, "the art and reason we have could not furnish us with the same voices that serve us naturally to express our passions, if we had lost the use of them." No doubt human cries, like those of animals, arise from some unknown necessity related to the inner workings of the passions, but such sounds are "as indifferent to signify the said passions, as are our words [*paroles*] to signify our conceptions, or the other things of which we wish to speak."[57] Signification thus required both intentionality and the use of reason; that is why the possession of language differentiated man from beasts. A causal, physiological connection between a passion and an utterance therefore failed by itself to qualify that sound as a signifier. Even if we should decide to use the utterance to signify its associated passion and thereby to make it a signifier, it would still not be a *natural* signifier. A thing is called "natural," says Mersenne, "because it is conformed to the principles and the nature of each thing." Consequently, we cannot show that

---

55. Ibid., p. 10. This remark resembles J. C. Scaliger's distinction (*De causis*, Cap. 1 pp. 2–3) between *vox* (equivalent to Aristotelian "matter") and *dictio* (*vox* plus meaning, the "form," giving *dictio*, the "substance"). Padley, *Grammatical Theory: Latin Tradition*, pp. 62–63, is to be read with caution on this point, owing to an apparent misunderstanding of the Aristotelian term "form."

56. Mersenne, *Harmonie universelle*, "De la voix," pp. 10–11.

57. Ibid., pp. 12, 14. On Mersenne's exploitation of the relation of the passions to sounds in his quest for a form of music that would have determinate effects on its hearers, see Dean T. Mace, "Marin Mersenne on Language and Music," *Journal of Music Theory* 14 (1970), 2–35; and Crombie, "Mathematics, Music." This "musique accentuelle" is also discussed by André Robinet, *Le langage à l'âge classique* (Paris, 1978), p. 131; this book is a Foucault-influenced treatment of ideas about language as a system of signs in the seventeenth and eighteenth centuries. Michel Foucault, *Les mots et les choses*—translated as *The Order of Things* (New York, 1973)—with its distinction between the view of verbal signs as "resemblances" in the sixteenth century and as "representations" in the "classical age" is unhelpful for my purposes, owing to the unnuanced nature of the periodization. On this point, see Hans Aarsleff's introduction to *From Locke to Saussure*, esp. 22–23. Foucault is also criticized in Sidonie Claus, "John Wilkins' Essay toward a Real Character," *Journal of the History of Ideas* 43 (1982), 531–53, which points out that debate on language schemes in the seventeenth century, far from exhibiting a monolithic conception of words as representations, was lively and divided.

something is natural to a body, since "this demonstration supposes the perfect knowledge of the animal, or body, which man cannot have in this world."[58] Mersenne means that a cry of fear, for instance, might be only an *accidental* attribute of fearfulness, not conformed to its essential principles. His argument shows clearly his exploitation of Aristotelian ontological concepts and categories even as it rejects Aristotelian epistemological assumptions.

For Aristotle and his scholastic followers, words related to the world by means of abstract mental concepts. The mind induced universals from sensory data and thereby determined species of things in the world; these natural species were the entities to which names had to be assigned. This account assumed that all members of a given species created the same concept in the minds of all observers. Thus mental concepts were themselves signs. They were distinct from words; unlike words—indeed, uniquely—they were truly *natural* signs because they necessarily conformed to the essences or principles of the things giving rise to them. "Concepts are natural signs of those things that they signify," wrote Fonseca. "For concepts, as Aristotle says, are the same with everyone."[59]

Mersenne, however, although he seems to have believed that any given sensory input creates the same conception in all minds,[60] rejected the idea that this psychological process succeeds in abstracting an object's specific nature. The mind learns only of the external, manifest properties of individuals. Naming is thus somewhat more problematic, because "it is most certain that the sounds [*dictions*] of all the languages that have existed or are still in usage in the entire world do not suffice to give each thing a name that will be proper and particular to it."[61] This point "ought to be understood of all the parts of a body, and of all individuals, and their parts." As a result, we are "constrained to use general terms [*vocables*] to signify particular things."[62] Mersenne's rejection of essentialism meant that such terms could be applied only to appearances, on a pragmatic basis. Summing up his views on names and naming in *La verité* and referring to the systematic artificial invention of new words, Mersenne said that it

58. Mersenne, *Harmonie universelle*, "De la voix," p. 15.

59. Fonseca, *Institutiones*, pp. 19–20.

60. In his *L'usage de la raison*, p. 118, Mersenne had noted in passing, while discussing the understanding and the will, that "as for language, if the external words [*paroles exterieures;* cf. Fonseca, *Institutiones*, p. 15] are Greek, Latin, or French, those of the mind are all the same." See also his discussion of the reliability of the senses in *La verité*, p. 191.

61. Mersenne, *Harmonie universelle*, "De la voix," p. 72.

62. Ibid., p. 73.

would be possible to form "as many diverse sounds [*dictions*] as there are diverse individuals in the world." However, "one cannot invent any that signify the nature and essence of things, inasmuch as we do not know it."[63]

Grammar, being semantically based and reflective of the outward relations between things, enabled language to act as a vehicle for expressing limited truths about the world, but language could never be isomorphic with nature, because Mersenne denied that words could signify essences. A number of implications followed. While entertaining the possibility of a universal language, Mersenne rejected attempts by contemporaries to develop a philosophical language expressing the true constitution of nature. That rejection in turn involved the idea of "method."

III

The hierarchical structure of faculties in the medieval university, the ordered curriculum of the Jesuit colleges, indeed, any educational scheme of the Middle Ages or Renaissance instantiated the encyclopedic ideal, the systematic arrangement of all knowledge. Mersenne's table in *Quaestiones in Genesim* reflects the same tendency.[64] During the sixteenth century, however, the encyclopedia had become more and more associated with "method."[65] The most famous exponent of method, Petrus Ramus, viewed it as essentially pedagogical; he furthered it not only by promoting his famous logic of dichotomies but also by placing a renewed emphasis on the establishment of rigid boundaries between disciplines.[66] Schemes of pedagogical reform similar to Ramus's (and there were many in the late sixteenth and early seventeenth centuries) all put forward plans of the layout and interrelations of knowledge as didactic methods. But their promoters regarded them as more than that, seeing them also as reflections of the genuine structure of knowledge and hence of the world. This vision of knowledge as a unified, interconnected system played a

---

63. Mersenne, *La verité*, p. 71. Slaughter presents the incorrect implication that Mersenne envisaged an essentialist philosophical language: Slaughter, *Universal Languages*, pp. 129–30.

64. Mersenne, *Quaestiones*, cols. 1205–10.

65. Gilbert, *Renaissance Concepts of Method*; E. Garin, *L'éducation de l'homme moderne*, pp. 190–216; Paolo Rossi, *Clavis universalis* (Milan, 1960), pp. 179–200; Frances A. Yates, *The Art of Memory* (Chicago, 1966), esp. chap. 10, "Ramism as an Art of Memory."

66. Ong, *Ramus*, esp. chap. 7; W. S. Howell, *Logic and Rhetoric in England, 1500–1700* (Princeton, 1956), pp. 151–52.

prominent role in seventeenth-century thought, and it encouraged suggestions for a language structured in the same way.[67]

Johann Amos Comenius, perhaps the preeminent seventeenth-century pedagogical projector, called his scheme *pansophia*, or "universal wisdom." *Pansophia* expressed both the organic unity of all knowledge and its availability to the human mind, and the juxtaposition of these two aspects involved a correspondence between language and the world: "For the divisions of things and words are the same; whoever sees the proportions of words in turn observes them more easily in things."[68] Comenius thus demonstrated how the view of all knowledge as unified related to the idea of a "philosophical language" reflecting reality; later, in his *Via lucis*, he advocated the construction of such a language.[69]

Far from being idiosyncratic, Comenius's linguistic interpretation of the unity of knowledge typified the period. Descartes, in another letter of 1629, replied to Mersenne's query about the possibility of a philosophical language:

> The invention of this language depends on the true philosophy, for it is impossible otherwise to enumerate all the thoughts of men, and to put them in order, or merely to distinguish them in such a way that they will be clear and simple, which is in my opinion the greatest secret that one could have to acquire true science [*la bonne science*]. And if someone had explicated well what are the simple ideas that are in the imagination of men, which compose all that they think, and that [explication] was received by everyone, I would dare to hope as a consequence for a universal language very easy to learn, to pronounce and to write, and, what's most important, that would aid the judgment, representing all things to it so distinctly that it would be almost impossible for it to err. . . .
>
> Now, I hold that this language is possible, and that one can find the science on which it depends, by means of which peasants could better judge the truth of things than the philosophers do now.[70]

67. See in general Padley, *Grammatical Theory: Trends*, chap. 5.
68. Johann Amos Comenius, *Linguarum methodus novissima* (1648), in *Veškeré Spisy* (Brno, 1911), 6:265. On *pansophia*, see E. Garin, *L'éducation*, pp. 212–14; Klaus Schaller, *Die Pädagogik des Johann Amos Comenius* (Heidelberg, 1967), esp. pp. 17–46.
69. For Comenius on language, see Padley, *Grammatical Theory: Trends*, pp. 336–49, which shows clearly the integration of Comenius's linguistic ideas with the vision behind *pansophia*; also Vivian Salmon, "Language-Planning in Seventeenth-Century England," in C. E. Bazell et al., *In Memory of J. R. Firth* (London, 1966), pp. 370–97; Brekle, "The Seventeenth Century," pp. 318–24 and references; Heinrich Geissler, *Comenius und die Sprache* (Heidelberg, 1959), esp. pp. 149–59; John Edward Sadler, *J. A. Comenius and the Concept of Universal Education* (London, 1966), pp. 149–58; Slaughter, *Universal Languages*, pp. 97–103.
70. Descartes to Mersenne, 20 November 1629, in Mersenne *Correspondance*, 2:328.

Descartes concluded by reflecting that it would be too much to expect for this language actually to come into currency, but he clearly considered its invention quite possible. The "science on which it depends" refers, of course, to something resulting from Descartes's own method, a method presupposing the deductive unity and completeness of all knowledge.

Mersenne objected to universal methods and to philosophical languages because they both supposed the accessibility of essentialist knowledge. He makes this plain in *La verité des sciences*, in a discussion of Francis Bacon's recently published *Novum Organum*.[71] Although himself an advocate of empirical practices, Mersenne is clearly unimpressed by Bacon's design, and his most fundamental criticism concerns the kind of knowledge Bacon seeks. The method, he says, cannot achieve the ends to which Bacon directs it: "Although one may anatomize, and dissolve bodies as much as one wishes, whether by fire, by water, or by the force of the mind, one will never arrive at the point of rendering our intellect equal to the nature of things. That is why I believe that Verulam's design is impossible, and that these instructions [i.e., Bacon's method] will be causes of nothing other than some new experiences which one will be able to explain easily by the ordinary philosophy."[72] Mersenne seems especially to have in mind here Book 2 of the *Novum Organum*, which gives examples of the method in action. Bacon's talk of "latent process," "latent configuration," simple natures, and the particles of bodies obviously violated Mersenne's conviction that the human mind cannot penetrate beyond appearances.[73] Unlike Mersenne's friend Gassendi, who advocated atomism only as a hypothesis, Bacon thought that he could discover the true natures of things rather than merely catalogue new phenomena. Bacon gave his account of the structure of matter as if it followed necessarily from the method itself, but Mersenne considered Bacon's explanations to be no improvement over "the ordinary philosophy," commenting on the "thousand other conceptions that we can have of all possible phenomena, by which the actions of natural

71. Mersenne, *La verité*, pp. 206–18. For discussion of that material, see Lenoble, *Mersenne*, pp. 329–31; Gaston Sortais, *La philosophie moderne depuis Bacon jusqu'à Leibniz* (Paris, 1920), 1:468–69. Mersenne may have criticized Bacon at the *cabinet* of the Dupuy brothers: see Philippe Fortin de la Hoguette to Pierre Dupuy, 1626, in Mersenne *Correspondance*, 1:379, and De Waard's note.

72. Mersenne, *La verité*, pp. 212–13.

73. See, e.g., Francis Bacon, *The New Organon*, trans. James Spedding (Indianapolis, Ind., 1960), p. 121; and Paolo Rossi, *Francis Bacon*, trans. Sacha Rabinovitch (Chicago, 1968), pp. 13–16.

things can be explained."[74] His criticism of Bacon's views on words followed the same lines.

Bacon enumerated as one of his four chief obstacles to knowledge the "Idols of the Market Place," the "ill and unfit imposition of words" which "wonderfully obstructs the understanding."[75] He considered that words not only signify concepts but also, to some extent, govern them, because they reflect and turn back "their force upon the understanding" and "are commonly applied according to the comprehension of the vulgar, and divide things by lines most obvious to the vulgar understanding."[76] Thus words obstruct the understanding if the concepts to which they attach are badly formed: that is, if they fail to classify things according to their true natures. Mersenne's reaction to this may be guessed from his mocking remarks, quoted earlier, about surnames and partridges. Words, he believed, are neither suitable nor unsuitable to the things they name, being merely arbitrary labels. In opposing Bacon, Mersenne asserted that "it matters very little how we speak, provided that we understand what we express by our ways of speaking, for words signify nothing other than what we wish."[77] He could ignore Bacon's points because their validity depended on the idea that names could and should attach to natural kinds. Like Bacon, Mersenne apparently assumed that under proper conditions of observation an object engendered the same concept in the minds of all observers. Unlike Bacon, however, he thought that names grouped individuals together solely on the basis of perceived similarities and pragmatic association. Man could not assign names to natural kinds because he was unable to perceive essential natures.

The proliferation in the seventeenth century of schemes and suggestions for philosophical languages (one thinks first of John Wilkins's *Essay* and the sketches of Leibniz) arose from the ambitions of those who—like Comenius, Bacon, and Descartes—in rejecting scholastic Aristotelianism, tried to replace it with other essentialist systems of

74. Mersenne, *La vérité*, p. 213. On the status of Gassendi's atomism, see Olivier René Bloch, *La philosophie de Gassendi* (The Hague, 1971), pp. 160–62; Popkin, *History of Scepticism*, pp. 141–46.

75. *Novum Organum*, vol. 1 of *The Works of Francis Bacon*, ed. J. Spedding, R. L. Ellis, and D. D. Heath (Boston, 1861), 1.43, p. 252. I deviate from Spedding's translation in Bacon, *New Organon*, p. 49; in particular, I translate *impositio* by "imposition" in place of Spedding's "choice." For Bacon on language, see Rossi, *Francis Bacon*, pp. 166–72; Brekle, "The Seventeenth Century," pp. 281–87; Slaughter, *Universal Languages*, pp. 85–97; Padley, *Grammatical Theory: Trends*, pp. 325–31.

76. Bacon, *Novum Organum*, 1.59, p. 262; I again deviate from Spedding's translation in Bacon, *New Organon*, p. 56.

77. Mersenne, *La vérité*, p. 209.

their own.[78] Descartes, for example, may have sought his essentialist accounts of the world in the quasi-mechanical interaction of particles instead of the scholastics' forms, substances, and causes, but the goal remained the same: to comprehend rationally the nature and workings of the world with absolute certainty; to know the world as God knows it. And in trying to emulate Aristotle and usurp Aristotle's place in the schools by developing a complete description and explanation of everything, using his universal method, Descartes also envisaged the possibility of a philosophical language that would be isomorphic with the structure of knowledge itself. The new essentialist philosophies of the seventeenth century in fact anticipated following the same route as scholastic Aristotelians.[79] The latter already had their own philosophical language, suited to their own kind of philosophy; indeed, scholasticism might be characterized as a mode of discourse based on a Latin taught explicitly as the proper medium of philosophical discussion and logical analysis. Purporting to speak of things absolutely, according to their true natures, scholastic Aristotelianism used names to designate natural kinds. Furthermore, as discussed above, scholastic Latin appeared in medieval textbooks as a grammatical system fully integrated with and explicated in terms of Aristotelian philosophy. Parsing a sentence correctly meant giving a philosophically correct account of the things of which it spoke; a statement could not, therefore, be correct grammatically without also being correct philosophically.[80] The Latin of scholastic Aristotelians was intended, as Descartes said of his own imagined philosophical language, to represent all things to the judgment "so distinctly that it would be almost impossible for it to err."

Mersenne discounted the possibility of a philosophical language because he discounted the feasibility of the kind of philosophical system that would have to underpin it. Descartes and many other anti-

78. In the considerable literature on Wilkins's scheme, the most recent treatments are Padley, *Grammatical Theory: Trends*, pp. 357–78; and Slaughter, *Universal Languages*, pp. 157–74, which provide many additional references. On Leibniz, see Louis Couturat, *La logique de Leibniz* (Paris, 1901), pp. 51–80, "La langue universelle"; also D. P. Walker, "Leibniz and Language," *Journal of the Warburg and Courtauld Institutes* 35 (1972), 294–307.

79. Aarsleff, introduction to *From Locke to Saussure*, p. 13, calls Wilkins's scheme an "anomaly" in light of Wilkins's otherwise apparently antiessentialist position; however, the great attractions of a philosophical language would seem to be confirmed by the "anomaly" itself.

80. Appropriate caveats to these generalizations center on a precise definition of "scholastic Aristotelianism": I mean broadly Thomist or Scotist scholastics, rather than nominalists (who still count as scholastics), and I exclude that brand of Aristotelianism, widespread in sixteenth century Italy, usually associated especially with Padua and usually described as "Averroist" (see Chapter 1, above).

scholastics retained the scholastic-Aristotelian explanatory ideal; all those who sought a philosophical language necessarily did so. Mersenne did not. He rejected the vision of all knowledge as a unified, interconnected edifice for which a correct, universal method (in the versions characteristic of the sixteenth and seventeenth centuries) could provide a means of negotiating. Comenius's all-encompassing *pansophia* and its concomitant philosophical language, *panglottia,* stood for a cognitive agenda quite different from Mersenne's.

In 1639 Mersenne received from London a copy of Comenius's recently published *Prodromus,* a work containing a version of the author's pansophic scheme.[81] He took special note of its final part, entitled "Conatuum pansophicorum dilucidatio," which describes the layout of a temple that serves to display the various branches of knowledge in ordered array according to its architectural plan.[82] Clearly reflecting the classical art of memory, the scheme nevertheless goes further in that Comenius intends it to express the *true* arrangement of knowledge rather than simply to provide a mnemonic aid.[83] On receipt of the book, Mersenne wrote a polite letter to its author, to be sent via Theodore Haak in London. Very formal, its Latin much more elaborate than Mersenne's usual style, the letter carefully skirted the central features of Comenius's ideas. Mersenne suggested in the accompanying letter to Haak that "Mr. Amos" should be alerted to the systematic works of Gassendi and Descartes, a remark indicating his view of Comenius's work as just another ambitious encyclopedic scheme with little to choose between it and the rest. He also observed to Haak, rather dryly, that "this kind of book usually sells well."[84] To Comenius himself, however, his tone was different. Treating the pansophic scheme as if it were nothing more than a compendium of knowledge (of the sort that he produced himself), Mersenne offered both to assist in publication of further such efforts and to send some things to help with Comenius's project, "such as what pertains to light, catoptrics, harmony, the prodigies of magnets, and motion." He made only one properly philosophical point: "It will be best, if I am not mistaken, if first you communicate to the literary world those common notions of the soul which you seem to have

81. See D. P. Walker, *The Ancient Theology* (London, 1972), pp. 173–74; Rossi, *Clavis universalis,* pp. 187–88; E. Garin, *L'éducation,* pp. 208–9.

82. Johann Amos Comenius, *Pansophiae prodromus* (London, 1639).

83. See Yates, *Art of Memory,* chap. 17 and passim.

84. Mersenne to Comenius, 1 November 1639, Mersenne *Correspondance,* 8:575–78; Mersenne to Haak, 1 November 1639, ibid., pp. 583, 581. See also Salmon, "Language-Planning," p. 390.

gathered for the basis of the entire work"; this recommendation appears again in Mersenne's other letter to Comenius a year later.[85]

Comenius's "common notions" corresponded exactly to the standard scholastic and Aristotelian category, comprising such metaphysical truths as "the whole is greater than its proper part"; however, he regarded them as of a kind with and the source of the whole subsequent edifice of knowledge (as is, in its way, also true of Descartes). For Mersenne, however, "common notions" related only indirectly to the task of discovering the contingent organization of the world.[86] Comenius intended his pansophic scheme to be absolute, like the classifications of a philosophical language, but Mersenne could not accord to either one any greater status than that of a division of convenience. Mersenne's interest in Comenius's ideas seems to have arisen chiefly from their pedagogical aims and, as D. P. Walker has suggested, from a sympathy with the irenical aspects of Comenius's project.[87] A genuine intellectual rapport never existed.

Mersenne's own views on language, by contrast, focused on its instrumental role as a tool for manipulating empirical data and encompassing the diversity found in nature—for mirroring, in effect, human experience and its limitations. Above all, it served as a means of communication, a central concern pinpointed in *La verité des sciences*. Mersenne expressed regret for the diversity of languages, "which began at the confusion of the tower of Babel to the great detriment of the sciences, for if there were only one language in the world, one would intercommunicate the sciences more easily and would employ all the time in learning them that one [now] spends studying foreign languages."[88] He explained his production of the Latin *Harmonicorum libri* in 1636 as a means of presenting material from *Harmonie universelle* to foreigners, a decision reflecting the status of Latin as the unchallenged international language of scholars.[89]

85. Mersenne *Correspondance*, 8:576–77. Comenius locates his "common notions" at the door of the temple; they are, he says, those principles from which particular sciences flow as rivers: Comenius, *Prodromus*, pp. 276–77. The subsequent letter is Mersenne to Comenius, 22 November 1640, Mersenne *Correspondance*, 10:263–74, esp. 264.

86. See the discussion in Mersenne, *La verité*, pp. 52–53.

87. Walker, *Ancient Theology*, p. 174; see also Mersenne's second letter to Comenius (n. 85, above). Irenicism became increasingly important for Mersenne during the 1630s and 1640s; see Chapter 8, below.

88. Mersenne, *La verité*, p. 72.

89. Mersenne, *Harmonicorum libri*, second page of original dedication to Montmor (the 1648 volume is a reissue of the material published in 1636 with some additions, including a new, extra dedication to Montmor). James R. Knowlson echoes the familiar story of the rise of vernaculars and decline of Latin in the seventeenth century in his

With the exception of *Harmonie universelle*, all Mersenne's more formal, less discursive treatments of mathematical subjects (whether compendia of the works of others or material of his own) appeared in Latin. Conversely, his choice of French for *L'impieté des deistes* and many subsequent works aimed at extending his audience among native French speakers.[90] However, he also considered the possibility of an *artificial* language deliberately adapted to the demands of a natural philosophy that concentrated on appearances and empirical reports.

Mersenne's discussions of an artificial language dealt almost exclusively with the construction of words; grammar presented no problem, because it already expressed the very relations between objects and their attributes that Mersenne took to be the appropriate subject matter of a workable natural philosophy. Now, words themselves could never group objects into natural kinds; at root, they were simply arbitrary labels. Mersenne explained in *Harmonie universelle* why even artificial words designed to encode the phenomenological properties of their referents failed to escape this conclusion:

> For one can give as many different names to water as there are other bodies in nature to which it can be compared, be it in hardness, or in weight; for example, if one compares it to gold, it will be necessary to give it a name that expresses that it is nineteen times lighter than gold, and to compose other names that express by how much it is more or less light or heavy than all the other bodies of which one can say the same thing as for water. From which it follows that as many different words [*dictions*] would be necessary to signify the relative properties of each body as there are different things in nature.[91]

Absolute attributes could not be signified because that would require a knowledge of their true natures: in order to signify the weight of a body without reference to another body, the cause and nature of

---

Universal Language Schemes in England and France, 1600–1800 (Toronto, 1975), pp. 27–32; as does Salmon, "Language-Planning," p. 371. The frequent implication of such accounts, that scholars ceased to know Latin and hence could no longer use it for international communication, is patently false; rather, the potential market for intellectual discourse became larger, including those sorts of people who had *never* been very conversant with Latin. This process can be seen in the case of Théophraste Renaudot's *Conférences*, in the 1630s and 1640s, weekly gatherings in Paris to which anyone could come and participate in intellectual discussion; Renaudot explicitly forbade the use of Latin in favor of French. See Howard M. Solomon, *Public Welfare, Science and Propaganda in Seventeenth Century France* (Princeton, 1972), p. 64.

90. Claude Bredeau commented on Mersenne's use of French for *L'impieté* in a letter to Mersenne of 24 October 1624, Bredeau resolving henceforth to write his letters to Mersenne in French: Mersenne *Correspondance*, 1:181.

91. Mersenne, *Harmonie universelle*, "De la voix," p. 74.

"heaviness" would have to be known. Consequently, labels could signify only relative properties, and the choice of standards of comparison, being arbitrary, would result in the names themselves having only a conventional relationship to attributes of the things named. With one notable exception, therefore (to be considered later), Mersenne concentrated on the systematic invention of arbitrary labels.

For reasons connected as much with his mathematical as his linguistic interests, Mersenne examined the implications of generating verbal labels using combinatorial techniques. He had adopted the approach in *La verité* when considering one of his favorite questions: what is the most beautiful tune possible on a given subject?[92] To render it manageable, Mersenne reduced the problem to one of determining the most beautiful tune that could be constructed from the five notes spanning a fifth, each note appearing only once. His somewhat aesthetically unsatisfying solution stopped at finding a way of ensuring a complete enumeration of the possible combinations; the combinatorial aspect really justified the whole exercise. Mersenne wrote down all 120 serial combinations of the notes designated *sol, fa, mi, re, ut* and regarded the problem as solved. Deciding which among them fulfilled the desideratum was an uninteresting matter of comparing and judging between them subjectively. He then generalized the procedure to greater numbers of notes, observing that the more notes used, the more impractical it became to list every combination. Therefore, he said, "I will content myself by putting here the number of tunes [*chans*] that can be found in all sorts of numbers of strings, sounds or voices, from 1 to 50."[93] That in itself constituted a lengthy table.[94] He characterized the exercise (repeated in *Harmonie universelle*) as an application of "*combinations,* in how many ways each multitude of things can be exchanged."[95]

Its application to words followed easily, except that Mersenne recognized an important difference: as he argued most forcibly in *Questions harmoniques*, music was essentially a study of reason;[96] a study of the natural world, by contrast, was empirical and involved a countless number of individuals. Whereas combinatorics delimited the field of investigation in music by determining the number and character of all the objects within it, words named an indeterminate number of things always liable to increase because contingent on God's will. Some propo-

92. Mersenne, *La verité*, pp. 544–45.
93. Ibid., pp. 546–48.
94. Ibid., pp. 549–50.
95. Ibid., p. 548.
96. Mersenne, *Questions harmoniques*, p. 235.

sitions in *Harmonie universelle,* however, showed the role combinatorics could play in establishing control even over such an indeterminate and open-ended field of inquiry. Although similarly open-ended, the combinatorial generation of words was nonetheless contrastingly *determinate.* Mersenne specified verbal brevity as the first requirement of the ideal language: "I say that the best language of all possible ought to be composed of all the words [*dictions*] that can be made from one letter, and then those of two, three, and four letters, until there was a sufficient number of words to express all the things that can be known and of which one can speak."[97] Employing combinatoric rules, Mersenne then calculated the number of words producible from sequences of vowels and consonants of given lengths. Observing that all existing languages in the world were together insufficient to provide a separate name for every individual thing, he noted that, nonetheless, an unlimited number of artificial names could in principle be invented to do the job. If God chose to create extra individuals, one could always develop new names by increasing the maximum number of letters allowed in a word.[98]

Ernest Coumet and Eberhard Knobloch have shown that Mersenne's combinatoric rules in *La verité* bear close affinities with those given in Clavius's commentary on *De sphaera,* which Mersenne studied at La Flèche; additional results presented in *Harmonie universelle* can be found in Cardano and others.[99] On one level Mersenne's application of combinatorics to language (as well as to music) reflects a lifelong interest in recreational mathematics. On another level, however, the association appears quite natural: Cabbalists and Lullists themselves employed versions of combinatorial rules in their examinations of the occult properties of words.[100] References to Cabbalism seem, in fact, to

97. Mersenne, *Harmonie universelle,* "De la voix," p. 66.

98. Ibid., pp. 72–73. See Ernest Coumet, "Mersenne: 'Dictions' nouvelles à l'infini," *XVIIᵉ siècle,* no. 109 (1975), 26–30, discussing Mersenne's idea with perhaps too imprecise a sense of its significance. It should be noted that Mersenne's position was not that of a nominalist; he did not deny the reality of true universals but simply doubted the possibility of coming to know them.

99. Eberhard Knobloch, "Marin Mersennes Beiträge zur Kombinatorik," *Sudhoffs Archiv* 58 (1974), 356–79, esp. 360–62, drawing on E. Coumet, "Mersenne: Dénombrements, répertoires, numérotations de permutations," *Mathématiques et sciences humaines* 10 (1972), 5–37. See also Coumet, "Mersenne: 'Dictions' nouvelles," perhaps the best treatment from a contextual rather than mathematical point of view; Eberhard Knobloch, "*Musurgia universalis,*" *History of Science* 17 (1979), 261–66. Also on Clavius and combinatorics, see Charles Naux, "Le père Christophore Clavius (1537–1612);" *Revue des questions scientifiques* 154 (1983), 339–41. Other contemporary, properly mathematical treatments of combinatoric problems are noted by De Waard in Mersenne *Correspondance,* 5:139–40.

100. Coumet, "Mersenne: 'Dictions' nouvelles," pp. 5–12; also Knowlson, *Universal Language Schemes,* p. 84. Apart from the long discussions of Cabbalism in *Quaestiones,*

have been common in contemporary discussions of language. Duret, as we saw earlier, dealt with it at great length (more than fifty pages), and in addition to listing the twenty-two letters of the Hebrew alphabet, known as the Ziruphs, he recorded the Cabbalists' calculation that these letters admitted of 112,400,259,082,719,680,000 combinations, an impressive number also noted by Mersenne.[101] In 1641, one of the weekly public conferences of Renaudot's Bureau d'Adresse in Paris considered the suitability of French for learning the sciences; two of the five interlocutors in this most intellectually commonplace of settings discussed Cabbalistic doctrines.[102] Mersenne thus followed a well-trodden path in connecting combinatorics and language, although his reasons for doing so differed sharply from those of the Cabbalists, who sought hidden, essential properties.

In a letter to Peiresc of 1635 Mersenne described another version of a combinatorically constructed universal language.[103] Again, he intended it to facilitate communication, not to model the world or partner a philosophical system. He brought the matter up in the course of remarking on his correspondent's ambitions to learn about Chinese culture. "I have imagined a sort of universal writing and language [*idiome*] which could serve you for this purpose, in constructing an alphabet that contains all possible languages, and all the words [*dictions*] that can serve to express each thing in whatever language one chooses. It has this property, that its reading alone can so teach the philosophy fitted to its order, that one cannot forget it, or if one forgets it, one can reestablish it without any help."[104] Mersenne's idea involved assigning a number to each possible combination of letters of

---

L'impieté, and *La verité*, Mersenne clearly adopts a Lullist example when talking about the ten attributes of God in *Harmonie universelle*, preface to "De la voix," p. 2. On Lullism, see Frances A. Yates, "The Art of Ramon Lull," in *Collected Essays*, vol. 1, *Lull and Bruno* (London, 1982), pp. 9–77.

101. Duret, *Thresor*, pp. 24–76; the number is on p. 24. See Coumet, "Mersenne: 'Dictions' nouvelles," p. 9, for Mersenne's citation of the number while discussing Cabbalism in *Quaestiones*, col. 1390; see also the list in Mersenne, *Harmonie universelle*, "Des chants," p. 108. Comenius plays with combinatorics and words in *Linguarum methodus*, cap. III.

102. Théophraste Renaudot, *Recueil general des questions traittees ès conferences du Bureau d'Adresse* (Paris, 1655), pp. 1–4. Despite Salmon's remarks in "Language-Planning," pp. 389–90, there is no evidence that Mersenne ever took part in the *Conférences*, and the arguments made by Solomon, *Public Welfare*, pp. 73–74, in support of the claim are weak and circumstantial. More important, even if Mersenne did occasionally frequent the meetings, the enormous diversity of opinions put forward there suffices to refute Salmon's suggestion that the proceedings somehow reflected Mersenne's views.

103. Mersenne to Peiresc, c. 20 April 1635, in Mersenne *Correspondance*, 5:134–40.

104. Ibid., p. 136.

an alphabet applicable to all languages.[105] The resultant ordered lexicon would necessarily contain every possible word of every language, each word designated by a number indicating its position in the sequence. Mersenne told Peiresc: "Your name is the 15,777,318,656th word of this alphabet, which consists of more millions of vocables than there are grains of sand in the entire world, although it is so easy to learn and retain that one has no need of any memory, provided that one had a little judgment."[106] He hoped his invention would give Peiresc "some light to invent the manner of communicating with all the peoples of the New World, who can help us with their observations."[107]

Unfortunately, he never made clear what the value of his "super-alphabet" might be.[108] Anyone learning the appropriate combinatorial rules (the "philosophy fitted to its order") could generate the sequence of letter combinations without having to learn it by heart as one does ABC; the rules served also to make the sequence boundless. However, a systematic arrangement of labels without any guide to their proper attachment to things clearly left a lot to be desired. Mersenne's suggestion attempted, once again, to come to grips with diversity—to produce more words than there were grains of sand in the world—and also to systematize the diversity of possible words, but it did not solve the problem of a universal language, as Mersenne himself evidently realized.

The context, Peiresc's interest in China, suggests strongly that Mersenne had in mind reports claiming that despite the diversity of languages within their realm, the Chinese used a common form of writing that enabled anyone who learned it to read a text even though ignorant of the language of its author; each person would read the text in his own tongue. This supposed property of Chinese characters aroused great interest in Europe throughout the seventeenth century. Mersenne mentions it in his *Questions inouyes* of 1634 and seems to have been quite taken with it as a means of universal communication.[109] His letter to Peiresc suggests a scheme drafted along different lines, but its goal, however unlikely the realization, surely owed something to the reports from China.

Two of Mersenne's fellow countrymen, Jean Le Maire and a certain

---

105. Mersenne, *Harmonie universelle,* "Des chants," pp. 140–42, contains a fuller discussion.

106. Mersenne *Correspondance,* 5:136–37.

107. Ibid., p. 137.

108. For a brief discussion of Mersenne's idea, see Coumet, "Mersenne: 'Dictions' nouvelles," pp. 23–26, although this sheds little light on the issue.

109. Cornelius, *Languages,* pp. 25–38; Mersenne, *Questions inouyes,* p. 117.

Des Vallées, attempted to produce more workable schemes for creating a technique of universal writing, apparently amounting to versions of the purported "universal character" of the Chinese. They interested Mersenne sufficiently to warrant their mention in his letters over quite a long period, from correspondence in 1629 with Descartes to that of the 1640s with Theodore Haak.[110] Des Vallées's approach, details of which are known only from Descartes's reply to Mersenne on the subject, seems to have involved a rationalized system of grammar that avoided the irregularities found in actual languages—irregularities arising, as Descartes commented, "from the corruption of usage." Des Vallées further envisaged a dictionary that would coordinate those words in different languages having the same signification. He proposed that the process be simplified by rationalizing vocabulary itself. Thus, "primitive words" in each language would be formed into their related words according to the same pattern: to the primitive words for "love," for example—"aymer, amare, φιλεῖν, etc."—the same standard affix would be added to construct the corresponding noun. As Descartes observed, the plan entailed that a Greek who was reading something by a Frenchman would need constant recourse to the dictionary.[111] Discussion of the scheme prompted Descartes's suggestion of a genuinely philosophical language in which "primitive words" would be invented so as to establish "an order between all the thoughts that can enter the human mind, just as there is one established naturally between numbers."[112] Had Des Vallées's artificial language attempted such a thing, however, Mersenne could not have taken so great an interest in it.

Le Maire's *Méthode universelle pour traduire les langues* was designed to teach children Greek, Latin, and Hebrew in a short time. Although no details remain, it appears to have centered on another universal writing scheme, which Mersenne, in a letter to Gassendi, explicitly compared to that of the Chinese.[113] Through its means, he said, all peoples might intercommunicate, even with inhabitants of the moon,

---

110. The notes in Mersenne *Correspondance* disagree with each other as to the identity of the man whose scheme Mersenne sent to Descartes in 1629. The last word is Bernard Rochot's, 10:271–73, identifying him convincingly with one Des Vallées. See also Knowlson, *Universal Language Schemes*, pp. 65–68.

111. Descartes to Mersenne, 20 November 1629, in Mersenne *Correspondance*, 2:323–26. Such "dictionary methods" were frequently proposed in the seventeenth century, e.g., by Gaspar Schott and Athanasius Kircher: see Couturat, *La logique de Leibniz*, pp. 51–53.

112. Mersenne *Correspondance*, 2:327.

113. See notes in ibid., 11:206 and 10:271; also Mersenne's description of the scheme to Comenius in 10:265. The remark to Gassendi is in ibid., 6:4.

"if there be such."[114] In *Quaestiones in Genesim*, Mersenne himself had referred to a way of learning a language in a single hour.[115] Apparently like Des Vallées and Le Maire, he saw language solely as a means of communication; all his discussions of it focus on that theme, whether dealing with missionary work or with the exchange of scientific information. The latter, of course, goes right to the heart of his lifelong efforts as correspondent and intelligencer, as well as his views on the kind of knowledge that could be sought from nature. Mersenne never expressed any interest in constructing a philosophical language to mirror the true constitution of things, because of what he saw as the impossibility of classifying the world according to natural kinds. His vision of a mathematical philosophy of appearances required accurate descriptions of those appearances, but the language employed could never transcend them.

The nearest he ever came to suggesting a "philosophical" language appears in Proposition XXIV of *Harmonie universelle*'s first book, "De la nature & des proprietez du Son." This attempts to discover whether one can "represent the quadrature of the circle, the duplication of the cube, and all things in the world by means of sounds."[116] Mersenne says that, knowing the relationship between sounds and string lengths,

> it is easy to represent in this way all geometry by means of sounds, but it is even easier to represent arithmetic, inasmuch as all numbers are measured by unity, and consequently they are all commensurable. . . .
>
> It is, furthermore, very easy to conclude that one can represent everything that is in the world, and consequently all the sciences, by means of sounds, for since all things are composed of weight, number, and measure, and sounds represent these three properties, they can signify all that one wishes, if one excepts metaphysics, which separates all its propositions from sensible and intellectual matter,[117] and which purifies them to such a point that they make us envisage the sovereign beauty of the being of beings. Whence it follows that the perfect musician can invent words [*dictions*], and a perfect language, which signifies things naturally, and that he can teach the sciences without using any other language than that of a lute, or some other instrument.

114. Mersenne to Comenius, ibid., 10:265. Mersenne also mentions Le Maire's ideas to Galileo (9:301–2) and to Haak (11:407).

115. Mersenne, *Quaestiones*, col. 471; see De Waard's note in Mersenne *Correspondance*, 2:329.

116. Mersenne, *Harmonie universelle*, "Du son," pp. 42–44; the passage is noted in Lenoble, *Mersenne*, p. 518.

117. I.e., the sensible matter of the physicist and the intelligible matter of the mathematician: see Chapter 4, sec. III, above, for a paraphrase of Blancanus's use of the terms.

By the same token, all the propositions of geometry, including those specified in the proposition's heading, certainly lend themselves to such a presentation. "But there is no man who has the ear sufficiently delicate and subtle for this subject, if it is not the perfect musician who has not yet at all appeared."[118]

Mersenne takes the idea no further, and he certainly never considered it the least bit practical. Even if he had, such a language would not have been "philosophical" in the sense envisaged by Descartes or Comenius, or even by John Wilkins in his celebrated "Real Character and Philosophical Language."[119] Those schemes required classifications according to the true natures of things;[120] Mersenne's suggestion promised no more than the provision of mathematical models of individual objects. Taking everything to be ordered in number, measure, and weight, according to the tenets of universal harmony, those quantitative characteristics of a body could be represented by a sound, itself characterized by the same three factors in the same proportions. The idea relied on Mersenne's three rules governing musical strings, "number" corresponding to string length; "weight," to string tension; and "measure," to the string's *grosseur* or thickness.[121] No single combination of the three variables uniquely specified a given note, of course; any note could arise from an infinite number of possible arrangements. Mersenne simply played with a conceit whereby the three basic quantifiable properties of bodies might be encoded. Discussing the same idea in *Questions théologiques*, Mersenne had acknowledged the practical impossibility of his "philosophical" language on the grounds that it required a complete knowledge of things such as was possessed only in heaven.[122] Purely descriptive, the

118. Mersenne, *Harmonie universelle*, "Du son," p. 43.

119. See n. 78, above.

120. Leibniz fully recognized the relationship between a true philosophical language and a correctly constituted encyclopedia, holding that the development of each would have to proceed in concert with that of the other, the former depending on the latter. See Couturat, *La logique de Leibniz*, chap. 3, esp. pp. 79–80.

121. See the discussion of this point in Mersenne, *Traité*, p. 332. On Mersenne's musical work in general, see Chapter 6, above.

122. See Lenoble, *Mersenne*, p. 518, quoting from the *expurgated* version of *Questions théologiques*, p. 158. The unexpurgated version contains a discussion of the motion of the earth; some copies had this section replaced with material on a science of sounds, for the benefit of the censor. There must be many more copies of the unexpurgated version than the expurgated, but it is impossible to tell in advance, even from the table of contents, which of the two versions any particular copy contains. For bibliographical details, see Lenoble, *Mersenne*, pp. xix–xx, 399–400. The fact that Mersenne used the material on a science of sounds merely as a cover for his Copernican section indicates clearly his lack of serious concern for the former. My interpretation of Mersenne's idea differs from that of Crombie, "Mersenne and Scientific Acceptability," pp. 186–204,

scheme would have depended on the prior establishment of the knowledge it represented; the perfect musician, said Mersenne, could *teach* the sciences this way, not discover them. Proponents of true philosophical languages recognized no such epistemological barrier: Descartes's vision required the establishment of the "true philosophy," a complete ontological and epistemological system.

Mersenne's rejection of essentialism as an attainable form of knowledge about the natural world meant that for him, philosophical systems could never be more than working hypotheses at best. True scientific knowledge represented a realistic goal only for mathematical sciences working with reliable data drawn from experience of appearances. Language therefore functioned as a scientific tool by enabling the communication of observations and discoveries; it could never assist in revealing the true constitution of the world. Human reason expressed itself through the structure of grammar, as scholastic doctrine asserted, and, like Aristotle, Mersenne held words to be arbitrary signs directly signifying notions and, thereby, things. He differed from Aristotle, however, on the important issue of the induction of universals: as we saw in Chapter 4, he regarded general concepts such as whiteness, for instance, as genuine universals in the Thomistic sense, but he believed it impossible to tell whether any particular attribute of a thing was essential or accidental. Induction of an individual's properties could not determine its specific characteristics. Hence, naming occurred on the basis of classifications made by grouping together perceived similarities, and not on the basis of natural classifications grouping together things of the same kind.

The conceptual materials going into Mersenne's ideas about language and its relation to natural philosophy thus derived in large part from orthodox teaching, scholastic and humanist. The conclusions he drew, however, differed from those of many self-declared anti-scholastic thinkers of the period—not because he remained orthodox and they did not but because, in rejecting the goal of essentialism, he undermined the assumptions on which the scholastic doctrine of signification related concepts to things in the world. The limits that Mersenne placed on language derived from those he placed on knowledge itself.

---

esp. 202, which seems to overestimate Mersenne's attachment to it; Crombie in any case uses the term "philosophical language" in a much looser sense than I do.

CHAPTER EIGHT

Mersenne's Later Career: A Philosophical Agenda and Its Limitations

I

THE PRECEDING chapters have concentrated on the earlier part of Mersenne's career, in the 1620s, and on his writings of the 1630s culminating in the great *Harmonie universelle*. The remaining ten or eleven years of his life saw no great letup in his literary or epistolary activities; in addition, there were such notable episodes as his trip to Italy in 1644–45, from which he brought back the Torricellian experiment; his related attempts to weigh the air; his involvement with the publication of Descartes's works, which incurred the displeasure as well as the indebtedness of the latter; and his conceit of an *Academia parisiensis* at which, if Hobbes is to be believed, he sat in judgment over the natural philosophical offerings of his colleagues.[1]

Important (and, for the most part, well known) as these things are, they serve as practical exemplifications of the agenda established by

1. See Cornélis de Waard, *L'expérience barométrique* (Thouars, 1936), esp. pp. 117–23; Lenoble, *Mersenne*, pp. 430–35; Pierre Duhem, "Le P. Marin Mersenne et la pesanteur de l'air," *Revue générale des sciences pures et appliquées* 17 (1906), 769–82, 809–17. On Mersenne and Descartes, see Lenoble, *Mersenne*, pp. 47–49; the *Academia parisiensis* is discussed in ibid., pp. 590–91. Hobbes's remarks appear in his *Dialogus physicus*, trans. Simon Schaffer, in Steven Shapin and Simon Schaffer, *Leviathan and the Air-Pump* (Princeton, 1985), p. 351. On Hobbes's relations with Mersenne, see Frithiof Brandt, *Thomas Hobbes' Mechanical Conception of Nature* (Copenhagen, 1928), esp. pp. 154–61, 167–74. Good accounts, by Armand Beaulieu, of Mersenne's trip to Italy and his subsequent trip to the Southwest of France in 1646 appear in Mersenne *Correspondance*, 13:234–48 and 14:212–16, respectively. In 1639 Mersenne published a French translation of Herbert of Cherbury's *De veritate*, apparently enamored of its irenical possibilities: Lenoble, *Mersenne*, pp. 562–63.

his earlier activity more than as significant developments of it. His *Academia* simply formalized, along conventional lines laid down in the sixteenth century, the informal contacts represented by his correspondence and the importance that he had always attached to open exchange of opinions and information. The same applies to his determination to bring Descartes into the open. From works of argumentation and polemic like *La verité des sciences*, from epistemological reflections such as are found in *Questions theologiques*, and from the grand endeavor of *Harmonie universelle*, Mersenne moved to concentrate on producing volumes of exemplification and compilation and on the further bringing-to-light of the works of others. His correspondence went on apace, furthering his project to require "of the most learned . . . their observations, and the remarks they will have made of different effects or phenomena of nature"[2]—and also, of course, fomenting dispute when purported demonstrations, such as that of Descartes concerning refraction, seemed to lack the force required to bring about consensus.[3]

Lenoble observed the change in Mersenne's religious stance from staunch Catholic apologist to conciliatory irenicist, which prompted André Pineau to describe him after his death as the "Huguenot Monk."[4] In fact, Mersenne's gradual shift towards a preference for religious toleration (observable in his dislike for the intellectualized discussions of grace inaugurated by Saint Paul and Saint Augustine)[5] cannot properly be regarded as gradual conversion to the opposite camp of Protestantism; Lenoble notes his gentle but sincere attempts at preaching to his Protestant friends to give up their erring ways.[6] A moderate, reconciliatory Catholicism had been, perhaps, more characteristic of the sixteenth than the seventeenth century,[7] but Mersenne came to choose it as a potentially more fruitful approach to the problem of controlling heresy and doctrinal anarchy than the Counter-Reformatory zeal of his early publications. His real enemies remained the same, however, and in a letter of 1637 to his frequent

2. Mersenne, *Questions theologiques*, p. 18.

3. Mahoney, *Mathematical Career of Pierre de Fermat*, pp. 375–90; A. I. Sabra, *Theories of Light from Descartes to Newton* (Cambridge, 1981), pp. 116–27.

4. Lenoble, *Mersenne*, chap. 14, and pp. 53, 578–80, summarizes his attitudes. For Pineau's remarks, see Harcourt Brown, *Scientific Organizations in Seventeenth Century France (1620–1680)* (Baltimore, Md., 1934), p. 36.

5. See Chapter 5, above.

6. Lenoble, *Mersenne*, p. 563.

7. Although it also motivated Isaac La Peyrère, whose heretical interpretations of biblical history did not prevent Mersenne from displaying an interest in his work: see Lenoble, *Mersenne*, pp. 510–11; Popkin, *History of Scepticism*, pp. 293–94.

correspondent André Rivet, himself a Protestant, the old concerns reappear:

> We are in a strange century for the different sorts of libertinism, which reach such a point in many minds that neither reasoning nor scripture can make them yield to the truth: some want demonstrations in religion, as in mathematics; and others imagine that everything is false, or at least that we cannot assure ourselves of anything, all things having two sides [*anses*]; and others maintain that everything is God, that all is good with respect to God, having neither evil of sin, nor of guilt, nor of affliction, following this verse:
>
> *Jupiter est quodcumque vides.*[8]
>
> We will always live amongst this confusion until we see no more in enigma, and the veil is lifted; and when *videbitur Deus Deorum in Sion,* we will no longer have wicked people to persecute us, nor impious people to mock God and religion.[9]

Conversion by sheer force of argument had, it seems, come to appear chimerical. The natural philosophical agenda spawned by Mersenne's attempts to circumvent philosophical and, by implication, theological unorthodoxy now stood on its own, a means of uniting under a deliberately restricted set of cognitive goals diverse, and even conflicting, philosophical outlooks. Operational and mathematical sciences of appearances might be hard pressed to confute the heretic, but they could provide common ground for an enterprise that heresy could not pollute.

Mersenne underpinned his promotion of this agenda with the "mitigated scepticism" that was the epistemological corollary to his frequent use of the metaphor of the veil: in the afterlife, we will at last see the truth in God; meanwhile, a veil hides that truth, leaving to us only appearances. As we saw in Chapter 3, such moderate scepticism informed humanist approaches to demonstration, and it appeared not only in Jesuit thought but also in Lutheran academic circles. A general feature of late humanist pedagogy, it observed no clear theological boundaries.[10] As a consequence, Mersenne easily found

---

8. A statement of pantheism; i.e., God is in everything and is identical to the world itself. The phrase is from Lucian and was cited by, e.g., La Mothe Le Vayer: see Mersenne *Correspondance*, 6:229n.1.

9. Mersenne to Rivet, 25 March 1637, in ibid., pp. 228–29.

10. It is interesting to note that the authors whose texts were used in the Jesuit schools were mostly Iberian, or associated with the Collegio Romano; features commonly regarded as typical of northern, particularly Protestant, humanism nonetheless appear in the work of these writers, as we have seen.

kindred spirits. Gassendi pursued his own version of "mitigated scepticism," as Popkin has shown; Roberval, with whom Mersenne closely associated in the 1630s and 1640s, loudly proclaimed his scepticism regarding physical systems and speculative hypotheses in a way clearly very congenial to the Minim.[11] One of Mersenne's more obscure correspondents, a fellow Minim named Jean Lacombe, put forward similar opinions in several letters of 1640, remarking that we "live in the shadows" and that "our greatest physical demonstrations usually go only to show that things can be according to the ideas that we conceive of them, and not that they are indeed thus." His own ideas, said Lacombe, expressed merely the "possibility of things, and not the truth of their being, which is hidden from us."[12] He summed up his position by asserting that if this kind of knowledge "does not suffice for perfect philosophy, it suffices at least for the feebleness of our minds."[13] Mersenne's was by no means a voice in the wilderness.

The three mathematical compendia of the 1640s most characteristically represent Mersenne's practical pursuit of his agenda. In 1644 appeared the *Universae geometriae, mixtaeque mathematicae synopsis* and the *Cogitata physico-mathematica;* in 1647, the *Novarum observationum . . . tomus III* (which completed the sequence).[14] The first of these, its title proclaiming its contents as falling within the traditional category of "mixed mathematics," was a new edition of the *Synopsis mathematica,* which had appeared, disjointedly, in 1626. All three works, however, had aims similar to those of the earlier collection. In 1639 Mersenne had expressed his estimation of the value of such compendia in a letter to Theodore Haak in England, commenting on a plan of John Pell's.

> His project is praiseworthy, but in place of the great collection he suggests of all those who have written on the subject of mathematics, it would be better to make a selection of a dozen of the best in each branch, and after having presented the ancients whose books we have, as Euclid, Apollonius, Archimedes, Theodosius, Pappus, Ptolemy, with their manuscript works as yet unpublished, of which Golius at Leiden has some, and others are at Rome, the best of the moderns would be presented, such as Vieta for analysis, Clavius for his five or six large volumes,

11. Popkin, *History of Scepticism,* pp. 141–50, on Gassendi. On Roberval, see Lenoble, *Mersenne,* pp. 414–18; and Léon Auger, *Gilles Personne de Roberval (1602–1675)* (Paris, 1962), pp. 134–48, which is mostly material quoted from Roberval himself.

12. Lacombe to Mersenne, 18 August 1640, in Mersenne *Correspondance,* 10:6.

13. Lacombe to Mersenne, 3 October 1640, in ibid., p. 134. See also, in general, Lacombe to Mersenne, 30 June 1640, in ibid., 9:441ff.

14. For full bibliographical details on these works see Lenoble, *Mersenne,* pp. xxvi–xxx.

and several others, including our Herigone [i.e., the *Cursus mathe-maticus*]. . . . And thus we should have all that is good, without caring about the rest.[15]

Mersenne lists, in addition, the appropriate authors for optics, arithmetic, spherical triangles and logarithmic computations, astronomy (Ptolemy and "several Arabs," together with compilers of tables from the Alphonsine to the Rudolphine—no mention of Copernicus), and finally, "for fortification, music, etc., about eight or ten of those who have been most successful, with those who have written on mechanics, statics, machines, hydraulics, etc.; so that in a dozen authors one would have everything necessary."[16]

Mersenne's scheme, manifested also in his letters of encouragement to Comenius,[17] formed part of a larger philosophical conception that gave a remarkably heavy weighting to the mathematical disciplines. "I even believe that everything that belongs to mathematics, pure and mixed, can be reduced to a single dozen volumes, all the best philosophy to three, all the liberal and mechanical arts to three, etc., such that one would be learned in short order [*à bon conte*]."[18] His use of conventional disciplinary categories, distinguishing "mathematics" from "philosophy," only serves to emphasize Mersenne's inversion of the usual hierarchical arrangement. For all practical purposes, those disciplines falling under the heading "mathematics" (supplemented, no doubt, by the mechanical arts) had supplanted "philosophy" properly so-called as the central accomplishments of one who could count himself "learned."

The three works of the 1640s follow closely the outline suggested to Haak.[19] In the preface to the first (and most extensive) Mersenne alerts the reader to Descartes's *Principia philosophiae*, which "we await any day"; this treatise, he reveals, attempts to "explain all the phenomena of nature"—"ex hypothesibus." He then compares it to the systems of such thinkers as Democritus; Descartes, if he ever troubled to read this passage, would surely not have welcomed the advertisement.[20] Mersenne intended his own work to follow different lines,

15. Mersenne to Haack [*sic*], 1 November 1639, in Mersenne *Correspondance*, 8:581; I follow here the translation in Brown, *Scientific Organizations*, pp. 45–46.
16. Mersenne *Correspondance*, 8:581–82.
17. Cf. Chapter 7, above.
18. Mersenne *Correspondance* 8:582–83.
19. See also the discussion in ibid., p. 585n.
20. Marin Mersenne, *Universae geometriae, mixtaeque mathematicae synopsis* (Paris, 1644), "Praefatio," [p. 8]. Curiously, Art. 202 of the *Principia*'s Part IV is devoted to distinguishing sharply between Descartes's ideas and those of Democritus: *Oeuvres de Descartes*, 8:325.

exploiting the precision and relative certainty of geometry and mixed mathematics. The pattern of the original *Synopsis*—a series of propositions and theorems, mostly without proofs—therefore remained appropriate, because the goal of presenting truths rather than opinions effectively rendered demonstrations otiose. If a conclusion were in doubt, the argument sustaining it would be essential to its statement; if, however, a conclusion were certain, then its truth would stand as an absolute, not dependent on dialectical construction but merely confirmed by it. Perfectly conventional, such a catechetical presentation of mathematical truth even had some philosophical basis: until Leibniz, the concept of truth contained no requirement of demonstrability.[21] Mersenne included in the *Universae geometriae . . . synopsis* a redaction of Ramus's epitome of Euclid's geometry (absent from the earlier version) "on account," he says, "of its great brevity." Ramus, the great pedagogue, had himself omitted proofs.[22]

The "mechanicorum libri" of Mersenne's new synopsis underline the purpose of both versions.[23] Exceptional in that they go beyond the simple listing of propositions that characterizes the other books, providing in addition discussion of their material, they ought best to display the changes wrought in Mersenne's ideas during the eighteen years separating them from their prototypes of 1626. On inspection, however, they prove to be an almost word-for-word reprinting, apart from occasional misprints and typographical corrections. Even the remarks on the inclined plane, drawn chiefly from Stevin, remain unchanged; Galileo does not appear. Mersenne repeats his virtual paraphrase of the pseudo-Aristotelian *Mechanica*, as well as the "Tertia pars: De utilitatibus, et mirabilibus circuli in mechanicis [i.e., concerning the usefulness and wonders of the circle in mechanics]."[24] The only major alteration is the elimination of the third of the three original "Mechanicorum libri," a fairly brief summary of hydrostatical theorems. Mersenne's avoidance of innovation relates to the intended status of the knowledge furnished by both versions. Galileo's name fails to appear in the 1644 edition, despite Mersenne's extensive discussions of him elsewhere, because the intention to provide only solid and incontestable truths ruled out a great deal.

21. Ian Hacking, "Proof and Eternal Truths," in Gaukroger *Descartes*, pp. 169–80.

22. Mersenne, *Universae geometriae . . . synopsis*, "Praefatio," [p. 1].

23. The bibliography in Lenoble, *Mersenne*, pp. xxvi–xxviii, indicates which sections were new and which covered the same ground as the original *Synopsis*, although Lenoble, as he says, was unable to compare the editions directly.

24. Pp. 269–82 of the "Mechanicorum libri" in Mersenne, *Synopsis;* pp. 456–60 in *Universae geometriae . . . synopsis*. A table listing the contents of the "Mechanicorum libri" may be found in Mersenne *Correspondance*, 14:686–87.

Concerning bodies on inclined planes, Mersenne says in both works that since it is difficult to demonstrate anything about them, "we therefore affirm of them only what is conceded by many people."[25] The single substantive variant actually serves to emphasize more strongly in the later version that the point under discussion should not be regarded as settled. In the *Synopsis mathematica,* a proposition at the beginning of the section "De centro universi" contains a clear caution:

> If the weight of bodies springs from the greater density of the parts, the center of the earth will be the densest of bodies: which only those assign, who take it [i.e., the earth] for the center of the universe, for to it they assign as much matter as in the rest of the bodies in the world.[26]

Mersenne subsequently decided on the stronger caveat found in the corresponding passage in the *Universae geometriae . . . synopsis:*

> If the weight of bodies springs from the greater density of the parts, whether the center of the earth is the densest of bodies? which density only those assign, who take it for the center of the universe, for to it they assign as much matter as in the rest of the bodies in the world: which are utterly uncertain [questions].[27]

Such care to preserve the integrity of the knowledge presented in his treatise indicates why Mersenne excluded Galileo's ideas. Appropriate though they might be for discursive treatment elsewhere, they lacked the apodeictic certainty necessary for the incorporation of their results into a synopsis.

The near-identity of the "Mechanicorum libri" of 1626 and 1644, moreover, does not result from a straightforward and uncritical reprinting of old material. The example just given shows how even apparently insignificant points could be subject to revision; other changes also reveal Mersenne's editorial hand at work. In addition to the dropping of the section on hydrostatics, the correction of misprints (at least in the case of proper names) probably results from Mersenne's efforts rather than the printer's.[28] The only substantive variants I have found, apart from the one already described, again bear witness to Mersenne's approval of the text of 1626 when he came

25. Mersenne, *Synopsis,* "Mechanicorum libri," p. 137.
26. Ibid., p. 13 (Proposition x).
27. Mersenne, *Universae geometriae . . . synopsis,* pp. 399–400.
28. E.g., the misprinted "Balbus" in *Synopsis,* "Mechanicorum libri," p. 306, is duly corrected to "Baldus."

to revise it in 1644. At the very end of the new version he remarks upon the absence of the old piece on hydrostatics, and at another place the words "hinc motus firmamenti, qui factus est a principio mundi usque ad annum 1626 ab Oriente in Occidentem" reappear with the date altered to 1644.[29] The continuity of Mersenne's basic aims, and their strict delimitation, are clear and characterize much of his later work.

II

We saw in Chapter 6 the evolution of Mersenne's mechanical thought up to its culmination in the Galileo-haunted pages of *Harmonie universelle*. Galileo's *Two New Sciences* provided further grist for his mill, being reconstituted in a thoroughly Mersennian guise as *Les nouvelles pensées de Galilée* (1638/9).[30] Mersenne found it easy to absorb the new material into the somewhat unsystematic framework within which he had previously accommodated Galileo's conceptions, and parts of it appear again in his other two compendia of the 1640s. Having already tentatively accepted Galileo's approach to the problem of falling bodies, and adapted it to his own program of empirical research, Mersenne found no difficulty in adopting the doctrine of

29. Mersenne, *Synopsis*, "Mechanicorum libri," p. 281; *Universae geometriae . . . synopsis*, p. 460. In the latter, p. 472, Mersenne introduces the "Opticae libri" by saying: "There follow, indeed, those [books] which had gone before in the first edition of the books of optics"; that assertion seems to be supported by my comparisons of the "Mechanicorum libri" in the two editions, showing almost complete identity. Nor does my more cursory comparison of such books as the paraphrases of Archimedes or Theodocius (for full titles see Lenoble, *Mersenne*, pp. xxvii–xxviii), which have much briefer and balder lists of propositions than do most parts of the "Mechanicorum libri," show significant differences. This apparent identity of most parts of the *Synopsis* of 1626 with their counterparts of 1644 makes it very probable that the optical books of the *Universae geometriae . . . synopsis* are simply reprints of the lost optical sections of 1626. The 1644 optical books, following a new preface with its mention of Descartes (pp. 473–76), comprise five sections—catoptrics, perspective, and so forth—all in the form of short-entry lists of "propositions" and "theorems" (libri 1–5, pp. 477–548), and two sections presenting new optical theories by William Warner and Thomas Hobbes (libri 6–7, pp. 549–66, 567–89). On Hobbes's piece, see A. E. Shapiro, "Kinematic Optics," pp. 145ff. The character of Mersenne's own optical books, together with their conservative content (e.g., the sine law of refraction is not mentioned), suggests strongly that they are identical to the earlier treatise of 1626.

30. Mersenne, *Nouvelles pensées;* for publication information on the original edition, and the reason for the ambivalent publication date (1638–9), see the introduction to the critical edition, pp. 28–31. An examination of the work, indicating differences in structure between it and its Galilean prototype (as well as Mersenne's tendency to miss the point on particular issues) is Shea, "Marin Mersenne," pp. 55–70; there is also a useful discussion of the work, concentrating on Mersenne's extreme concern for pre-

the parabolic path of projectiles. In the *Nouvelles pensées* he presents a derivation of that path and then proceeds, in typical fashion, to observe that it is not actually found in nature and that Galileo's demonstration leaves out the important factor of air resistance.[31] In the *Cogitata physico-mathematica* of 1644 Mersenne discusses parabolic paths at some length,[32] asking in one proposition why jets of water do not actually follow them. Again, he has resort to the effect of the air, "which insinuates itself and interposes between the droplets, and divides them bit by bit as into foam."[33] This attitude directly parallels that found a few years earlier in *Questions theologiques*, in which Mersenne considered the odd-number rule for free fall as a means of examining the ways in which actual cases of fall deviated from it.[34] The final book of *Harmonie universelle*, entitled "Nouvelles observations physiques & mathematiques"—and apparently written during 1637, according to the rather piecemeal production of that work[35]— had pointed to the new possibilities opened up by an empirical exploitation of the odd-number rule. Among these "new observations" Mersenne describes experiments for measuring the relative rates of fall of bodies of differing densities in air and in water. His idea, he explains, is to compare the densities, or "weights," of water and other bodies with that of air, via a premise based on his observation of "the different speed of falling weights, which ought to be greater when they weigh more,[36] although this difference isn't easily perceptible in the

---

cise experimental verification, by Jean Bernhardt, "Mersenne, commentateur de Galilée," *Revue d'histoire des sciences* 28 (1975), 169–77. Bound with some copies of the *Nouvelles pensées* is a 68-page work entitled *L'usage du quadran, ou d'horloge physique universel* (Paris, 1639), which appears to be by Mersenne, although his name nowhere appears (the item is not included in Lenoble's bibliography). It concerns practical applications of the quadrant, as well as of the pendulum as a time-keeper: see the introduction to the critical edition of *Nouvelles pensées*, pp. 29n.81, 30n.82. The work is contained in the copy of the Rocolet *Nouvelles pensées* in the Rosenwald Collection of the Institute for Advanced Study, Princeton, where I have had access to it.

31. Mersenne, *Nouvelles pensées*, pp. 225–32.

32. Mersenne, *Cogitata*, e.g., in the section "Ballistica," pp. 65–73. *Oeuvres de Descartes*, 10:582–99, contains bibliographical details of the *Cogitata* together with a description of its contents, followed by quoted passages that allude to Descartes or apparently cite his letters. Pp. 588–90 reprint Mersenne's *éloge* of Galileo from *Cogitata*, "Hydraulica, pneumatica," pp. 193–95; the latter can also be found, with notes and a French translation by Pierre Costabel and Pierre Piveteau, in *Revue d'histoire des sciences* 18 (1965), 221–26.

33. Mersenne, *Cogitata*, "Hydraulica, pneumatica," Proposition XXIII, pp. 117–119.

34. Mersenne, *Questions theologiques*, p. 17.

35. Mersenne, *Harmonie universelle*; on the vicissitudes of its publication, see the introduction to the critical edition of Mersenne, *Nouvelles pensées*, pp. 20–24.

36. Mersenne's annotations to his own copy insert at this point the observation that the bodies can also be of the same weight but of lesser volume.

ordinary heights from which one drops them, if they aren't very different in their weights." The whole analysis relies on considering the resistance of the medium.[37]

Clearly, Mersenne's examinations of the effects of air resistance on unconstrained motion required his adoption of Galileo's ideal generalizations about free fall and projectile motion. The omission of Galileo's results from the *Universae geometriae . . . synopsis* indicates Mersenne's true evaluation of their status, however; he never accepted them unreservedly and treated them only as highly probable empirical rules, not mathematical or mechanical conclusions. Nonetheless, during the years from *Harmonie universelle* to the compendia of 1644, he accepted them as practically effective and experientially justified. In the *Cogitata*, for example, he remarks that were it not for air resistance, a ball on a smooth horizontal plane would continue in motion, once started, indefinitely. He also discusses the parabolic paths of projectiles, considers again the effects of air resistance on bodies in free fall, and devotes an entire proposition to the question of whether the motion of such things as pendulums and missiles really would continue indefinitely in the absence of air resistance; he decides that it probably would.[38] None of his epistemological or methodological commitments, therefore, appeared to be threatened by a quite firm, although ultimately provisional, acceptance of Galilean mechanics. Galileo's work accorded closely enough with Mersenne's own physico-mathematical agenda to enable him to adopt it without major difficulties.

That state of affairs had altered radically by October 1646, when Mersenne wrote on these matters to Christiaan Huygens, then seventeen years old. Constantijn Huygens had relayed to Mersenne a letter written by his son to the younger Constantijn, Christiaan's elder brother, because it contained some mathematical results that the youth had lately produced.[39] The last of them maintained that a body in free fall would follow the odd-number rule and if thrown sideways would describe a parabola (all this in apparent ignorance of Galileo). Mersenne responded as a courtesy to Christiaan's father, and confined his observations to this question of falling bodies.[40] His objec-

37. Mersenne, *Harmonie universelle,* "Nouvelles observations," p. 3.

38. Mersenne, *Cogitata,* "Ballistica," pp. 48, 65–73, 132–35, 136–38 (Proposition XXXVIII); Mersenne says he "supposes" that God maintains motion in a perpetual creation (p. 138).

39. Christiaan Huygens to Constantijn Huygens, his brother, 3 September 1646, in Mersenne *Correspondance,* 14:434–36; relayed by Constantijn Huygens to Mersenne, 12 September 1646, in ibid., pp. 448–53.

40. Mersenne to Christiaan Huygens, 13 October 1646, in ibid., pp. 538–41.

tions to what were Galilean characterizations of motion now went far beyond the identification of the perturbing effects of the air.

Mersenne starts out by questioning whether Christiaan has a demonstration of his assertions. Somewhat pontifically, he goes on to make his own assertion, that "heavy bodies [*graves*] that fall do not go always augmenting their speed following the odd numbers, 1, 3, 5, 7, etc., even if we pretend [*faignons*] that there is no air at all to impede them, because every heavy body is not capable of receiving a movement as fast as that of a body that descended from a height of one or several leagues . . . if it is not sufficiently heavy to receive such a great impetuosity."[41] Mersenne counters Christiaan's mathematical result, therefore, with a *physical* consideration, implicitly invoking some unspecified cause of fall and its associated acceleration. He had never stressed such an objection previously; indeed, it appears to undermine his ambition to push forward a mathematically certified kind of natural philosophy, by infecting its techniques with physical uncertainties.[42] He continues in similar vein, saying that even *in vacuo* a falling body could not follow the claimed proportion exactly, since such behavior would necessitate that at the start of its descent it pass through all the degrees of slowness from rest, "which does not occur, whatever Galileo thought, for the stone already has a certain speed in beginning the fall."[43]

This second physical objection at first looks strange in light of Mersenne's previous acceptance (originally in his *Les mechaniques de Galilée*) of Galileo's arguments concerning the indefinitely small degrees of speed of balls moving on inclined planes approximating ever more closely to a horizontal surface.[44] However, his concern here is actually quite different: instead of some average or overall speed of a ball on a plane and its variation depending on different inclinations, he is considering one ball, subjected to a single downward tendency, passing successively through all degrees of speed from rest. But neither did Mersenne's difficulty arise from a rejection of the mathematical concept of a body passing through an infinite number of degrees of speed in a finite time. Rather, Huygens's, and Galileo's, claim about free fall challenged Mersenne's understanding of the physical relationship between force and speed.

41. Ibid., pp. 538–39.
42. In *Harmonie universelle*, "Du mouvement des corps," p. 129, Mersenne endorses the doctrine of a terminal velocity: "ce qui semble probable"; he seems, however, simply to relate it to the effects of air resistance.
43. Mersenne *Correspondance*, 14:539.
44. See, e.g., Mersenne, *Harmonie universelle*, "Du mouvement des corps," p. 110.

We saw in Chapter 6 his perennial tendency to treat speed as dependent upon and proportional to applied force; we also saw his criticisms of Isaac Beeckman's advocacy of uniform acceleration in free fall, which centered not just on a denial of the doctrine's empirical adequacy but on a rejection of its *physical* coherence. If all causal factors remain the same during fall, Mersenne held, then the effect should also remain constant: a constant downward force should generate a constant downward speed. Evidently, Mersenne's subsequent acceptance of Galileo's arguments in favor of Beeckman's position never fully erased that intuition.[45] In 1646, his assertion that a body "always has a certain speed in beginning the fall" seems to be based on the same conceptualization of the phenomenon: namely, that a heavy body on release is set in motion by a certain finite force impelling it towards the center of the earth, and so, the force acting all at once as soon as the body is allowed to fall, it must at once take on a corresponding finite speed. Mersenne had shown an equal disregard for discontinuities in his treatments of vibrating strings: his analysis implied that at extreme positions of the string its speed would jump instantaneously from zero to a considerable finite quantity when a finite restitutive force came into play.[46] Between 1633 and 1646, however, he had not seen fit to apply such an analysis to free fall.

As if to complete his about-face regarding Galilean accounts of motion, Mersenne turns finally to criticize Huygens's claims concerning the paths of projectiles. Where previously he had concentrated on the perturbing effects of air resistance in bringing about deviations from the mathematical ideal of the parabola, Mersenne now disapproves of Huygens's espousal of that ideal on more fundamental grounds. These are, yet again, physical.[47] Going straight to the heart of the matter, Mersenne says that "the air not being considered at all," the parabolic path still fails exactly to fit the true behavior of a projectile, "for it would be necessary that the impetuosity communicated to the missile never cease; now, the qualities that impress themselves easily, like impetus, dissipate themselves [*se perdent*] also very easily and quickly. *Violentum non durabile*."[48] Parabolic projectile motion is impossible, therefore, because a missile can never conserve its hori-

---

45. The proportionality between cause and effect was a basic tenet of Aristotelian physics.

46. See Chapter 6, sec. IV, above.

47. Armand Beaulieu's note to this passage, Mersenne *Correspondance,* 14:539n.2, misses the difference between this and Mersenne's previous criticisms of Galileo's claim of the parabolic path of projectiles.

48. Ibid., pp. 539–40. Inexplicably, Beaulieu (p. 540n.1), interprets the passage quoted as tantamount to a version of Torricelli's principle.

zontal component of velocity even in the absence of air resistance. Implicitly rejecting Galileo's lessons, he characterizes the horizontal motion as violent and sustained by a spontaneously dissipating impetus—a routine late-scholastic position integrated with basic Aristotelian physical conceptions.

Mersenne had employed these ideas before but not with such confident self-consciousness. At a number of places in *Harmonie universelle* confusions become apparent between scholastic physics and Galilean mechanics; Mersenne's attempts at absorbing Galileo's work into the mixed-mathematical, nonphysical structure of statics frequently failed, throwing him back on physical assumptions seldom much modified from their school prototypes. But his use of them against the young Huygens served a contrary purpose: the unavoidable presence of qualitative physical causes not only compromised the absolute certainty of Galileo's new science of motion but provided reasons for doubting even the plausibility of its premises.[49]

The letter to Huygens dates from 1646, and its highly sceptical attitude departs sharply from the tone of the *Cogitata* of 1644. In that work there is, to be sure, a consideration of possible alternatives to the odd-number rule for free fall, but the latter receives a strong, although not unreserved, endorsement on the basis of experimental tests.[50] The sequences 1, 2, 4, 8, 16 . . . and 1, 2, 3, 4, 5 . . . governing distances traveled in successive time intervals fail the test of experience. "Since therefore that progression of ours by odd numbers . . . has seemed always to correspond to our experience, and is confirmed by its incremental changes of ratios,[51] we will retain it."[52] A subsequent mild qualification, considered below, does little to weaken this endorsement of the odd-number ratio. The corroborative explanation to which Mersenne refers, which uses the idea of accumulating increments of impetus, is in fact the very means by which Christiaan himself arrived at his Galilean result two years later. Mersenne had

---

49. For a brief summary of Mersenne's correspondence with the young Christiaan Huygens, see Beaulieu's note, ibid. 14:35–39; also Armand Beaulieu, "Christiaan Huygens et Mersenne l'inspirateur," in *Huygens et la France* (Paris, 1982), pp. 25–31.

50. Mersenne, *Cogitata*, "Ballistica," pp. 51–52.

51. The phrase here is "suisque rationum momentis"; despite this verbal obscurity, Mersenne clearly refers to the account of uniform acceleration in free fall first communicated to him by Beeckman, involving the successive compounding of acquired downward impulses by the mobile (see Chapter 6, sec. II, above). He had described it a few pages earlier, in Proposition XVII, pp. 46–48; it relies, of course, on the concept of impetus.

52. Ibid., p. 52. On Mersenne's discussion, see Beaulieu's note in Mersenne *Correspondance*, 12:301–2, identifying the sequence 1, 2, 4, 8 . . . with Pierre Le Cazre, who had a dispute with Gassendi on the matter, and the sequence 1, 2, 3, 4 . . . with Honoré Fabri.

rejected it when Beeckman used it as an argument in 1629, and he would reject it again in 1646; in 1644, however, he considered it to support his empirical establishment of uniform acceleration in free fall.

The letter of 1646 was no aberration; it signals a change in Mersenne's views expressed more coolly in his *Novarum observationum . . . tomus III*, published in the following year. He returns there to the question of the numerical sequences governing free fall and covers the same ground as the corresponding section in the *Cogitata*.[53] His conclusions lack the earlier confidence, however; the actual proportion followed by heavy bodies, he says, depends on the *cause* of fall, and that we do not know. All he can say is that bodies seem to follow the series of odd numbers for middling heights.[54] He points out that results such as the mean-speed theorem, which measures the distance traveled by a uniformly accelerated mobile in terms of a uniform speed sustained over an equal period, conclude necessarily once we accept their premises.[55] Mersenne's problem, however, lay in moving beyond formal demonstration of that kind to establish scientific knowledge about nature, which required that the conditions establishing theorems also be accredited as true of things in the world. Accordingly, in the immediately following discussion, he tries to assess Galileo's "doctrine of the natural acceleration of heavy bodies." His observations here echo those in the letter to Huygens and paint a pessimistic picture of the prospects for a mathematical science of gravitational motion.

That opinion [of Galileo's] is promoted if it is shown that the motion of heavy bodies is natural, but since some people contend that it is violent, or from an external cause [*a principio externo*], because [heavy bodies] never descend without the force of a subtle matter being applied . . . , or by the attraction of the earth, it is not promoted from that direction. Secondly, neither [is it promoted] through consideration of infinite degrees of slowness, since he does not at all show that a heavy body passes through infinite, or all, degrees of slowness. Thirdly, neither [is it promoted] by the consideration that geometers, relying on reasons of great weight, cannot at all allow that heavy bodies under any circumstances [*quaelibet*], even if considered to be moved *in vacuo*, are able to receive

---

53. Marin Mersenne, *Novarum observationum . . . tomus III* (Paris, 1647), pp. 131–35; for some remarks on this material, see P. Boutroux, "Le Père Mersenne et Galilée," p. 353.

54. Mersenne, *Novarum observationum . . . tomus III*, pp. 132–33.

55. Ibid., p. 134.

any velocity whatever; rather, they affirm that to particular bodies can be communicated just a single highest velocity, beyond which they cannot receive successively higher velocities.[56]

And fourthly, Galileo never demonstrated his fundamental postulate that the speed acquired by a body falling down an inclined plane depends only on initial vertical elevation, not on degree of slope.[57] Altogether, Mersenne's criticisms appear devastating to any attempt at establishing a demonstrative science of motion on Galilean foundations. The uncertainty of physical causes, as well as the obscurity of certain effects, once more cast a shadow of scepticism over the possibility of a true science of nature.

Mersenne's second and third points parallel the first two of those made to Huygens. His first point connects with the explanation given above of his doubt surrounding the idea that, upon release, a body proceeds to pass through all degrees of slowness; it considers the physical causes of descent. Clearly, between the middle of 1644 (when the *Cogitata* appeared) and October of 1646 (the date of the Huygens letter), Mersenne had found new reasons to emphasize, on physical grounds, the uncertainty of Galileo's laws, and he pursued them forcefully in the treatise of 1647. The change of perspective from pragmatic adoption to principled rejection, therefore, falls squarely between the two earlier dates.

During 1646 there appeared an important work on local motion and free fall by the Jesuit Honoré Fabri. His ideas resemble those in a volume of G. B. Baliani's dated the same year, although Mersenne seems not to have seen the latter until well into 1647.[58] Both rejected, for similar reasons, Galileo's assertion that the distances traversed in equal times during fall follow the sequence of odd numbers. The details of their arguments have been admirably exposed by Stillman Drake in an important article; for present purposes it suffices to say that Baliani and Fabri held physical acceleration to occur as an aggre-

56. Ibid., p. 136. Mersenne concludes (p. 141): "From all which [considerations about falling bodies] it seems to me sufficiently to be established that nothing has thus far been demonstrated about accelerated motion, not only where air is considered but also *in vacuo*: hence it is that in this matter, and in other similar things, we are yet able to assert with Saint Paul, I Cor. 8:3, 'If anyone imagines that he knows something, he does not yet know as he ought to know'" (I give the quotation, which is there I Cor. 8:2, from the Revised Standard Version).

57. Mersenne, *Novarum observationum . . . tomus III*, p. 136. He had already observed the undemonstrated nature of this postulate in *Harmonie universelle*, "Du mouvement des corps," p. 109, while opining that it appeared to be *veritable*.

58. See Baliani to Mersenne, 30 July 1647, in Mersenne *Correspondance*, 15:333–34.

gate effect of minuscule but not indivisible instants during each of which the speed of the mobile's descent remained constant. In the first instant a speed of one unit traversed a distance of one unit; in the second instant, a speed of two units traversed a distance of two units, and so on in the sequence 1, 2, 3, 4, 5 . . . . Over sensible intervals of time and space the behavior of a mobile accelerating in such a fashion approximates that proposed by Galileo; the point of contention lay in Galileo's use of continuous rather than discontinuous acceleration, which for Baliani and Fabri presented both mathematical and physical difficulties.[59]

These ideas immediately formed the subject of considerable discussion; Mersenne's correspondence throughout 1647, for example, frequently refers to Fabri's opinions on the issue.[60] At the beginning of January 1647 Mersenne indicated in a letter to Christiaan Huygens his continuing doubts about Galileo's rule by means of drawing Huygens's attention to Fabri's views.[61] He did not, however, endorse Fabri's position but concluded with a characteristic remark about how little we know of physical things. In fact, as we shall see shortly, Mersenne may have failed to grasp the point of Fabri's and Baliani's arguments, taking them to be asserting a simple sequence of 1, 2, 3, 4, 5 . . . as against Galileo's 1, 3, 5, 7, 9 . . . , but he clearly recognized that Galileo's claims were open to more dispute than he had once thought. Yet Fabri had explained his ideas to Mersenne in a letter of 1643 without having a visible impact on the latter's endorsement of Galileo in the following year's *Cogitata* (we have already seen the dismissive treatment given to non-Galilean sequences in that work).[62] Although prompting Mersenne to realize that properly physical, rather than mathematical, considerations might serve to undermine

59. Drake, "Free Fall," esp. pp. 350–51, 360–66; see also Stillman Drake, "Impetus Theory and Quanta of Speed before and after Galileo," *Physis* 16 (1974), 47–65, which covers almost identical ground, with discussion of Fabri and Baliani (pp. 54–62). See also Serge Moscovici, *L'expérience du mouvement* (Paris, 1967), pp. 56–72. Additional references may be found in Mersenne *Correspondance*, 15:173n.2. Fabri's work was the *Tractatus de motu locali corporis. Ex praelectionibus Hon. Fabry a Petro Mousnerio* (1646); Baliani's was *De motu naturali gravium solidorum et liquidorum* (1646), which actually appeared at the beginning of 1647 (see note in Mersenne *Correspondance*, 15:147).

60. See, e.g., the letter of 13 April 1647, in Mersenne *Correspondance*, 15:173–99, in which Jacques Le Tenneur responds to Mersenne's request for his opinion of Fabri's anti-Galilean writings. On Le Tenneur's involvement in the lively debates over free fall in these years, in which Gassendi also participated, see Stillman Drake, "Le Tenneur, Jacques," *DSB*, 8:267–69. A frequent correspondent of Mersenne, Le Tenneur was a staunch defender of Galileo's doctrines.

61. Mersenne to Christiaan Huygens, 8 January 1647, in Mersenne *Correspondance*, 15:24–39.

62. Honoré Fabri to Mersenne, 21 August 1643, in ibid., 12:285–302.

the solidity of Galileo's rule, Fabri's work does not seem a sufficient explanation of his change of mind.

A clue lies in Mersenne's means of stressing (in the passage quoted above from the *Novarum observationum . . . tomus III*) our lack of an undisputed causal account of gravitational motion. "Some people contend that it is violent," he says, and cites as an example the suggestion that it results from the force of a "subtle matter." This example evidently refers to another anti-Galilean view of gravity and fall, postdating the *Cogitata* and emphasizing much more starkly than Fabri or Baliani the dependence of free fall on the nature of underlying physical causes: it appears in Descartes's *Principia philosophiae*, which was published in 1644—just after Mersenne's two treatises of that year.[63] Mersenne seems to have had only a sketchy knowledge of Descartes's account of gravity prior to the appearance of the *Principia*; indeed, Descartes usually preferred not to reveal his cosmology in snippets but to present his explanations of particular phenomena as elements in a comprehensive structure that would serve to justify them.[64] His letters to Mersenne touched only briefly on the vortical construction of the universe, therefore. Unfortunately, Mersenne's correspondence provides no direct indications of the Minim's first reactions to the *Principia*: there are no extant letters to or from Descartes throughout 1644 and 1645; and when they start appearing again in 1646, Mersenne wants chiefly to know about centers of oscillation.[65] Nonetheless, as we saw earlier, in the *Universae geometriae . . . synopsis* he had looked forward to Descartes's book with some interest. On the specific issue of falling bodies, moreover, Descartes's reservations concerning Galileo's theorems receive mention at the end of the discussion in the *Cogitata*. Mersenne has said that he will

---

63. See above for Mersenne's remarks in the preface to the *Universae geometriae . . . synopsis*; similarly, in the *Cogitata*, "Tractatus mechanicus," p. 96, he looks forward to explanations of such phenomena as the tides to come forth shortly from Descartes. Clearly, Mersenne was still ignorant of the contents of Descartes's *Principia*, which appeared on 10 July 1644.

64. See, e.g., Descartes to Mersenne, 19 June 1639, in Mersenne *Correspondance*, 8:454–55, on subtle matter and the cause of fall; also Descartes to Mersenne, 6 August 1640, in ibid., 9:547–50, explaining the cause of tides while saying that he cannot do it properly without the entire system. Similarly, when responding to Mersenne's queries about the "false suns" phenomenon in 1629, Descartes said that because he would have to lay out the whole of his system to explain it, he would prefer to wait until he had completed his treatise *Le monde* (which never appeared in his lifetime and was preempted by the *Principia*). See Mahoney's introduction to his translation of Descartes, *The World*, esp. pp. vii–viii. The essays of 1637, published with the "Discourse on Method," count only as a partial exception, explicitly divorced (at least in the case of the "Dioptrics" and "Meteorology") from the system that would fully establish them.

65. See letters from Descartes to Mersenne in Mersenne *Correspondance*, 14:112ff.

retain the odd-number rule on the basis both of experience and of the supporting (merely probable) argument from the compounding of impulses. But he adds the proviso that such a retention should hold "until another [rule governing fall] has been demonstrated by the 'Illustris vir' [i.e., Descartes], who, although he believes that heavy bodies do not pass through all degrees of slowness from [rest], none-theless acknowledges that this progression is very close to the truth."[66] Mersenne explicitly invokes Descartes, then, as one who might provide grounds for doubting the odd-number rule. The *Principia philosophiae*, with its gravitational theory, apparently proved adequate for the task.

Contrary to Mersenne's assumption, however, Descartes did not undermine Galileo's rule by asserting and rendering plausible a different mathematical progression for free fall. Instead, he gave a physical explanation of fall that lent no support whatever to the odd-number rule and could even be seen as incompatible with it, except over short distances and as an approximation (the opinion Mersenne had already attributed to Descartes).[67] Mersenne, confronted by an ingenious and plausible physical explanation of gravity that defied any neat mathematical analysis but undoubtedly compromised hopes of portraying Galileo's work as genuinely demonstrative, effectively abandoned his previous qualified adherence to Galileo's doctrines— not because he accepted Descartes's explanation as true or even likely (he did not), but because it was *possible*. It brought home to Mersenne the extent to which accounts of gravity and fall relied on an under-standing of physical causes, something that even Fabri's arguments had failed to do.

Galileo had presented his treatment of free fall and projectile motion as if its validity rested on a methodologically sound combination of mathematical and experiential reasoning akin to Archimedean statics. He had successfully disguised the physical assumptions (mostly negative) necessarily implicated in his work and had gone so far as to ridicule pretensions of understanding the cause of fall, as if he could establish his "new science" of local motion without it.[68] Mersenne found the prospect of doing so attractive, while remaining uncon-vinced that Galileo had actually achieved it. The very concreteness of

---

66. Mersenne, *Cogitata*, "Ballistica," p. 52. See Chapter 6, above, for more on Des-cartes's reservations about Galileo's rule; for his equivocation on its practical validity, see esp. Nardi, "Descartes 'presque galiléen,'" pp. 3–16.

67. For the theory of gravity, involving the centrifugal tendencies of a vortex of subtle matter surrounding the earth and the concomitant inward tendency of heavy bodies, see *Oeuvres de Descartes*, 8:212; for a good discussion, see E. J. Aiton, *The Vortex Theory of Planetary Motions* (London, 1972), pp. 55–58.

68. See Galileo, *Dialogue Concerning the Two Chief World Systems*, pp. 234–35.

Descartes's causal account of gravity, however, seems to have persuaded him of its impossibility. Descartes's ideas seem to have had a part, too, in Mersenne's new disinclination to credit the view that a falling body traverses all degrees of speed from rest.[69] In the *Cogitata* he had mentioned Descartes's denial of this view, but without endorsement; indeed, he intimated that Descartes ought to give a demonstration of his contrary claims if they were to be given credence. But the *Principia* renewed his awareness that physical causes could not be abstracted out of the problem of fall and led, together with the objections of Fabri, to his unkind remarks to the young Christiaan Huygens and to his discussion in the *Novarum observationum . . . tomus III*. Mersenne recognized the plausibility of Descartes's account of fall as a sign of the unavoidable place of physical explanations in establishing mathematical accounts of the natural world.

As he always did when faced with physical inscrutability, Mersenne resorted to experiment. Where it had once served to refute Beeckman's support of uniform acceleration in free fall and had subsequently modulated an acceptance of Galileo's identical opinion, experiment now obliged Mersenne by justifying that opinion only as an accidental approximation. He reported, in the compilation of 1647, experiments on falling bodies conducted during his Italian journey of 1645–46, including an exploitation of the facilities afforded in Rome by Saint Peter's, and we have seen the attitude he adopted in that treatise towards their subject matter.[70] When he produced a new edition of the *Harmonicorum libri* in the following year, Mersenne also took the opportunity to reassert his independence from the Galilean doctrine, using, not the arguments centered on considerations of physical uncertainty, but his favorite claims of simple empirical inadequacy. Thus, the new dedication to Habert de Montmor states that "the spaces which are run through by heavy bodies in falling, whether perpendicularly or obliquely on inclined planes, are not perpetually in the duplicate ratio of the times"; experience shows that a lead weight dropped from a height of three hundred feet takes six seconds to reach the ground rather than the five computed from its initial acceleration.[71]

The basis for this assertion was an experiment reported in the four-page "Liber novus praelusorius" inserted into some copies of the new edition of *Harmonicorum libri*, between the volume's two independent-

69. This was, however, also a crucial part of Fabri's and Baliani's arguments.

70. See Lenoble, *Mersenne*, p. 389, on the Saint Peter's experiments; the general account of Mersenne's mechanics in ibid., pp. 461–78, is not always reliable.

71. Mersenne, *Harmonicorum libri*, "Dedication," [p. 2], the first of the two dedications to Montmor.

ly paginated halves.[72] The second proposition is headed: "It is certain that sufficiently heavy bodies, such as metallic globes, in that space of about 150 feet which we can conveniently employ, fall in such a way that the ratio of spaces that they run through is roughly [*proxime*] the duplicate of the times in which their fall is completed."[73] The positive value of this statement lies in its confutation of those other suggested ratios considered and rejected in both the *Cogitata* and the *Novarum observationum . . . tomus III*. Thus Mersenne considers once more the two chief candidates, rejecting them easily and confidently for what he by now regarded as their well-established incompatibility with experience. Baliani, he says, proponent of the arithmetical progression 1, 2, 3, 4, 5 . . . , puts audacity (a bold conjecture) before truth. Dropping a ball of lead from a height of twelve feet takes a second;[74] from a height of forty-eight feet, if Baliani doesn't find the time of fall then to be two seconds, Mersenne will underwrite his boldness, because according to the arithmetical progression it ought to fall only thirty-six feet in that time.[75] The discussion probably misrepresents Baliani's views;[76] nonetheless, Mersenne's sarcasm displays full confidence in the applicability of the duplicate ratio to this case and explains the title of the proposition. But his faith in the testimony of experiment also serves to qualify the Galilean rule in typical post-1644 fashion: he goes on to say that "it is established from many experiences that heavy bodies do not always observe the same ratio of acceleration in descent, since they change it sensibly while falling from 300 feet," taking about six seconds to fall instead of five. This effect, he says, is difficult to observe for a height of 150 feet, and he cites by way of example the vault of St. Peter's in Beauvais, which permits drops of 144 feet.[77]

Mersenne's assertive deployment of experiential claims to deflate the pretensions of conclusions based on reasoning a priori still allowed some room for positive pronouncements. At the end of this discussion he concludes: "I add only that no proportion hitherto invented agrees more closely with observations of falling bodies than Galileo's as long as the bodies are endowed with much gravity, such as

72. For bibliographical details, see Lenoble, *Mersenne*, p. xxx.

73. Mersenne, *Harmonicorum libri*, "Liber novus praelusorius," p. 2.

74. Mersenne discusses units of measurement at length in the first book of the *Cogitata*.

75. Mersenne, *Harmonicorum Libri*, "Liber novus praelusorius," p. 2.

76. Baliani was frequently misunderstood on this point, e.g., by Riccioli: see Stillman Drake, "Baliani, Giovanni Battista," *DSB*, 1:424–25; Moscovici, *L'expérience du mouvement*, pp. 79–83.

77. Mersenne, *Harmonicorum Libri*, "Liber novus praelusorius," p. 3.

metallic things; in the next place, truly that proportion deviates most from the truth when things are lighter, like cork, the pith of the elder-tree, and other things of that kind . . . for cork completes forty-eight feet in three seconds, elder-pith in five, and the inflated swim-bladder of a carp eight seconds, which [distance] wood as well as lead traverses in two seconds."[78]

The most interesting aspect of Mersenne's remarks lies in the way that experimental work first reported ten or eleven years previously, in *Harmonie universelle*, reappears as part of a subtly different argument. Where originally Mersenne placed the observations within the context of an examination of terminal velocities due to air resistance (extending it also to fall in water), no such explanation occurs here. He wishes only to show that falling bodies do not, as a matter of observed fact, follow an arithmetical progression, and that they follow the sequence of odd numbers only to the degree that they are heavier rather than lighter. The conceptual framework of the earlier presentation had rendered the empirical material the focus for an investigation of the way in which the medium disturbed the ideal uniform acceleration of a freely falling body. Here, deviations from Galileo's rule appear not as controllable modulations of an immanent mathematical law but simply as evidence of the inadequacy of a generalization. In asking Christiaan Huygens to justify his assertion of the odd-number rule, Mersenne no doubt had in mind not only epistemological and physical objections but also the necessity of demonstrating its actual empirical veracity.

Mersenne's principled abandonment, towards the end of his life, of strict Galilean mechanics had little apparent impact on his general philosophical position or activities. It did not represent a warning of the futility of his physico-mathematical agenda; if it had, he would not have continued to pursue it in the *Novarum observationum . . . tomus III*, which, apart from the sceptical caveats about doctrines of free fall, closely resembles the *Cogitata* in its approach and subject matter. Nor did it compromise the optical work published posthumously as *L'optique et la catoptrique du Reverend Pere Mersenne Minime* (1651). The mixed mathematical sciences, with their rigorous exploitation of the quantitative characteristics of manifest experience, still remained Mersenne's paradigms for attainable knowledge of the natural world. Only the classification of Galileo's kinematics as a potential example of one of these admirable sciences had changed. Mersenne had never, in any case, been entirely sanguine about the absolute certainty even

---

78. Ibid. For his original report of these experiments, Mersenne refers in this passage to *Harmonie universelle*, "Nouvelles observations," Obs. 1, of which pp. 1–2 are the most relevant.

of the well-established examples, discussing as he did in *Questions theologiques* the relative degrees of uncertainty possessed by music and optics, owing to their inevitable use of suppositions drawn from physics.[79] Abandoning his attachment to Galilean ideas (never unreservedly accepted in any case) really only amounted to a shift of Mersenne's judgmental weighting in light of Descartes's striking emphasis on determinate physical explanation. The theme of the inscrutability of nature sounds throughout Mersenne's career. In that sense, nothing changed. Galileo had always presented a problem; he went too far beyond experience.

At the end of his volume of 1647, in a passage written near the close of his life, Mersenne moved from a discussion of the descent of different bodies in different liquid media to more general epistemological reflections. We know our observations in such matters to be true, he says, just as much as that "this is the hand with which I write this on St. Augustine's day in the year 1647."

> But why this or that thing is [i.e., exists] (which is its final cause), or by what cause [*ratione*] it exists, and performs its operations in whatever way these are subject to our senses, or even, seeing that we are approaching a trope, why bad things follow these, good those, and countless things of this kind which depend on the will of God, if anyone supposes that he knows, and through his entire life exhausts the greatest labors in considering such things, it is truly possible to affirm that so far he has walked in image [*in speculo*] and enigma.[80]

Mersenne questions not the reality of the kinds of cause sought by Aristotelian philosophy but their knowability. When the Coïmbra commentators observed that mathematicians "consider the nature and essence of no real being," they implicitly sanctioned just that enterprise which Mersenne abandoned.[81] He spent his entire life in an endeavor to avoid walking in image and enigma, taking as his guide the scientific ideal of the Conimbricenses' mathematical colleagues. The rationality of nature never implied its total comprehensibility.

---

79. See Chapter 4, above.
80. Mersenne, *Novarum observationum . . . tomus III*, p. 234.
81. Coïmbra *Dialectic*, 2:507 (see Chapter 4, above).

CHAPTER NINE

Summary and Conclusions

I

To say that Mersenne's thought owed much to the learning of the schools is to endorse a trivial proposition. No one can fail to exhibit in later life certain habits of thought once acquired through formal education and from exposure to the intellectual commonplaces of established academic culture; they provide an inevitable substratum of values and expectations from which even the most rebellious prove unable to detach themselves. Despite Descartes's passion for originality, Étienne Gilson could detail, in *Index scolastico-cartésien*, his use of scholastic terminology and ideas.[1] Mersenne had no such passion, and his intellectual debts are correspondingly more obvious. This book has attempted to do more than merely catalogue them.

Mersenne did not reflect passively the intellectual standards of the schools. He appropriated and used humanist and scholastic conceptual resources, and adopted also some of their associated values, as tools for the promotion of his own purposes. The essential conservatism of his apologetic aims, although moderated by an irenical turn as his life proceeded, entailed an attachment to the central philosophical and theological commitments of the Church. Among the available doctrinal variants Mersenne seems—not unnaturally, given his educational background—to have felt closest to that of the Jesuits. When, in *Harmonie universelle*, he praised the value of learning to piety (for which Saint Augustine provided the best example), he observed that

1. Étienne Gilson, *Index scolastico-cartésien* (Paris, 1913).

there was no need to restrict oneself to the Church Fathers to find endorsement, "since our century shows us the great sanctity of life, joined to such profound sciences, in that admirable society which carries the holy name of the Savior for its arms and its device."[2]

Jesuit academic culture itself contained doctrinal variety, of course, and Mersenne took sides with the mathematicians rather than the philosophers regarding the status of the mathematical sciences. Some of the ammunition in the debate, however, arose from a shared intellectual context in which humanist estimations of the importance of probable argument sanctioned open admissions of the inconclusiveness of most natural philosophical demonstrations. Mersenne, like Clavius and many others, turned this moderate sceptical stance on its head to argue that the greater certainty of the mathematical sciences recommended them as alternatives to ordinary natural philosophy. Clavius did so as a means of elevating disciplinary prestige; Mersenne did so as a means of meeting the challenge of Pyrrhonism. He needed a weapon that could both defeat the Pyrrhonist threat to the possibility of knowledge (with its theological and moral implications) and close the door on various philosophical unorthodoxies such as magic and naturalism. Ciceronian probabilism, informing Jesuit notions of demonstration, allowed Mersenne to grant the sceptic a measure of uncertainty in natural philosophy while preserving the cognitive status of mathematics as well as of observations of manifest appearances. Conventional pedagogy supported a disciplinary and conceptual division between physics and mathematics legitimating such a demarcation. In *La verité des sciences* Mersenne's argument therefore dwelt on those available sources of certainty that demanded no specific natural philosophical commitment. Dangerous natural philosophical alternatives, meanwhile, foundered on the rocks of scepticism itself, the dialogue's Alchemist encountering the unanswered criticisms of its Sceptic. Mersenne complements this strategy in *La verité* with an entirely appropriate, albeit halfhearted, probabilistic defense of Aristotelian physics based on its general acceptance, but his interests and purposes necessarily gravitated towards the mathematical sciences and away from natural philosophy, or physics, properly so-called.

This "mitigated scepticism" nonetheless led mathematics back to natural philosophy, despite the institutionalized structure of intellectual options constraining Mersenne's choice. He came to adopt Isaac Beeckman's term "physico-mathematics," but not because he subscribed to a corpuscular-mechanical explanatory ideal and not because he returned to a search for the true natures of things behind

---

2. Mersenne, *Harmonie universelle*, "De l'utilité," p. 24.

appearances—the goal of a genuine physics. He did it because the scope of the mathematical sciences seemed extendable over such a range of phenomena and with so much more genuinely scientific— that is, demonstrative—precision that they far outstripped in practice the unrealizable pretensions of any properly physical system, whether Aristotle's, Descartes's, or Gassendi's. Their scope and scientificity rendered them the best means of understanding the natural world, and to that extent they usurped the place of physics, if not its explanatory ambitions.

Those mathematical disciplines dealing with the natural world, represented in the quadrivium by astronomy and music, therefore acted as paradigms for attainable scientific knowledge of physical things. Mersenne conceived of them, in the standard Aristotelian way, as "subordinate sciences" depending on arithmetic and geometry but discussing mathematical properties abstracted from material objects. The nature of mathematical objects themselves, shorn in this way of physical existence, was the nub of the dispute—in which Mersenne sided with Clavius—over the causal properties of mathematical demonstrations. Mersenne held that mathematical relationships constrained the possible behavior and attributes of physical objects and to that extent expressed genuine causes explaining why certain things must be as they are. The objects of mathematics, far from being fictions, had exemplary existence in the mind of God in the same manner as did the objects of physics, but the realization of the latter necessarily involved the simultaneous instantiation of the former, thereby guaranteeing an intelligible mathematical aspect to nature. The metaphysical property of unity that scholastic philosophy attached to individuals in the world provided the fundamental exemplification of God's inevitable utilization of mathematics in His Creation, because unity, Mersenne argued, stood at the foundation of all mathematics; it was also an essential attribute of God himself.

By these means, Mersenne attempted to establish the mathematical sciences, and, in particular, the mixed mathematical sciences, at the center of the study of nature. Far from dealing with merely accidental attributes of things, they now appeared in his presentation as concerned with quasi-essential properties grounded at a metaphysical level. Reconstructing the status of mathematical objects in a way similar to that of contemporary Jesuit mathematicians supported the dignity and value of a mathematical approach to nature, while the solidity of mathematical knowledge and its attendant value-neutrality kept it safe from the moral objections of the Pyrrhonists. Nonetheless, because essential knowledge of the kind sought by Aristotelian physics remained unattainable, the certainty even of a science such as optics was compromised to the extent that the physical nature of its objects might have a bearing on their measurable behavior. That Mersenne still regarded mixed mathematics as worth pursuing shows that the degree of importance he had attached to absolute certainty in *La verité des sciences* was higher, owing to the specific argumentative goals of that book, than he otherwise deemed necessary to validate claims to knowledge. To a limited extent, therefore (but the limits were very narrow), Mersenne retained a probabilistic view of knowledge even for the mathematical sciences.

The profound relationship between mathematics, God, and the logic of Creation that the concept of unity both mediated and indicated lent itself to a further elaboration designed to justify a positive program of seeking out material analogues of mathematical structures. This program, focusing on ratios of various kinds, found legitimation in Augustinian statements about the immanence of number harmonies in the natural world. Mersenne's reliance on standard accounts, drawn from school texts, of the nature of mathematics had served to reinforce the impression of uncontentious orthodoxy surrounding his work. Using Augustine to sanction the further extension of the mathematical investigation of nature, Mersenne displayed a similar attempt at invoking the authority of precedent, as well as the protection of a Father of the Church. What look like "Platonic" aspects of Mersenne's thought were thus constituted by a quite different set of philosophical appeals from those of "Fludd and the neo-Platonists," whom he so despised. Connecting the Thomistic emphasis on God's creative constraint by logical possibilities with the Augustinian notion of "wisdom," *sapientia*, Mersenne could introduce Augustine's stress on number as the characteristic exemplification of God's wisdom manifested in the Creation and reflected in our own minds. God had made the world in accordance with mathematical ratios and proportions, and man could know it by his participation, through divine illumination, in God's wisdom thus expressed. "Universal harmony" existed, and the mathematical sciences served to display it.

Augustinian doctrines had always had a place within scholastic philosophy and theology; in addition, seventeenth-century France witnessed an Augustinian theological renascence connecting with a longer-standing Christian humanist predilection for the saint. Mersenne fits well within a contemporary intellectual and cultural setting; his employment both of Augustinian arguments and of Augustine's name displays his acceptance of their validity and his desire to acquire the authority associated with them.[3] Augustinian thought informed

3. Augustine's moderate scepticism should also be taken into account.

Descartes's accounts of the intellect and its sources of knowledge in a comparable way, with the significant difference that Descartes wished greatly to appear original as well as religiously orthodox. Mersenne saw no advantage in appearing original.

Far from being mere justificatory rhetoric designed to ease acceptance of his physico-mathematical agenda, however, Mersenne's construal of the relation between mathematics and the world determined the character and cognitive achievements of his work in the sciences of music and mechanics. In his earlier writings on the latter subject— indeed, throughout his career—the approach and techniques of the pseudo-Aristotelian *Mechanica* served as a guide, apparently because of its rather physical interpretation of mechanics. The use of physical causes in the *Mechanica*'s explanation of the law of the lever, implicit in its hidden reliance on a direct proportionality between speed and force, certainly compromised the mathematical integrity of statics; Guidobaldo del Monte rejected such conflations of subject matter. Mersenne's adoption of an approach to a mathematical science that introduced in this way the uncertainties of physics clearly stemmed from the possibilities that a dynamic account of statical situations suggested for an extension of mathematical mechanics to the study of motion.

The resemblance here to Galileo's approach provided the basis for Mersenne's qualified acceptance of the former's own mechanical ideas. A crucial difference, however, lay in Galileo's faith that a true demonstrative science of motion might be constructed. Mersenne tried to compensate for the unavoidable uncertainty of the physical concepts required in a science of motion by reducing it as much as possible to a doctrine concerning appearances. This meant a constant appeal to experiments, not as illustrative or even regulative examples but as the very content of the science itself. That is, Mersenne's way of developing a mathematical treatment of motion—specifically, of falling bodies—centered not on the abstract physical process, which individual cases might instantiate, but on the generalized description of such cases; their details, their precise parameters, held an importance for him altogether lacking for Galileo. Mersenne did not believe that no unifying causal agency existed; indeed, his belief in the regularity of nature required the existence of such an agency. However, his doubt that it could be known had the direct implication that a true science of motion must remain elusive. That is why, in sharp contrast to Galileo, he took an interest in the empirical determination of *deviations* from the odd-number rule.

His belief in "universal harmony" prevented Mersenne from questioning the presence and mathematical character of regularities underlying phenomena of motion, despite his recognition of difficulties in discovering them. The prior assumption that mathematical ratios and proportions governed the structure of the world led Mersenne to defend the Pythagorean basis of musical harmony, which had come under threat, by the expedient of grounding consonance and dissonance in the mechanical properties of sounding bodies. The mechanization of music did not signify the reduction of harmonic relationships to accidental mechanical rules, however. The model whereby musical consonances corresponded to particular patterns of concurrence among pulses could not in itself explain the nature of harmony as harmony; it simply provided an alternative way of evidencing the identity of harmony and simple numerical ratios. Hence the establishment of characteristically musical relationships in mechanics acted to demonstrate the harmony hidden in the behavior of motion, force, and machines and gave a further guarantee of the presence of Augustinian "wisdom" in the created world. Mersenne's close association of music and mechanics produced his statement and proof of the inverse-square law governing the frequency of a pendulum with respect to its length, and in this way his construal of the relationship of mathematics to nature and his image of "universal harmony" appear constitutive of his scientific work even in the generation of precise technical results.

The interaction between the general and the specific, the philosophical idiom and the statement of a truth about a particular aspect of the natural world, found explicit expression in Mersenne's characterizations of language. Only recently has the importance of schemes for the reform of language and for the development of artificial languages been adequately recognized as part of the seventeenth century's reassessment of the grounds and goals of knowledge. Language appeared in the medieval scholastic scheme of learning as the embodiment both of logic—a logic of *verbal* propositions—and of philosophy; grammar was taught with reference to Aristotelian philosophical concepts. Humanist restructuring of grammar, rhetoric, and dialectic shifted the emphasis towards language as a medium of persuasion, with grammatical rules justified primarily by appeal to correct usage, but none of that ran counter to the traditional scholastic view of the nature of words or of the general philosophical significance of grammatical categories. Humanism moved the pedagogical emphasis away from philosophy without denying the principal doctrines of the older approach.[4] Language therefore remained uncontroversially the vehicle of reason, and words—in humanist pedagogy just as in Aristotle's

4. This despite the tendency of some humanist writers to disparage scholasticism.

pronouncements—were arbitrarily imposed signs bearing no more than a conventional relationship to whatever they signified. The wholesale rejection of Aristotelian philosophy in any of its guises by many thinkers in the seventeenth century therefore involved reconsideration of the nature of language and its role in describing the world.

Scholastic Latin—the technical, philosophical Latin of the schools— was a kind of "philosophical language" designed to mirror the structure of the world by expressing real relations between things (such as cause and effect), real categories (such as things and actions, corresponding to nouns and verbs), and especially the natural groupings of individuals constituting real species of things. The philosophical-language projects of the seventeenth century each attempted to replace scholastic Latin with a new but functionally equivalent language tailored according to its author's own philosophical system. Mersenne thus rejected these kinds of language schemes for the same reason he rejected Aristotelian epistemology: each presupposed that essential natures could be known behind appearances and that individuals could be grouped into species accordingly. Nonetheless, Mersenne fully accepted the usual accounts of grammar and of the "institutional" character of words themselves, just as they appeared in the standard textbooks of the Jesuit colleges. He could do this because such aspects of scholastic Aristotelian linguistic doctrine applied perfectly well to appearances alone; in Mersenne's interpretation, denial of cognitive access to essences still left the fundamental grammatical structure of language (common to all languages) as the embodiment of precisely those phenomenological relationships that *could* be known. Mersenne defended the reliability of language as a way of formulating knowledge, and expressing reason, through the use of schoolroom commonplaces—no doubt to the considerable advantage of the defense's effectiveness.

Mathematics also formed part of an appropriate language for understanding the world because the things it demonstrated to be self-contradictory or self-consistent were in fact respectively impossible or possible in the world. A self-consistent account of the quantitative interrelations of a physical system such as a pendulum therefore expressed truths that might apply to actual pendulums and certainly applied to possible pendulums. Experiment established the applicability of a mathematical description in particular cases. The problems of generalization and demonstrability, the desiderata of a true science, ultimately proved incorrigible on this basis and led Mersenne, in the face of a Cartesian physics that exhibited clearly the unfathomable extent of the possible, to reduce his acceptance of Galilean doctrines about fall from qualified assent to resigned scepticism. All along, the point of promoting an approach to natural knowledge built around the mathematical sciences had been to avoid conflict and controversy, to abandon the dangers of dogmatism that fueled the criticisms of the Pyrrhonists by restricting knowledge claims to the evident and demonstrable matter of appearances and mathematics. The establishment of a unified scientific community depended on developing a language of consensus, but Galileo's work finally showed itself to be as reliant upon hidden assumptions about physical causes and as much a generator of dissension as Aristotle's or Descartes's philosophies. Mersenne's desire to achieve Christian unity and freedom from religious strife had gradually led him from quite vigorous Catholic apologetics to an irenicist tolerance that required the tenets of faith to be as few, and as firm, as could successfully command common assent.[5] He had consistently placed the same demands on his associated philosophical program.

Mersenne's Thomistic assurance of the importance of philosophy to theology thus underlay his entire agenda for the study and understanding of nature. Certainty, assurance, and uncontentiousness were his goals; the tools he used to achieve them suited their purpose to the extent that they acquired their legitimacy from a doctrinally orthodox, well-established source: the learning of the schools. Mersenne did not create a new system of natural philosophy or a new epistemology to support his view of the sorts of questions that the student of nature should ask. Instead, his program of research depended on conceptual elements and stock arguments drawn from contemporary scholastic-Aristotelian and humanist teaching, materials that Mersenne would initially have met during his education by the Jesuits. His philosophical agenda, although concentrating on mathematical, operational knowledge of appearances, was thus formulated in a preexisting philosophical idiom suited to essentialism, and his ideas often display a borrowed rather than intrinsic coherence. Mersenne preferred the sanction of orthodoxy to the rhetoric of "innovation" favored by many of his contemporaries, not least because novelty usually implied system, and system implied essentialism. Since a defense of any particular world view ran counter to his aims, Mersenne avoided the difficulty by lifting (in a somewhat piecemeal fashion) well-entrenched, familiar ideas out of their usual context and building a new context around them.

Mersenne does not belong in the pantheon of the creators of a

---

5. One thinks of his interest in such people as Herbert of Cherbury, Comenius, and La Peyrère.

"new science" because he invented a new vision of nature or major new techniques for its understanding; in any direct way he did neither. He belongs there because of his role in developing, through his correspondence and publications, a new kind of philosophical community for studying nature; in a sense, by no means entirely anachronistic, a new *scientific* community. He endeavored to do so by redefining the goals of natural knowledge and recharacterizing the proper— and attainable—ambitions of the natural philosopher. That is why the term "agenda," rather than "system" or even "philosophy," has seemed appropriate to describe the characteristically novel aspect of his work. Mersenne advocated as the principal techniques for investigating nature those of the mixed mathematical sciences. The real novelty lay in his moving them to the center of the philosophical stage. Aristotelian natural philosophy, a physics sharply demarcated from mathematics, allowed the mathematician to play at best a tributary role in understanding the physical world. Mersenne simply asserted that the kind of knowledge sought by the physicist could not be had or that the degree of certainty accruing to it failed to meet appropriate criteria. An operational understanding of appearances, centered on the mathematical sciences, took its place; in that sense Mersenne's adoption of the term "physico-mathematics" has a clear justification even though, according to strict contemporary usage, most of the things he put under this head were not "physical."[6]

In effect, therefore, Mersenne retained the usual scholastic boundaries between disciplines. He rejected essentialist physics and exalted the mathematical disciplines, but he never claimed that the subject matter of physics had no real meaning or was illusory. Mersenne was not a positivist; he believed that what man could not verify, God already knew. Natural kinds existed in nature, and things had essential definitions, but man could not know them in this life; hence, physics was either a futile or, at best, a wholly conjectural endeavor— and dogmatic conjectures bred social division. The pursuit of scientific knowledge, he thought, should proceed according to a realizable plan calculated to command common assent rather than to generate philosophical dispute, and he constructed such a plan out of the least questionable forms of knowledge and most generally accepted argu-

6. Gaspar Schott, *Magia universalis naturae et artis* (Würzburg, 1657–59), 3:212, classifies Mersenne's approach to mechanics as "mathematical" rather than "physico-mechanical" because Mersenne does not consider the physical causes of motion. As Mersenne's interest in the *Mechanica* shows, this critique goes a little too far (Schott lists Aristotle in the second category), but it indicates Mersenne's care to distance himself from physics proper. (One might note that Beeckman's usage of the term "physico-mathematics" *was* correct because of its corpuscular basis.)

ments available. Seeing Mersenne's approach to natural philosophy as a new "agenda" pursued through the selective use of existing conceptual resources thus locates his work firmly within its proper context. The full significance of this view appears when one considers its contrast with versions of the "continuity thesis" developed in the twentieth century following the work of Pierre Duhem.

II

Duhem, focusing on fourteenth-century discussions of motion at Oxford and Paris, argued that Galileo's mechanics represented a development of that medieval tradition, the Renaissance being little more than an unfortunate interlude.[7] Subsequent scholars, most notably Anneliese Maier and Ernest Moody, refined and qualified his contention and revealed important differences as well as similarities between Galileo and impetus theorists of the fourteenth century (although Maier's claims never entirely convinced Moody that Galileo and Jean Buridan were as far apart as she maintained).[8] The prevailing consensus holds that while elements of the work on motion in medieval Oxford and Paris clearly found their way to Galileo, the nature of his enterprise differed sufficiently to render them of only secondary value in understanding the development of his mechanics. Thus recent studies of the "Oxford Calculators" by John Murdoch and Edith Sylla have tended more and more to treat the fourteenth-century work in its own context and to leave aside the connections with the sixteenth century that once provided the chief incentive for studying it.[9]

Nonetheless, another version of the continuity thesis retains some vigor. Different from Duhem's yet partly inspired by his example, it concentrates on "scientific method." It first appeared in John Randall's influential argument of 1940 that Galileo's approach to natural

7. Pierre Duhem, *Études sur Léonard de Vinci* (Paris, 1906–13).

8. Maier's long list of published studies includes several volumes under the general title of *Studien zur Naturphilosophie der Spätscholastik*; for a full bibliography and relevant essays see Anneliese Maier, *On the Threshold of Exact Science*, ed. and trans. Steven D. Sargent (Philadelphia, 1982). See also Ernest A. Moody, *Studies in Medieval Philosophy, Science, and Logic* (Berkeley, 1975), esp. "Galileo and His Precursors," pp. 393–408 (an essay first published in 1966).

9. See, e.g., Edith Dudley Sylla, "The Oxford Calculators," in Kretzmann, Kenny, and Pinborg, *Cambridge History of Later Medieval Philosophy*, pp. 540–63; John E. Murdoch, "The Analytic Character of Late Medieval Learning," in Lawrence D. Roberts, ed., *Approaches to Nature in the Middle Ages* (Binghamton, N.Y., 1982), pp. 171–213.

philosophy descended directly from the methodological speculations of Averroist Aristotelians at Padua, especially Zabarella. A number of scholars have successfully challenged Randall's view, noting that experience plays a very different role in Galileo's methodology from that in Zabarella's and pointing out alternative sources for certain relevant concepts in Galileo's writings.[10] Nonetheless, Randall's thesis has found a successor that takes over some of its stronger features and shores them up with direct textual evidence of Galileo's borrowing from scholastic sources. The attention to methodology remains, but its locus has shifted.

William Wallace, and Alistair Crombie and Adriano Carugo, have shown during the last decade or so that certain of Galileo's works previously dismissed as juvenile or purely derivative bear close affinities to Jesuit teachings at the Collegio Romano in the later sixteenth century.[11] Arguing that these writings represent Galileo's crit-

---

10. John Herman Randall, Jr., "The Development of Scientific Method in the School of Padua," *Journal of the History of Ideas* 1 (1940), 177–206; also idem, *The School of Padua and the Emergence of Modern Science* (Padua, 1961). Randall's position, developed from remarks by Cassirer, has been undermined most notably by Neal W. Gilbert, "Galileo and the School of Padua," *Journal of the History of Philosophy* 1 (1963), 223–31; Charles Schmitt, "Experience and Experiment," *Studies in the Renaissance* 16 (1969), 80–138, showing quite different concepts of experience in Zabarella and Galileo; Nicholas Jardine, "Galileo's Road to Truth and the Demonstrative Regress," *Studies in History and Philosophy of Science* 7 (1976), 277–318, like Gilbert tracing the roots of Galileo's conception of "analysis" and "synthesis" to mathematical sources rather than to Zabarella; Paolo Rossi, "The Aristotelians and the 'Moderns'," *Annali dell'Istituto e Museo di Storia della Scienza di Firenze* 7 (1982), fasc. 1, 3–28, using Zabarella as the representative Aristotelian and denying the validity of claims to "continuity." Alistair C. Crombie, *Robert Grosseteste and the Origins of Experimental Science, 1100–1700* (Oxford, 1953), attempted to extend Randall's chain of development back to Grosseteste at the beginning of the thirteenth century. For criticisms of Crombie's characterization of Grosseteste as an advocate of "experiment," see Bruce S. Eastwood, "Medieval Empiricism," *Speculum* 43 (1968), 306–21; and James McEvoy, *The Philosophy of Robert Grosseteste* (Oxford, 1983), pp. 206–11. The influence of Zabarella has also been claimed for other seventeenth-century "new philosophers," including William Harvey and Thomas Hobbes: see the assessment of such claims by Charles Schmitt, "Aristotelianism in the Veneto and the Origins of Modern Science," in Luigi Olivieri, ed., *Aristotelismo veneto e scienza moderna* (Padua, 1983), 1:104–23, rejecting strong claims about the role of the "School of Padua" (which Schmitt denies existed in any definitive way) in the creation of modern science; William F. Edwards, "Paduan Aristotelianism and the Origins of Modern Theories of Method," in Olivieri, *Aristotelismo*, 1:206–20, attributes a large debt to Zabarella on the part of Descartes and Hobbes. Aldo G. Gargani, *Hobbes e la scienza* (Turin, 1971), maintains the importance of the resolutive/compositive method of Zabarella for Hobbes. No doubt the debate will continue.

11. Most importantly, Wallace, *Prelude to Galileo* and *Galileo and His Sources*; Alistair C. Crombie, "Sources of Galileo's Early Natural Philosophy," in M. L. Righini Bonelli and W. R. Shea, eds., *Reason, Experiment and Mysticism in the Scientific Revolution* (New York, 1975), pp. 157–75; Adriano Carugo and Alistair C. Crombie, "The Jesuits and Galileo's Ideas of Science and of Nature," *Annali dell'Istituto e Museo di Storia della Scienza di Firenze* 8 (1983), fasc. 2, 3–68.

ical appropriation of scholastic ideas,[12] they contend that throughout his career Galileo's conception of the nature of a science, and the ways in which he framed and described his procedures especially in the study of motion, derived in large measure from Jesuit antecedents. The principal difference between this thesis and Randall's is that whereas Randall connects Galileo to Aristotelian traditions via the Paduan Averroists, these authors do so via the Jesuits of the Collegio Romano. The difference is by no means insignificant, and Wallace distinguishes convincingly between "fundamentalist" Aristotelians at Padua (and elsewhere) and "progressive" Jesuit Aristotelians. Wallace's *Galileo and His Sources* makes a good case for Galileo's methodological ideals having retained throughout his career at least some family resemblance to the Jesuit doctrines with which he had early become acquainted, and Wallace is careful to conclude with the admission that Galileo also innovated in important ways, including an original use of mathematical techniques in natural philosophy and the employment of new experimental procedures.[13] Despite such moderation, however, Wallace's overall aim remains clear. He wishes to establish that certain basic elements of Galileo's science, elements contributing crucially to the success of that science, derived from a Jesuit version of a scholastic philosophical enterprise stretching back to the thirteenth century. This was broadly Thomistic and ultimately rooted in Aristotle.

Wallace explicitly describes his argument as a "continuity thesis." The same label clearly fits Crombie's and Carugo's work along similar lines, although they have themselves denied it, asserting that their intention goes no further than to show the roots of Galileo's thought in the specific context of late sixteenth-century Jesuit teaching. Since few would deny the intellectual filiations between the scholasticism of the Jesuits and that of the High Middle Ages (whatever the originality of the former), this distinction seems unnecessary. Furthermore, the analytical assumptions of Crombie and Carugo differ in no essential respects from those of Wallace or, indeed, Randall; "scientific method" provides the thread linking Galileo with his proper antecedents.

There are a number of objections to these methodological varieties of the continuity thesis. The strongest is that "science" differs radically from "applied scientific method." As Paolo Rossi has written,

12. But see Ernan McMullin's criticisms of this point in his review of Wallace's *Prelude to Galileo* (1981) in *Philosophy of Science* 50 (1983), 171–73; Wallace provides a scorching reply, "Galileo and the Continuity Thesis," in ibid., 51 (1984), 504–10.

13. Though even this seems less clear in light of Dear, "Jesuit Mathematical Science." Wallace's claims here are more moderate than in some of his previous writings.

one cannot explain the Scientific Revolution in terms of the development or application of correct scientific method, because such a method—taken as a regulative, determinate procedure generating objective knowledge of nature—does not exist; science is not that simple.[14] Most attempts at a continuity thesis presuppose as their central historical explanandum the production in the seventeenth century of new and important discoveries, of true facts about nature. Galileo almost invariably appears as the central focus, the historian adopting the role of assayer to determine how the evidence of Galileo's work weighs for or against an argument pertaining to the Scientific Revolution as a whole. Indeed, for Wallace, Galileo is still the Father of Modern Science. The implicit premises supporting such an approach are, first, that Galileo did indeed discover true things about the world; secondly, that doing so required the use of correct scientific method; and thirdly, that this method became the standard for seventeenth-century science. Thus, Galileo's method accounts for the Scientific Revolution as a phenomenon, and discovering the sources for that method explains it historically.

The historian cannot legitimately employ any of these premises, however. Sanctioning Galileo's knowledge claims as true is irrelevant to a historical understanding of their nature and origins. People do not believe things *because* they are true.[15] Consequently, quite apart from Rossi's surely correct observation that there is no "scientific method" or set of rules for producing true knowledge,[16] we may say that even if there were, it could never, even in principle, assist in producing historical accounts or explanations of Galileo's work in particular or the Scientific Revolution in general. Understanding seventeenth-century natural philosophy requires consideration of "scientific method" in the sense that ideas and discussions about method figured largely in the creation of the new attitudes towards knowledge characterizing the period. The pronouncements of Bacon or Descartes or Galileo concerning proper procedure in learning and speaking about the natural world are important, regardless of judgments as to whether or not we ought to agree with them. One can also, perhaps, ask whether and in what sense their general theories of knowledge shaped, or became instantiated in, or even were constituted by specific pieces of formal scientific accomplishment: the

14. Rossi, "The Aristotelians and the Moderns," esp. pp. 3–6.
15. I mean this in a strict logical sense.
16. Recent work in the sociology of scientific knowledge has pressed this point with reference to the work of Wittgenstein. See, e.g., David Bloor, *Wittgenstein* (London, 1983); H. M. Collins, *Changing Order* (London, 1985).

sine law of refraction; the proportionality between speed and time for falling bodies. At no point, however, will considerations of the truth or falsity of these individual results enter into their historical evaluation, and so the "correctness" of the method involved in their production loses any explanatory significance. Similarly, one need not develop firm political views on absolutism in order to discuss Hobbes's *Leviathan* as a historical document. Only a historical actor's claims or beliefs, not their validity, can properly play a part in the historian's accounts. It would be futile, for example, to try to explain Mersenne's opinions on whether falling bodies undergo uniform acceleration by reference to the actual behavior of falling bodies. Before 1633 he denied uniform acceleration; subsequently, until 1644 or so, he accepted it; finally, he doubted it once more. Yet he based his assertions at every stage on the authority of clear sensory experience.

The question of the continuity or discontinuity between thinkers of the Scientific Revolution and scholastic philosophers of whatever stripe in the Middle Ages does not entirely disappear, of course, simply by rejecting a concern with some timeless "scientific method." We still find, for example, that Galileo talks of accidents and causes, natural and violent motion, uniformly difform motion, the demonstrative regress—terms and concepts, concerning both method and particular subject matters, the sources of which represent no great mystery. However, like Descartes's or Mersenne's, Galileo's retention of elements of school learning—specifically, commonplace late-scholastic Aristotelian physics and logic—ought only to be expected. Galileo surely perceived the distinction between the significant, novel aspects of his own work and the mere "residues of the past" differently from the way such a distinction appears to us—he would never have retained anything that seemed to him redundant. If Galileo did not regard certain concepts as "residues," then they did not play that role in his thought. What, then, should we make of their presence in his philosophical vocabulary? The answer is simply that he found them useful.

The value of taking Mersenne's work as an example of apparent continuity within a process of equally apparent change and novelty arises from the extent to which he avoids embodying within himself the seeming paradox of his situation. That is to say, unlike Descartes or Galileo or others with whom he corresponded or whose ideas he promoted, Mersenne never cast himself as an innovator. Consequently, his writings afford a less rhetorically layered, or cluttered, object of analysis. He feels less need to hide intellectual debts; indeed, he frequently parades them (or, perhaps, incurs them) as authoritative endorsements of his own arguments. His rhetorical style relies much more on the persuasiveness of familiar doctrines than do those of his more heroic contemporaries, yet he is as much a representative figure of the Scientific Revolution as they are; the practical implications of his philosophy, and his own scientific activities, bear much the same characteristics. If he differs from Descartes and from Galileo, the differences do not exceed that between those two men themselves. Mersenne's promotion of the mathematical sciences as the most effective means of understanding nature signals his alignment with a major development in seventeenth-century natural philosophy; his experimental bias, although different from Descartes's on the one hand and Galileo's on the other, does likewise. Furthermore, his activities as an intelligencer, which form a crucial aspect of his agenda, helped to consolidate an emerging community to act as the social locus of these new approaches. Even if, contrary to the arguments given above, Mersenne's importance were also deemed to rest on his production of specific scientific results, "true facts about nature," his musical or acoustical studies alone would qualify. His chief significance, however, lies in his intellectual sympathy with mathematical and even mechanistic approaches to natural philosophy and in his attempts to make them the basis of a new philosophical consensus.

The analytical difficulties of creating order from the contradictory signs of continuity and discontinuity, or novelty, result only from a confusion of conceptual and rhetorical resources with the uses to which they are put. Ideas themselves do not determine their applications; in a sense, they do not even possess any definitive meaning. The "Merton mean-speed theorem" had no physical significance until Galileo (or Domingo de Soto, perhaps) used it as a way of speaking about free fall; Galileo's action simultaneously devalued the theorem's previously preeminent logical or sophismatic significance.[17] Mersenne's new agenda for natural knowledge, his account of the direction it should follow and the questions it should ask, drew heavily on existing techniques, ideas, and arguments, but it too gave them new meanings defined by his novel purposes. Lenoble and Popkin identified Mersenne's goals, the goals of his agenda and hence of his deployment of ideas, with the generally apologetical aims of destroying the credibility of naturalism, magic, and scepticism—all tools of heresy. More broadly, he worked at creating consensus, both religious and philosophical.

The picture that has emerged from this study shows Mersenne constructing an ideal of natural knowledge, based on mathematics

17. On sophismata, see Sylla, "The Oxford Calculators"; on De Soto, see William A. Wallace, "The Enigma of Domingo de Soto," *Isis* 59 (1968), 384–401.

and the appearances of things, which constituted a new agenda for the investigation of the physical world. The ultimate purposes of the new agenda, to undermine alternatives perceived as subversive of true religion and social order and to establish a new basis for consensus, provided the criteria for evaluating its acceptability. Its actual character, however, depended equally on the conceptual resources available for its construction. Mersenne's agenda thus resulted from a dialectic between goals and resources. It was determined neither by the goals it served nor by the conceptual resources it employed; however, the suitability of the available resources to yield an agenda consonant with Mersenne's apologetical and social goals necessarily shaped that agenda into a particular form inexplicable through simple consideration of its purpose. The sources of particular ideas or arguments contributed to their rhetorical effectiveness: Mersenne *wanted* to look orthodox. His development of a way of creating community among natural philosophers of diverse persuasion relied on the exploitation of ideas that no one had learned seriously to question.

The case of Mersenne does not, then, support the "continuity thesis" in any of the senses discussed above. Discovering conceptual elements of school learning, whether humanist or scholastic, in the work of important figures of the Scientific Revolution fails to establish their thought as an internal development of a preexisting intellectual enterprise. The ends for which they used those conceptual elements, and the choice they exercised in selecting them, also require investigation. True continuity would reside in a continuity of natural philosophical agendas, presupposing a continuity not only of specific ideas but also of goals. Mersenne continued to use traditional ideas while developing a new agenda responding to the changing role of knowledge of the natural world in his cultural environment. His value as a focus of historical examination lies in the clarity of his purposes and the undisguised character of his intellectual debts.

Bibliography

This bibliography contains full publication data for all items cited in the notes, together with some additional sources not otherwise noticed.

AARSLEFF, HANS. *From Locke to Saussure*. Minneapolis: University of Minnesota Press, 1982.
———. "Leibniz on Locke on Language." *American Philosophical Quarterly* 1 (1964), 165–88. Reprinted, with quotations translated, in Aarsleff, *From Locke to Saussure*, pp. 42–82.
———. "The Study and Use of Etymology in Leibniz." In Aarsleff, *From Locke to Saussure*, pp. 84–100.
———. " The Tradition of Condillac: The Problem of the Origin of Language in the Eighteenth Century and the Debate in the Berlin Academy before Herder." In Aarsleff, *From Locke to Saussure*, pp. 146–209.
———. "Wilkins, John." In *Dictionary of Scientific Biography*, 15:239–77.
ABERCROMBIE, NIGEL. *Saint Augustine and French Classical Thought*. Oxford: Oxford University Press, 1938.
AGUILONIUS, FRANCISCUS. *Opticorum libri sex, Philosophis iuxta ac Mathematicis utiles*. Antwerp: apud Viduam et Filios Io. Moreti, 1613.
AITON, E. J. *The Vortex Theory of Planetary Motions*. London: Macdonald, 1972.
AMMANN, PETER J. "The Musical Theory and Philosophy of Robert Fludd." *Journal of the Warburg and Courtauld Institutes* 30 (1967), 198–227.
ARIOTTI, PIERO E. "Aspects of the Conception and Development of the Pendulum in the 17th Century." *Archive for History of Exact Sciences* 8 (1972), 329–410.
———. "Bonaventura Cavalieri, Marin Mersenne, and the Reflecting Telescope." *Isis* 66 (1975), 303–21.
ARISTOTLE. *Posterior Analytics*.
——— [Pseudo-Aristotle]. *Mechanica*. Translated by E. S. Forster. In J. A. Smith

and W. D. Ross, eds., *The Works of Aristotle*, vol. 6. Oxford: Clarendon Press, 1913.

———. *Topics.*

ARMSTRONG, C. J. R. "The Dialectical Road to Truth: The Dialogue." In Sharratt, *French Renaissance Studies*, pp. 36–51.

ASHWORTH, E. J. "Do Words Signify Ideas or Things? The Scholastic Sources of Locke's Theory of Language." *Journal of the History of Philosophy* 19 (1981), 299–326.

———. *Language and Logic in the Post-Medieval Period.* Dordrecht: D. Reidel, 1974.

ASHWORTH, WILLIAM B., JR. "Catholicism and Early Modern Science." In Lindberg and Numbers, *God and Nature*, pp. 136–66.

AUGER, LÉON. *Gilles Personne de Roberval (1602–1675).* Paris: Blanchard, 1962.

———. "Le R. P. Mersenne et la physique." *Revue d'histoire des sciences* 2 (1948), 33–52.

AUGUSTINE. *Contra Academicos.* Translated by Denis J. Kavanagh. In Ludwig Schopp, ed., *Writings of Saint Augustine*, vol. 1. New York: Cima, 1948.

———. *De civitate Dei.* Translated by Gerald G. Walsh et al. In Vernon J. Bourke, ed., *Saint Augustine: The City of God.* New York: Image Books, 1958.

———. *De diversibus quaestionibus.*

———. *De libero arbitrio.* Translated by John H. S. Burleigh. In John H. S. Burleigh, ed., *Augustine: Earlier Writings.* Library of Christian Classics, vol. 6. Philadelphia: Westminster Press, 1953.

———. *De magistro.* Translated by John H. S. Burleigh. In John H. S. Burleigh, ed., *Augustine: Earlier Writings.* Library of Christian Classics, vol. 6. Philadelphia: Westminster Press, 1953.

———. *De musica.* Translated by Robert Catesby Taliaferro. In Ludwig Schopp, ed., *Writings of Saint Augustine*, vol. 2. New York: Cima, 1947.

———. *De ordine.* Translated by Robert P. Russell. In Ludwig Schopp, ed., *Writings of Saint Augustine*, vol. 1. New York: Cima, 1948.

———. *De trinitate.* Translated by A. W. Haddan. In Whitney J. Oates, ed., *Basic Writings of Saint Augustine*, vol. 2. New York: Random House, 1948.

———. *Soliloquia.* Translated by John H. S. Burleigh. In John H. S. Burleigh, ed., *Augustine: Earlier Writings.* Library of Christian Classics, vol. 6. Philadelphia: Westminster Press, 1953.

BACON, FRANCIS. *The New Organon.* Translated by James Spedding. Indianapolis, Ind.: Bobbs-Merrill, 1960.

———. *Novum Organum.* In J. Spedding, R. L. Ellis, and D. D. Heath, eds., *The Works of Francis Bacon*, vol. 1. Boston: Brown & Taggart, 1861.

BAUMGARTNER, FREDERICK J. "Scepticism and French Interest in Copernicanism to 1630." *Journal for the History of Astronomy* 17 (1986), 77–88.

BAYLEY, PETER. *French Pulpit Oratory, 1598–1650.* Cambridge: Cambridge University Press, 1980.

BEAULIEU, ARMAND. "Christiaan Huygens et Mersenne l'inspirateur." In *Huygens et la France: Table Ronde du CNRS, Paris, 27–29 Mars 1979*, pp. 25–31. Paris: J. Vrin, 1982.

———. "Découverte d'un livre de Mersenne." *Revue d'histoire des sciences* 35 (1982), 55–56.

———. "Lumière et matière chez Mersenne." *XVIIᵉ siècle*, no. 136 (1982), 311–16.

———. "Problèmes d'édition de la correspondance d'un homme prodigieux: Marin Mersenne." In Trevor Levere, ed., *Editing Texts in the History of Science and Medicine*, pp. 101–16. New York: Garland, 1982.

———. "Les réactions des savants français au début du XVIIᵉ siècle devant l'héliocentrisme de Galilée." In Paolo Galluzzi, ed., *Novità Celesti e Crisi del Sapere: Atti del Convegno Internazionale di Studi Galileiani*, pp. 373–81. Supplement, *Annali dell'Istituto e Museo di Storia della Scienza*, 1983, fasc. 2.

———. "Secret ou mystification? *Aristarchi de mundi systemate*, avec notes de Roberval." *Recherches sur le XVIIᵉ siècle* 4 (1980), 37–45.

BERKEL, KLAAS VAN. "Beeckman, Descartes et 'la philosophie physico-mathématique.'" *Archives de philosophie* 46 (1983), 620–26.

BERNHARDT, JEAN. "Mersenne, commentateur de Galilée: À propos d'une édition critique des 'Nouvelles pensées de Galilée.'" *Revue d'histoire des sciences* 28 (1975), 169–77.

BETTS, C. J. *Early Deism in France.* The Hague: Martinus Nijhoff, 1984.

BLANCANUS, JOSEPHUS. *Aristotelis loca mathematica ex universis ipsius Operibus collecta, & explicata.* Bologna: apud Bartholomaeum Cochium, 1615.

———. *De mathematicarum natura dissertatio: Una cum clarorum mathematicorum chronologia.* Bologna: apud Bartholomaeum Cochium, 1615.

———. "Echometria." In Josephus Blancanus, *Sphaera mundi*, pp. 415–43. Bologna: typis Sebastiani Bonomii, 1620.

BLOCH, OLIVIER RENÉ. *La philosophie de Gassendi.* The Hague: Martinus Nijhoff, 1971.

BLOOR, DAVID. *Wittgenstein: A Social Theory of Knowledge.* London: Macmillan, 1983.

BODIN, JEAN. *La méthode de l'histoire.* French translation by Pierre Mesnard of *Methodus ad facilem historiarum cognitionem.* Algiers: Maison-Carrée, 1941.

BOETHIUS. *De institutione musica.*

BOLGAR, R. R. *The Classical Heritage and Its Beneficiaries.* Cambridge: Cambridge University Press, 1954.

BOUTROUX, EMILE. *Des vérités éternelles chez Descartes.* French translation by Georges Canguilhem of *De veritatibus aeternis apud Cartesium.* Paris: Alcan, 1927.

BOUTROUX, PIERRE. "Le Père Mersenne et Galilée." *Scientia* 31 (1922), 279–90, 347–60.

BOUWSMA, WILLIAM J. "The Two Faces of Humanism: Stoicism and Augustinianism in Renaissance Thought." In Heiko O. Oberman and Thomas A. Brady, Jr., eds., *Itinerarium Italicum*, pp. 3–60. Studies in Medieval and Reformation Thought, vol. 14. Leiden: E. J. Brill, 1975.

BRANDT, FRITHIOF. *Thomas Hobbes' Mechanical Conception of Nature.* Copenhagen: Levin & Munksgaard, 1928. (Available through University Microfilms, Ann Arbor, Mich.)

BREHIER, ÉMILE. "The Creation of the Eternal Truths in Descartes's System" (1937). Translated from the French in Willis Doney, ed., *Descartes: A Collection of Critical Essays,* pp. 192–208. New York: Anchor Books, 1967.

BREKLE, HERBERT E. "The Seventeenth Century." In Sebeok, *Historiography of Linguistics,* pp. 277–382.

BREVA-CLARAMONTE, MANUEL. "Sanctius' *Minerva* of 1562 and the Evolution of His Linguistic Theory." *Historiographia Linguistica* 2 (1975), 49–66.

———. *Sanctius' Theory of Language: A Contribution to the History of Renaissance Linguistics.* Studies in the History of Linguistics, vol. 27. Amsterdam: John Benjamin, 1983.

BROCKLISS, L. W. B. "Philosophy Teaching in France, 1600–1740." *History of Universities* 1 (1981), 131–68.

BROWN, HARCOURT. *Scientific Organizations in Seventeenth Century France (1620–1680).* Baltimore: Williams & Wilkins, 1934.

BROWN, JOSEPH E. "The Science of Weights." In Lindberg, *Science in the Middle Ages,* pp. 179–205.

BUBACZ, BRUCE. *St. Augustine's Theory of Knowledge: A Contemporary Analysis.* Texts and Studies in Religion, vol. 11. New York: Edwin Mellen, 1981.

BURNYEAT, MYLES, ed. *The Skeptical Tradition.* Berkeley: University of California Press, 1983.

BURSILL-HALL, G. L. "The Middle Ages." In Sebeok, *Historiography of Linguistics,* pp. 179–230.

BURTT, EDWIN A. *The Metaphysical Foundations of Modern Physical Science.* Rev. Ed. New York, 1932.

BUSARD, H. L. L. "Clavius, Christoph." In *Dictionary of Scientific Biography,* 3:311–12.

BUZON, FRÉDÉRIC DE. "Descartes, Beeckman, et l'acoustique." *Archives de philosophie* 44 (1981), Bulletin Cartésien X, pp. 1–8.

———. "Science de la nature et théorie musicale chez Isaac Beeckman (1588–1637)." *Revue d'histoire des sciences* 38 (1985), 97–120.

CARTWRIGHT, W. C. *The Jesuits: Their Constitution and Teaching.* London: John Murray, 1876.

CARUGO, ADRIANO, AND ALISTAIR C. CROMBIE. "The Jesuits and Galileo's Ideas of Science and of Nature." *Annali dell'Istituto e Museo di Storia della Scienza di Firenze* 8 (1983), fasc. 2, 3–68.

CASSIRER, ERNST. "Mathematical Mysticism and Mathematical Science." In McMullin, *Galileo,* pp. 338–51.

CHARLES-DAUBERT, FRANÇOISE. "Le libertinage et la recherche contemporaine." *XVIIᵉ siècle,* no. 149 (1985), 409–32.

CHARTIER, ROGER, DOMINIQUE JULIA, AND MARIE-MADELEINE COMPÈRE. *L'éducation en France du XVIᵉ au XVIIIᵉ siècle.* Paris: Société d'édition d'enseignment supérieur, 1976.

CLAGETT, MARSHALL. *The Science of Mechanics in the Middle Ages.* Madison: University of Wisconsin Press, 1959.

CLARKE, DESMOND. *Descartes' Philosophy of Science.* Manchester: Manchester University Press, 1982.

CLAUS, SIDONIE. "John Wilkins' Essay toward a Real Character: Its Place in the Seventeenth-Century Episteme." *Journal of the History of Ideas* 43 (1982), 531–53.

CLAVELIN, MAURICE. *The Natural Philosophy of Galileo.* Translated by A. J. Pomerans. Cambridge, Mass.: M.I.T. Press, 1971.

CLAVIUS, CHRISTOPH. "Modus quo disciplinae mathematicae in scholis Societatis possent promoveri." In *Monumenta paedagogica Societatis Iesu quae primam Rationem Studiorum anno 1586 praecessere,* pp. 471–74. Madrid, 1901.

——. *Operum mathematicorum tomus primus.* Mainz: Reinhardus Eltz, 1611.

CODINA MIR, GABRIEL. *Aux sources de la pédagogie des Jésuites: Le "Modus Parisiensis."* Rome: Institutum Historicum S. I., 1968.

COHEN, H. F. *Quantifying Music. The Science of Music at the First Stage of the Scientific Revolution, 1580–1650.* Dordrecht: D. Reidel, 1984.

COLLINS, H. M. *Changing Order: Replication and Induction in Scientific Practice.* London: Sage, 1985.

COMENIUS, JOHANN AMOS. *Linguarum methodus novissima.* In Johann Amos Comenius, *Veškeré Spisy,* vol. 6. Brno, 1911.

——. *Pansophiae prodromus.* London: Fawne & Gellibrand, 1639.

Commentarii Collegii Conimbricensis e Societate Iesu: In universam dialecticam Aristotelis Stagiritae. Cologne: apud Bernardum Gualtherium, 1607; facsimile rpt., Hildesheim: Georg Olms, 1976.

Commentariorum Collegii Conimbricensis Societatis Iesu, in octo libros physicorum Aristotelis Stagiritae . . . tomi. Cologne: L. Zetzner, 1596.

COPLESTON, FREDERICK. *A History of Philosophy,* vol. 3. Westminster, Md.: Newman Press, 1963.

CORNELIUS, PAUL. *Languages in Seventeenth and Early Eighteenth Century Imaginary Voyages.* Geneva: Droz, 1965.

COSENTINO, GIUSEPPE. "L'insegnamento delle matematiche nei collegi gesuitici nell'Italia settentrionale." *Physis* 13 (1971), 205–17.

COSTABEL, PIERRE. "L'initiation mathématique de Descartes." *Archives de philosophie* 46 (1983), 637–46.

——. "La roue d'Aristote et les critiques françaises à l'argument de Galilée." *Revue d'histoire des sciences* 17 (1964), 385–96.

—— AND PIERRE PIVETEAU. Translation of *éloge* of Galileo from Mersenne, *Cogitata. Revue d'histoire des sciences* 18 (1965), 221–26.

COUMET, ERNEST. "Mersenne: 'Dictions' nouvelles à l'infini." *XVIIe siècle,* no. 109 (1975), 3–32.

COUTURAT, LOUIS. *La logique de Leibniz.* Paris: Alcan, 1901.

—— AND LÉOPOLD LEAU. *Histoire de la langue universelle.* Hildesheim: Georg Olms, 1979.

CRANZ, F. EDWARD. *A Bibliography of Aristotle Editions, 1501–1600.* 2d ed., with addenda and revisions by Charles B. Schmitt. Bibliotheca Bibliographica Aureliana, vol. 38*. Baden-Baden: Valentin Koerner, 1984.

CROMBIE, ALISTAIR C. "Experimental Science and the Rational Artist in Early Modern Europe." *Daedalus* 115 (1986), 49–74.

——. "Marin Mersenne and the Seventeenth-Century Problem of Scientific Acceptability." *Physis* 17 (1975), 186–204.

——. "Mathematics and Platonism in the Sixteenth-Century Italian Universities and in Jesuit Educational Policy." In Y. Maeyama and W. G. Saltzer, eds., *Prismata: Naturwissenschaftsgeschichtliche Studien (Festschrift für Willy Hartner)*, pp. 63–94. Wiesbaden: Franz Steiner, 1977.

——. "Mathematics, Music and Medical Science." In *Actes du XIIe Congrès International d'Histoire des Sciences, Paris 1968*, 1B:295–310. Paris: Albert Blanchard, 1971. (Also in *Organon* 6 [1969], 21–36.)

——. "Mersenne, Marin." In *Dictionary of Scientific Biography*, 9:316–22.

——. *Robert Grosseteste and the Origins of Experimental Science, 1100–1700*. Oxford: Clarendon Press, 1953.

——. "Science and the Arts in the Renaissance: The Search for Truth and Certainty, Old and New." In Shirley and Hoeniger, *Science and the Arts*, pp. 15–26.

——. "Sources of Galileo's Early Natural Philosophy." In M. L. Righini Bonelli and W. R. Shea, eds., *Reason, Experiment and Mysticism in the Scientific Revolution*, pp. 157–75. New York: Science History Publications, 1975.

CRONIN, TIMOTHY J. *Objective Being in Descartes and in Suarez*. Analecta Gregoriana, vol. 154. Rome: Gregorian University Press, 1966.

CURLEY, E. M. "Descartes on the Creation of the Eternal Truths." *Philosophical Review* 93 (1984), 569–97.

DAINVILLE, FRANÇOIS DE. *L'éducation des Jésuites XVIe–XVIIIe siècles*. Paris: Minuit, 1978.

——. "L'enseignment des mathématiques dans les Collèges Jésuites de France du XVIe au XVIIIe siècle." *Revue d'histoire des sciences* 7 (1954), 6–21, 109–23.

——. "Foyers de culture scientifique dans la France méditerranéenne du XVIe au XVIIIe siècle." *Revue d'histoire des sciences* 1 (1948), 289–300.

——. *La géographie des humanistes*. Paris: Beauchesne, 1940.

——. *La naissance de l'humanisme moderne*. Paris: Beauchesne, 1940.

DALBIEZ, R. "Les sources scolastiques de la théorie cartésienne de l'être objectif." *Revue d'histoire de la philosophie* 3 (1929), 464–72.

DEAR, PETER. "Jesuit Mathematical Science and the Reconstitution of Experience in the Early Seventeenth Century." *Studies in History and Philosophy of Science* 18 (June 1987).

DEBUS, ALLEN G. *The English Paracelsians*. London: Oldbourne, 1965.

——. "Fludd, Robert." In *Dictionary of Scientific Biography*, 5:47–49.

DE COSTE, HILARION. *La vie du R. P. Marin Mersenne, théologien, philosophe et mathématicien, de l'Ordre des Pères Minimes*. Paris, 1649. Reprinted in Philippe Tamizey de Larroque, ed., *Les correspondants de Peiresc*, 2:436–97. 1879–97; facsimile rpt., Geneva: Slatkine, 1972.

DEE, JOHN. *The Mathematicall Preface to the Elements of Geometrie of Euclid of Megara* (1570). Introduction by Allen G. Debus. New York: Science History Publications, 1975.

DEHNERT, EDMUND JOHN. "Music as Liberal in Augustine and Boethius." In *Arts libéraux et philosophie au moyen âge*, pp. 987–91. Actes du quatrième congrès international de philosophie médiévale, 1967. Montreal: Institut d'études médiévales, 1969.

DE MOTT, BENJAMIN. "The Sources and Development of John Wilkins' Philosophical Language (1668)." *Journal of English and Germanic Philology* 57 (1958), 1–13.

DESCARTES, RENÉ. *Discours de la méthode, texte et commentaire par Étienne Gilson.* Paris: J. Vrin, 1967.

——. *Oeuvres de Descartes.* Publiées par Charles Adam & Paul Tannery. Paris: J. Vrin, 1964–71.

——. *Règles utiles et claires pour la direction de l'esprit en la recherche de la vérité.* Translated by Jean-Luc Marion. The Hague: Nijhoff, 1977.

——. *The World.* Translated by Michael S. Mahoney. New York: Abaris Books, 1979.

DE WAARD, CORNÉLIS. "À la recherche de la correspondance de Mersenne." *Revue d'histoire des sciences* 2 (1948), 13–28.

——. *L'expérience barométrique.* Thouars, 1936.

DICTIONARY OF SCIENTIFIC BIOGRAPHY. Edited by Charles C. Gillespie. 16 vols. New York: Scribner, 1970–80.

DOIG, JAMES C. "Suarez, Descartes, and the Objective Reality of Ideas." *New Scholasticism* 51 (1977), 350–71.

DONAHUE, WILLIAM H. *The Dissolution of the Celestial Spheres.* New York: Arno Press, 1981.

DOSTROVSKY, SIGALIA. "Early Vibration Theory: Physics and Music in the Seventeenth Century." *Archive for History of Exact Sciences* 14 (1975), 169–218.

DOYLE, JOHN P. "Suarez on the Reality of the Possibles." *Modern Schoolman* 45 (1967), 29–48.

DRABKIN, ISRAEL E. "Aristotle's Wheel: Notes on the History of a Paradox." *Osiris* 9 (1950), 162–98.

DRAKE, STILLMAN. "Baliani, Giovanni Battista." In *Dictionary of Scientific Biography,* 1:424–25.

——. "Free Fall from Albert of Saxony to Honoré Fabri." *Studies in History and Philosophy of Science* 5 (1975), 347–66.

——. *Galileo at Work: His Scientific Biography.* Chicago: University of Chicago Press, 1978.

——. *Galileo Studies.* Ann Arbor: University of Michigan Press, 1970.

——. "Impetus Theory and Quanta of Speed before and after Galileo." *Physis* 16 (1974), 47–65.

——. "Le Tenneur, Jacques." In *Dictionary of Scientific Biography,* 8:267–69.

——. "Physics and Tradition before Galileo." In Drake, *Galileo Studies,* pp. 19–42.

——. "Renaissance Music and Experimental Science." *Journal of the History of Ideas* 31 (1970), 483–500.

——. "Vincenzo Galilei and Galileo." In Drake, *Galileo Studies,* pp. 43–62.

—— AND I. E. DRABKIN, eds. *Mechanics in Sixteenth-Century Italy.* Madison: University of Wisconsin Press, 1969.

DROIXHE, DANIEL. *La linguistique et l'appel de l'histoire (1600–1800).* Geneva: Droz, 1978.

——. "Le prototype défiguré: L'idée scythique et la France gauloise (XVIIᵉ–

XVIIIᵉ siècles)." In Konrad Koerner, ed., *Progress in Linguistic Historiography*, pp. 123–37. Amsterdam: John Benjamin, 1980.

DUGAS, RENÉ. *Mechanics in the Seventeenth Century*. Translated by Freda Jacquot. Neuchâtel: Griffon, 1958.

DUHEM, PIERRE. *Études sur Léonard de Vinci*. 3 vols. Paris: Hermann, 1906–13.

——. *Les origines de la statique*. 2 vols. Paris, 1905–6.

——. "Le P. Marin Mersenne et la pesanteur de l'air." *Revue générale des sciences pures et appliquées* 17 (1906), 769–82, 809–17.

DUNCAN, DAVID ALLEN. "The Tyranny of Opinions Undermined: Science Pseudo-Science and Scepticism in the Musical Thought of Marin Mersenne." Diss., Vanderbilt University, 1981.

DURET, CLAUDE. *Thresor de l'histoire des langues de cest univers*. 2d ed. Yverdon: Société helvetiale baldoresque, 1619.

DURKHEIM, ÉMILE. *L'évolution pédagogique en France*. 2 vols. Paris: Alcan, 1938.

EASTWOOD, BRUCE S. "Medieval Empiricism: The Case of Grosseteste's Optics." *Speculum* 43 (1968), 306–21.

EDWARDS, SANDRA. "The Realism of Aquinas." *New Scholasticism* 59 (1985), 79–101.

EDWARDS, WILLIAM F. "Paduan Aristotelianism and the Origins of Modern Theories of Method." In Olivieri, ed., *Aristotelismo veneto e scienza moderna*, 1:206–20.

ENGELBERG, DON, AND MICHAEL GERTNER. "A Marginal Note of Mersenne concerning the 'Galilean Spiral.'" *Historia mathematica* 8 (1981), 1–14.

ESPINAS, A. "Pour l'histoire du cartésianisme." *Revue de métaphysique et de morale* 4 (1906), 265–93.

FENNER, DUDLEY. *The Artes of Logike and Rethorike* (1584). In Robert D. Pepper, ed., *Four Tudor Books on Education*, pp. 143–80. Gainesville, Fl.: Scholars' Facsimiles and Reprints, 1966.

FERREYROLLES, GÉRARD. "L'influence de la conception augustinienne de l'histoire au XVIIᵉ siècle." *XVIIᵉ siècle* 34 (1982), 216–41.

FIELD, JUDITH V. "Kepler's Rejection of Numerology." In Vickers, *Occult and Scientific Mentalities*, pp. 273–96.

FLUDD, ROBERT. *Sophiae cum moria certamen . . .* Frankfurt, 1629.

FONSECA, PEDRO DA. *Commentariorum in metaphysicorum Aristotelis Stagiritae libros tomi quatuor*. Cologne, 1615; facsimile rpt., Hildesheim: Georg Olms, 1964.

——. *Institutionum dialecticarum libri octo*. Venice: apud Vincentium Florinum, 1611.

FOUCAULT, MICHEL. *The Order of Things*. Translation of *Les mots et les choses*. New York: Vintage Books, 1973.

FRANCE, PETER. *Rhetoric and Truth in France: Descartes to Diderot*. Oxford: Oxford University Press, 1972.

FRANKFURT, H. "Descartes on the Creation of the Eternal Truths." *Philosophical Review* 86 (1977), 36–57.

FUMAROLI, MARC. *L'âge de l'éloquence: Rhétorique et "res literaria" de la Renaissance au seuil de l'époque classique*. Geneva: Droz, 1980.

FUNKENSTEIN, AMOS. "Descartes, Eternal Truths and the Divine Omnipotence." In Gaukroger, *Descartes*, pp. 181–95.

GALILEO GALILEI. *Dialogue Concerning the Two Chief World Systems.* Translated by Stillman Drake. 2d ed. Berkeley: University of California Press, 1967.

———. *On Motion and On Mechanics.* Translated by I. E. Drabkin and Stillman Drake. Madison: University of Wisconsin Press, 1960.

———. *Two New Sciences.* Translated by Stillman Drake. Madison: University of Wisconsin Press, 1974.

GARGANI, ALDO G. *Hobbes e la scienza.* Turin: Einaudi, 1971.

GARIN, EUGENIO. *L'éducation de l'homme moderne.* French translation from the Italian by Jacqueline Humbert. [Paris]: Fayard, 1968.

GARIN, PIERRE. *Thèses cartésiennes et thèses thomistes.* Paris: Desclée de Brouwer, 1932.

GAUKROGER, STEPHEN. *Explanatory Structures: A Study of Concepts of Explanation in Early Physics and Philosophy.* Atlantic Highlands, N.J.: Humanities Press, 1978.

———, ed. *Descartes: Philosophy, Mathematics and Physics.* Brighton, Sussex: Harvester Press, 1980.

GEISSLER, HEINRICH. *Comenius und die Sprach.* Heidelberg: Quelle & Meyer, 1959.

GENTILE, GIOVANNI. "Il concetto dell'uomo nel rinascimento." In *Opere complete,* 11:47–113. Florence: G. C. Sansoni, 1940.

GERSON, LLOYD. "Augustine's Neoplatonic Argument for the Existence of God." *Thomist* 45 (1981), 571–84.

GILBERT, NEAL W. "Galileo and the School of Padua." *Journal of the History of Philosophy* 1 (1963), 223–31.

———. *Renaissance Concepts of Method.* New York: Columbia University Press, 1960.

GILSON, ÉTIENNE. *Études sur le rôle de la pensée médiévale dans la formation du système cartésien* (1921). Paris: J. Vrin, 1951.

———. *Index scolastico-cartésien.* Paris: Alcan, 1913.

———. *Introduction à l'étude de Saint Augustin.* Paris: J. Vrin, 1929.

———. *La liberté chez Descartes et la théologie.* Paris: Alcan, 1913.

———. *The Philosophy of St. Thomas Aquinas.* Translation by G. A. Elrington of *Le Thomisme,* 3d ed. Cambridge: Heffer, 1924.

GODWIN, JOSCELYN. *Robert Fludd: Hermetic Philosopher and Surveyor of Two Worlds.* London: Thames & Hudson, 1979.

GOUHIER, HENRI. *Cartésianisme et augustinisme au XVIIe siècle.* Paris: J. Vrin, 1978.

———. "La crise de la théologie au temps de Descartes." *Revue de théologie et de philosophie,* 3d ser., 4 (1954), 19–54.

———. *La pensée métaphysique de Descartes.* Paris: J. Vrin, 1962.

———. *La pensée religieuse de Descartes.* 2d ed. Paris: J. Vrin, 1972.

GRACIA, JORGE J. E. *Suarez on Individuation.* Milwaukee: Marquette University Press, 1982.

GRAFTON, ANTHONY T. "Teacher, Text and Pupil in the Renaissance Classroom: A Case Study from a Parisian College." *History of Universities* 1 (1981), 37–70.

GRAY, HANNA H. "Renaissance Humanism: The Pursuit of Eloquence." *Jour-*

nal of the History of Ideas 24 (1963), 497–514. Reprinted in P. O. Kristeller and P. Wiener, eds., *Renaissance Essays*. New York: Harper Torchbooks, 1968.

GRUBER, ALBION. "Mersenne and Evolving Tonal Theory." *Journal of Music Theory* 14 (1970), 36–67.

GUARINO, BATTISTA. *De ordine docendi et studendi*. Translated by William Harrison Woodward. In Woodward, *Vittorino da Feltre*, pp. 159–78.

GUERLAC, RITA. *Juan Luis Vives against the Pseudo-Dialecticians*. Dordrecht: D. Reidel, 1979.

GUIDOBALDO DEL MONTE. *Mechanicorum liber*. Pesaro, 1577. Abridged translation by Stillman Drake. In Drake and Drabkin, *Mechanics*, pp. 239–328.

HACKING, IAN. *The Emergence of Probability*. Cambridge: Cambridge University Press, 1975.

———. "Proof and Eternal Truths: Descartes and Leibniz." In Gaukroger, *Descartes*, pp. 169–80.

HANNAWAY, OWEN. "Laboratory Design and the Aim of Science: Andreas Libavius versus Tycho Brahe." *Isis* 77 (1986), 585–610.

HEATH, TERRENCE. "Logical Grammar, Grammatical Logic, and Humanism in Three German Universities." *Studies in the Renaissance* 18 (1971), 9–64.

HEATH, THOMAS. *Mathematics in Aristotle*. Oxford: Clarendon Press, 1949.

HEILBRON, JOHN L. *Electricity in the 17th and 18th Centuries: A Study in Early Modern Physics*. Berkeley: University of California Press, 1979.

HERMELINK, HEINER. "Marin Mersenne und seine Naturphilosophie." *Philosophia naturalis* 1 (1950), 223–42.

HILL, DAVID K. "Galileo's Work on 116v: A New Analysis." *Isis* 77 (1986), 283–91.

HINE, WILLIAM L. "The Interaction between Science and Religion in the Circle of Marin Mersenne." Diss., University of Oklahoma, 1967.

———. "Marin Mersenne: Renaissance Naturalism and Renaissance Magic." In Vickers, *Occult and Scientific Mentalities*, pp. 165–76.

———. "Mersenne and Copernicanism." *Isis* 64 (1973), 18–32.

———. "Mersenne and Vanini." *Renaissance Quarterly* 29 (1976), 52–65.

———. "Mersenne Variants." *Isis* 67 (1976), 98–103.

HOBBES, THOMAS. *Dialogus physicus*. Translated by Simon Schaffer. In Steven Shapin and Simon Schaffer, *Leviathan and the Air-Pump: Hobbes, Boyle and the Experimental Life*, pp. 345–91. Princeton: Princeton University Press, 1985.

HOLTON, GERALD. "Johannes Kepler's Universe: Its Physics and Metaphysics." In Robert M. Palter, ed., *Toward Modern Science*, 2:192–216. New York: Noonday Press, 1961. Reprinted in Gerald Holton, *Thematic Origins of Scientific Thought, Kepler to Einstein*, pp. 69–90. Cambridge: Harvard University Press, 1973.

HOOYKAAS, R. *Humanisme, science et réforme: Pierre de la Ramée (1515–1572)*. Leiden: E. J. Brill, 1958.

HOWELL, W. S. *Logic and Rhetoric in England, 1500–1700*. Princeton: Princeton University Press, 1956.

HUCHZERMEYER, HELMUT, AND HANS HUCHZERMEYER. "Die Bedeutung des Rythmus in der Musiktherapie der Griechen von der Frühzeit bis zum Beginn des Hellenismus." *Sudhoffs Archiv* 58 (1974), 113–48.

HUMBERT, PIERRE. "Mersenne et les astronomes de son temps." *Revue d'histoire des sciences* 2 (1948), 29–32.

HUNT, FREDERICK VINTON. *Origins in Acoustics: The Science of Sound from Antiquity to the Age of Newton.* New Haven: Yale University Press, 1978.

HYDE, FREDERICK BILL. "The Position of Marin Mersenne in the History of Music." Diss., Yale University, 1954.

JARDINE, LISA. *Francis Bacon: Discovery and the Art of Discourse.* Cambridge: Cambridge University Press, 1974.

——. "Lorenzo Valla and the Intellectual Origins of Humanist Dialectic." *Journal of the History of Philosophy* 15 (1977), 143–64. Revised as "Lorenzo Valla: Academic Skepticism and the New Humanist Dialectic," in Burnyeat, *The Skeptical Tradition*, pp. 253–86.

JARDINE, NICHOLAS. *The Birth of History and Philosophy of Science. Kepler's "A Defence of Tycho against Ursus" with Essays on Its Provenance and Significance.* Cambridge: Cambridge University Press, 1984.

——. "The Forging of Modern Realism: Clavius and Kepler against the Sceptics." *Studies in History and Philosophy of Science* 10 (1979), 141–73.

——. "Galileo's Road to Truth and the Demonstrative Regress." *Studies in History and Philosophy of Science* 7 (1976), 277–318.

——. "The Significance of the Copernican Orbs." *Journal for the History of Astronomy* 13 (1982), 168–94.

——. "Skepticism in Renaissance Astronomy: A Preliminary Study." In C. B. Schmitt and R. H. Popkin, eds., *Skepticism from the Renaissance to the Enlightenment.* Wolfenbüttel: Herzog August Bibliothek, forthcoming.

JONES, R. F. "Science and Language in England of the Mid-Seventeenth Century." *Journal of English and Germanic Philology* 31 (1932), 315–31.

JORDAN, MARK D. "The Intelligibility of the World and the Divine Ideas in Aquinas." *Review of Metaphysics* 38 (1984), 17–32.

KAHN, VICTORIA. *Rhetoric, Prudence, and Skepticism in the Renaissance.* Ithaca: Cornell University Press, 1985.

KASSLER, JAMIE KROY. "Music as a Model in Early Science." *History of Science* 20 (1982), 103–39.

KAUFMAN, PETER IVER. *Augustinian Piety and Catholic Reform.* Macon, Ga.: Mercer University Press, 1982.

KELLER, ALEX. "Mathematical Technologies and the Growth of the Idea of Technical Progress in the Sixteenth Century." In Allen G. Debus, ed., *Science, Medicine and Society in the Renaissance*, 1:11–27. New York: Science History Publications, 1972.

KEOHANE, NANNERL O. *Philosophy and the State in France.* Princeton: Princeton University Press, 1980.

KLEIN, JACOB. *Greek Mathematical Thought and the Origin of Algebra.* Cambridge, Mass.: M.I.T. Press, 1968.

KNOBLOCH, EBERHARD. "Marin Mersennes Beiträge zur Kombinatorik." *Sudhoffs Archiv* 58 (1974), 356–79.

——. "*Musurgia universalis*: Unknown Combinatorial Studies in the Age of Baroque Absolutism." *History of Science* 17 (1979), 258–75.

KNOESPEL, KENNETH J. "The Narrative Matter of Mathematics: John Dee's Preface to the *Elements* of Euclid of Megara (1570)." *Philological Quarterly*, forthcoming.

KNOWLSON, JAMES R. *Universal Language Schemes in England and France, 1600–1800.* Toronto: Toronto University Press, 1975.

KOTTMAN, KARL A. "Fray Luis de León and the Universality of Hebrew: An Aspect of 16th and 17th Century Language Theory." *Journal of the History of Philosophy* 13 (1975), 297–310.

KOYRÉ, ALEXANDRE. "A Documentary History of the Problem of Fall from Kepler to Newton." *Transactions of the American Philosophical Society* 45 (1955), 329–95.

——. "An Experiment in Measurement." In Koyré, *Metaphysics and Measurement*, pp. 89–117.

——. "Galileo and Plato." In Koyré, *Metaphysics and Measurement*, pp. 16–43. Reprinted from *Journal of the History of Ideas* 4 (1943), 400–428.

——. *Galileo Studies.* Translation by John Mepham of *Études galiléennes.* Brighton, Sussex: Harvester Press, 1978.

——. "Giambattista Benedetti, Critic of Aristotle." In McMullin, *Galileo*, pp. 98–117.

——. *Metaphysics and Measurement.* Cambridge: Harvard University Press, 1968.

——. *La philosophie de Jacob Boehme.* Paris: J. Vrin, 1929.

KRETZMANN, NORMAN, ANTHONY KENNY, AND JAN PINBORG, eds. *The Cambridge History of Later Medieval Philosophy.* Cambridge: Cambridge University Press, 1982.

KRISTELLER, PAUL OSKAR. "The Modern System of the Arts." In *Renaissance Thought and the Arts*, pp. 163–227. Princeton: Princeton University Press, 1980.

——. "The Renaissance." In Michael Mooney, ed., *Renaissance Thought and Its Sources*, pp. 242–59. New York: Columbia University Press, 1979.

——. *Renaissance Concepts of Man and Other Essays.* New York: Harper & Row, 1972.

——. *Renaissance Thought: The Classic, Scholastic, and Humanist Strains.* New York: Harper Torchbooks, 1961.

KUKENHEIM, LOUIS. *Contributions à l'histoire de la grammaire grecque, latine et hebraïque à l'époque de la Renaissance.* Leiden: E. J. Brill, 1951.

LAIRD, W. R. "The Scope of Renaissance Mechanics." *Osiris*, n.s., 2 (1986), 43–68.

LAKOFF, ROBIN. Review of *Grammaire générale et raisonnée*. *Language* 45 (1969), 343–64.

LENIHAN, J. M. A. "Mersenne and Gassendi: An Early Chapter in the History of Sound." *Acustica* 1 (1951), 96–99.

LENOBLE, ROBERT. "À propos du tricentenaire de la mort de Mersenne."

Archives internationales d'histoire des sciences 28 (1949), 583–97.

——. "Histoire et physique: À propos des conseils de Mersenne aux historiens et de l'intervention de Jean de Launoy dans la querelle gassendiste." *Revue d'histoire des sciences* 6 (1953), 112–34.

——. *Mersenne ou la naissance du mécanisme.* Paris: J. Vrin, 1943, 1971.

——. "Quelques aspects d'une révolution scientifique: À propos du troisième centenaire du P. Mersenne (1588–1648)." *Revue d'histoire des sciences* 2 (1948), 53–79.

LEWIS, CHRISTOPHER. *The Merton Tradition and Kinematics in Late Sixteenth and Early Seventeenth Century Italy.* Padua: Antenore, 1980.

LINDBERG, DAVID C. "Science and the Early Church." In Lindberg and Numbers, *God and Nature*, pp. 19–48.

——, ed. *Science in the Middle Ages.* Chicago: Chicago University Press, 1978.

—— AND RONALD L. NUMBERS, eds. *God and Nature: Historical Essays on the Encounter between Christianity and Science.* Berkeley: University of California Press, 1986.

LLOYD, G. E. R. *Magic, Reason and Experience: Studies in the Origin and Development of Greek Science.* Cambridge: Cambridge University Press, 1979.

LOHR, CHARLES H. "Jesuit Aristotelianism and Sixteenth-Century Metaphysics." In Harry George Fletcher III and Mary Beatrice Schulte, eds., *Paradosis: Studies in Memory of Edwin A. Quain*, pp. 203–20. New York: Fordham University Press, 1976.

LOWINSKY, EDWARD E. "Music in the Culture of the Renaissance." *Journal of the History of Ideas* 15 (1954), 509–53.

MACE, DEAN T. "Marin Mersenne on Language and Music." *Journal of Music Theory* 14 (1970), 2–35.

McEVOY, JAMES. *The Philosophy of Robert Grosseteste.* Oxford: Clarendon, 1983.

MACHABEY, ARMAND, SR. "Quelques savants-musiciens de l'époque de Mersenne." *Revue d'histoire des sciences* 11 (1958), 193–206.

McKIRAHAN, RICHARD D. "Aristotle's Subordinate Sciences." *British Journal for the History of Science* 11 (1978), 197–220.

McMULLIN, ERNAN, ed. *Galileo, Man of Science.* New York: Basic Books, 1967.

——. Review of William A. Wallace, *Prelude to Galileo* (1981). *Philosophy of Science* 50 (1983), 171–73.

McRAE, ROBERT. "Innate Ideas." In R. J. Butler, ed., *Cartesian Studies*, pp. 32–54. Oxford: Blackwell, 1972.

MAHONEY, MICHAEL S. "The Beginnings of Algebraic Thought in the Seventeenth Century." In Gaukroger, *Descartes*, pp. 141–55.

——. *The Mathematical Career of Pierre de Fermat.* Princeton: Princeton University Press, 1973.

——. "Mathematics." In Lindberg, *Science in the Middle Ages*, pp. 145–78.

——. "The Royal Road: The Development of Algebraic Analysis from 1550 to 1650, with Special Reference to the Work of Pierre de Fermat." Diss., Princeton University, 1967.

MAIER, ANNELIESE. *On the Threshold of Exact Science: Selected Writings of An-*

neliese Maier on Late Medieval Natural Philosophy. Edited and translated by
Steven D. Sargent. Philadelphia: University of Pennsylvania Press, 1982.

MARGOLIN, JEAN-CLAUDE. "L'enseignment des mathématiques en France
(1540–70): Charles de Bovelles, Fine, Peletier, Ramus." In Sharratt, *French
Renaissance Studies*, pp. 109–55.

MARION, JEAN-LUC. *Sur la théologie blanche de Descartes.* Paris: Presses Universitaires de France, 1981.

MARRONE, STEPHEN P. *William of Auvergne and Robert Grosseteste: New Ideas of
Truth in the Early Thirteenth Century.* Princeton: Princeton University Press,
1983.

MAURER, ARMAND. "St. Thomas and Eternal Truths." *Mediaeval Studies* 32
(1970), 91–107.

MERSENNE, MARIN. *Cogitata physico-mathematica.* Paris, 1644.

———. *Correspondance du P. Marin Mersenne, religieux minime.* Edited by C. de
Waard, R. Pintard, B. Rochot, A. Beaulieu. 16 vols. to date. Paris: Beauchesne (vol.1); Presses Universitaires de France (vols. 2–4); Centre Na-
tionale de la Recherche Scientifique (vols. 5–), 1932–.

———. *Harmonicorum libri XII.* Paris, 1648. Rpt., Geneva: Minkoff, 1972.

———. *Harmonie universelle.* Paris, 1636–37. Facsimile rpt. of author's anno-
tated copy, Paris: Centre National de la Recherche Scientifique, 1963.

———. *L'impieté des deistes.* 2 vols. Paris, 1624. Rpt. vol. 1, Stuttgart-Bad Cannstatt: Friedrich Frommann, 1975.

———. *Les mechaniques de Galilée, mathematicien et ingenieur du Duc de Florence.*
Paris, 1634. Critical ed. by Bernard Rochot, Paris: Presses Universitaires de
France, 1966.

———. *Les nouvelles pensées de Galilée.* Paris, 1638–39. Critical ed. by Pierre
Costabel and Michel-Pierre Lerner, Paris: J. Vrin, 1973.

———. *Novarum observationum . . . tomus III.* Paris, 1647.

———. *Observationes et emendationes ad Francisci Georgii Veneti problemata.* Paris,
1623.

———. *L'optique et la catoptrique du Reverend Pere Mersenne Minime: Nouvellement
mise en lumiere, après la mort de l'Autheur.* Paris, 1651.

———. *Les preludes de l'harmonie universelle.* Paris, 1634.

———. *Quaestiones celeberrimae in Genesim.* Paris, 1623.

———. *Questions harmoniques.* Paris, 1634. Rpt., Stuttgart–Bad Cannstatt:
Friedrich Frommann, 1972.

———. *Questions inouyes, ou recreation des sçavans.* Paris, 1634. Rpt., Stuttgart-Bad
Cannstatt: Friedrich Frommann, 1972.

———. *Questions rares et curieuses, theologiques, naturelles, morales, politiques, et de
controverse, resoluës par raisons tirées de la Philosophie, & de la Theologie.* Paris:
Pierre Billaine, 1630. Reprint from same plates, with new front matter, of
L'impieté des deistes, vol. 1.

———. *Questions theologiques, physiques, morales, et mathematiques.* Paris, 1634.

———. *Synopsis mathematica.* Paris, 1626.

———. *Traité de l'harmonie universelle.* Paris, 1627.

———. *Universae geometriae, mixtaeque mathematicae synopsis.* Paris, 1644.

———. *L'usage de la raison.* Paris, 1623.

——. *L'usage du quadran, ou d'horloge physique universel.* Paris: Rocolet, 1639.

——. *La verité des sciences contre les septiques ou Pyrrhoniens.* Paris, 1625. Rpt., Stuttgart–Bad Cannstatt: Friedrich Frommann, 1969.

METCALF, GEORGE G. "The Indo-European Hypothesis in the Sixteenth and Seventeenth Centuries." In Dell Hymes, ed., *Studies in the History of Linguistics: Traditions and Paradigms,* pp. 233–57. Bloomington: Indiana University Press, 1974.

MIETHE, TERRY L. "Augustine and Sense Knowledge." In *Augustinian Bibliography, 1970–1980, with Essays on the Fundamentals of Augustinian Scholarship,* pp. 171–83. Westport, Conn.: Greenwood Press, 1982.

MILTON, JOHN R. "The Origin and Development of the Concept of the 'Laws of Nature.'" *Archives européennes de sociologie* 22 (1981), 173–95.

Monumenta Paedagogica Societatis Iesu quae Primam Rationem Studiorum anno 1586 praecessere. Madrid, 1901.

MOODY, ERNEST A. *Studies in Medieval Philosophy, Science, and Logic: Collected Papers, 1933–1969.* Berkeley: University of California Press, 1975.

—— AND MARSHALL CLAGETT, eds. *The Medieval Science of Weights.* Madison: University of Wisconsin Press, 1960.

MORRIS, JOHN. "Descartes' Natural Light." *Journal of the History of Philosophy* 11 (1973), 169–87.

MORSE, JOANN S. "The Reception of Diophantus' *Arithmetic* in the Renaissance." Diss., Princeton University, 1981.

MOSCOVICI, SERGE. *L'expérience du mouvement: Jean-Baptiste Baliani, disciple et critique de Galilée.* Paris: Hermann, 1967.

MUELLER, IAN. "Geometry and Scepticism." In Jonathan Barnes et al., eds., *Science and Speculation: Studies in Hellenistic Theory and Practice,* pp. 69–95. Cambridge: Cambridge University Press, 1982.

MURDOCH, JOHN E. "The Analytic Character of Late Medieval Learning: Natural Philosophy without Nature." In Lawrence D. Roberts, ed., *Approaches to Nature in the Middle Ages,* pp. 171–213. Binghamton, N.Y.: Center for Medieval and Early Renaissance Studies, 1982.

NARDI, ANTONIO. "Descartes 'presque galiléen': 18 février 1643." *Revue d'histoire des sciences* 39 (1986), 3–16.

NASH, RONALD H. *The Light of the Mind: St. Augustine's Theory of Knowledge.* Lexington: University Press of Kentucky, 1969.

NAUX, CHARLES. "Le père Christophore Clavius (1537–1612): Sa vie et son oeuvre." *Revue des questions scientifiques* 154 (1983), 55–67, 181–93, 325–47.

NEIMAN, ALVEN MICHAEL. "The Arguments of Augustine's *Contra Academicos.*" *Modern Schoolman* 59 (1982), 255–79.

NORENA, CARLOS P. "Ockham and Suarez on Universal Concepts." *New Scholasticism* 55 (1981), 348–62.

OBERMAN, HEIKO. *Masters of the Reformation.* Cambridge: Cambridge University Press, 1981.

O'CONNELL, ROBERT J. *Art and the Christian Intelligence in St. Augustine.* Oxford: Blackwell, 1978.

OLIVIERI, LUIGI, ed. *Aristotelismo veneto e scienza moderna.* 2 vols. Padua: Antenore, 1983.

ONG, WALTER J. Ramus: Method, and the Decay of Dialogue. New York: Octagon Books, 1979.

OSLER, MARGARET J. "Eternal Truths and the Laws of Nature: The Theological Foundations of Descartes' Philosophy of Nature." *Journal of the History of Ideas* 46 (1985), 349–62.

———. "Providence and Divine Will in Gassendi's Views on Scientific Knowledge." *Journal of the History of Ideas* 44 (1983), 549–60.

OWEN, G. E. L. "Aristotle: Method, Physics, and Cosmology." In *Dictionary of Scientific Biography*, 1:250–58.

OWENS, JOSEPH. "Faith, Ideas, Illumination, and Experience." In Kretzmann, Kenny, and Pinborg, *The Cambridge History of Later Medieval Philosophy*, pp. 440–59.

PADLEY, G. A. *Grammatical Theory in Western Europe, 1500–1700: The Latin Tradition.* Cambridge: Cambridge University Press, 1976.

———. *Grammatical Theory in Western Europe, 1500–1700: Trends in Vernacular Grammar I.* Cambridge: Cambridge University Press, 1985.

PAGANINI, GIANNI. "L'anthropologie naturaliste d'un esprit fort: Thèmes et problèmes pomponaciens dans le *Theophrastus Redivivus*." *XVIIᵉ siècle*, no. 149 (1985), 349–77.

PAGEL, WALTER. *Paracelsus: An Introduction to Philosophical Medicine in the Era of the Renaissance.* Basel: S. Karger, 1958.

PALISCA, CLAUDE V. "The Science of Sound and Musical Practice." In Shirley and Hoeniger, *Science and the Arts*, pp. 59–73.

———. "Scientific Empiricism in Musical Thought." In Hedley Howell Rhys, ed., *Seventeenth Century Science and the Arts*, pp. 91–137. Princeton: Princeton University Press, 1961.

PANIZZA, LETIZIA A. "Lorenzo Valla's *De vero falsoque bono*, Lactantius and Oratorical Scepticism." *Journal of the Warburg and Courtauld Institutes* 41 (1978), 76–107.

PASCAL, BLAISE. *Les lettres provinciales.*

PATEY, DOUGLAS LANE. *Probability and Literary Form: Philosophic Theory and Literary Practice in the Augustan Age.* Cambridge: Cambridge University Press, 1984.

PERCIVAL, W. KEITH. "The Grammatical Tradition and the Rise of the Vernaculars." In Sebeok, *Historiography of Linguistics*, pp. 231–75.

———. "The Reception of Hebrew in Sixteenth-Century Europe: The Impact of the Cabbala." *Historiographia linguistica* 11 (1984), 21–38.

PETER OF SPAIN. *Tractatus, called afterwards Summule logicales.* First critical ed. from the MSS. Edited by L. M. de Rijk. Assen: Van Gorcum, 1972.

PINTARD, RENÉ. *Le libertinage érudit dans la première moitié du XVIIᵉ siècle.* Paris: Boivin, 1943. Rpt., Geneva: Slatkine, 1983.

POPKIN, RICHARD H. "Father Mersenne's War against Pyrrhonism." *Modern Schoolman* 34 (1956–57), 61–78.

———. *The History of Scepticism from Erasmus to Spinoza.* Berkeley: University of California Press, 1979.

———. "Le scepticisme pour ou contre les sciences à la fin du XVIᵉ siècle." In *VIIIᵉ Congrès International de Tours: Sciences de la Renaissance*, pp. 83–90. Paris: J. Vrin, 1973.

PRIMAUDAYE, PETER DE LA. *The French Academy.* Translated by T. B. London, 1602.

PSEUDO-ARISTOTLE. *See* Aristotle.

QUINN, JOHN M. "The Scholastic Mind of Galileo: The Jesuit Connection." *International Philosophical Quarterly* 20 (1980), 347–62.

RANDALL, JOHN HERMAN, JR. "The Development of Scientific Method in the School of Padua." *Journal of the History of Ideas* 1 (1940), 177–206.

———. *The School of Padua and the Emergence of Modern Science.* Padua: Antenore, 1961.

Ratio studiorum et institutiones scholasticae Societatis Iesu per Germaniam olim vigentes collectae. 4 vols. Published by G. M. Pachtler. Berlin: Hofmann, 1887–94.

REIF, MARY RICHARD. "Natural Philosophy in Some Early Seventeenth Century Scholastic Textbooks." Diss., St. Louis University, 1962.

REMSBERG, ROBERT GOTWALD. *Wisdom and Science at Port-Royal and the Oratory.* Yellow Springs, Ohio: Antioch Press, 1940.

RENAUDOT, THÉOPHRASTE. *Recueil general des questions traittees ès conferences du Bureau d'Adresse, sur toutes sortes de matieres, par les plus beau esprits de ce temps.* Paris, 1655.

ROBINET, ANDRÉ. *Le langage à l'âge classique.* Paris: Klincksieck, 1978.

ROCHEMONTEIX, CAMILLE DE. *Un collège de Jésuites aux XVIIe & XVIIIe siècles: Le collège Henri IV de La Flèche.* 4 vols. Le Mans: Leguicheux, 1889.

ROCHOT, BERNARD. *La correspondance scientifique du Père Mersenne.* Paris: Palais de la Découverte, 1966.

———. "Le P. Mersenne et les relations intellectuelles dans l'Europe du XVIIe siècle." *Cahiers d'histoire mondiale* 10 (1966), 55–73.

RODIS-LEWIS, GENEVIÈVE. *L'oeuvre de Descartes.* Paris: Vrin, 1971.

ROSE, PAUL LAWRENCE. *The Italian Renaissance of Mathematics: Studies on Humanists and Mathematicians from Petrarch to Galileo.* Geneva: Droz, 1975.

——— AND STILLMAN DRAKE. "The Pseudo-Aristotelian *Questions in Mechanics* in Renaissance Culture." *Studies in the Renaissance* 18 (1971), 65–104.

ROSS, J. F. "Introduction." In Francisco Suarez, *On Formal and Universal Unity,* translated by J. F. Ross. Milwaukee: Marquette University Press, 1964.

ROSSI, PAOLO. "The Aristotelians and the Moderns: Hypothesis and Nature." *Annali dell'Istituto e Museo di Storia della Scienza di Firenze* 7 (1982), fasc. 1, 3–28.

———. *Clavis universalis.* Milan: Riccardo Ricciardi, 1960.

———. *Francis Bacon: From Magic to Science.* Translated by Sacha Rabinovitch. Chicago: University of Chicago Press, 1968.

RUBY, JANE E. "The Origins of Scientific 'Law'." *Journal of the History of Ideas* 47 (1986), 341–59.

SABRA, A. I. *Theories of Light from Descartes to Newton.* Cambridge: Cambridge University Press, 1981.

SADLER, JOHN EDWARD. *J. A. Comenius and the Concept of Universal Education.* London: George Allen & Unwin, 1966.

SALMON, VIVIAN. "John Wilkins' *Essay* (1668): Critics and Continuators." *Historiographia linguistica* 1 (1974), 147–63. Reprinted in Salmon, *The Study of Language,* pp. 191–206.

————. "Language-Planning in Seventeenth-Century England: Its Context and Aims." In C. E. Bazell et al., *In Memory of J. R. Firth*, pp. 370–97. London: Longmans, 1966. Reprinted in Salmon, *The Study of Language*, pp. 129–56.

————. "'Philosophical' Grammar in John Wilkins' 'Essay.'" *Canadian Journal of Linguistics* 20 (1975), 131–60. Reprinted in Salmon, *The Study of Language*, pp. 97–126.

————. "Pre-Cartesian Linguistics." *Journal of Linguistics* 5 (1969), 165–87. Reprinted in Salmon, *The Study of Language*, pp. 63–85.

————. *The Study of Language in 17th-Century England.* Amsterdam: John Benjamin, 1979.

SCALIGER, J. C. *De causis linguae Latinae libri tredecim.* N.p.: Petrum Santandreanum, 1580.

SCALIGER, JOSEPH. "Diatriba de Europaeorum linguis." In Joseph Scaliger, *Opuscula*, pp. 119–22. Paris, 1610.

SCHALLER, KLAUS. *Die Pädagogik des Johann Amos Comenius.* Heidelberg: Quelle & Meyer, 1967.

SCHIFFMAN, ZACHARY S. "Montaigne and the Rise of Skepticism in Early Modern Europe: A Reappraisal." *Journal of the History of Ideas* 45 (1984), 499–516.

SCHMITT, CHARLES B. "Aristotelianism in the Veneto and the Origins of Modern Science: Some Considerations on the Problem of Continuity." In Olivieri, *Aristotelismo veneto e scienza moderna*, 1:104–23.

————. *Aristotle and the Renaissance.* Cambridge: Harvard University Press, 1983.

————. *Cicero Scepticus: A Study of the Influence of the* Academica *in the Renaissance.* The Hague: Martinus Nijhoff, 1972.

————. "Experience and Experiment: A Comparison of Zabarella's View with Galileo's in *De motu*." *Studies in the Renaissance* 16 (1969), 80–138.

————. "The Recovery and Assimilation of Ancient Scepticism in the Renaissance." *Rivista critica di storia della filosophia* 27 (1972), 363–84. Revised as "The Rediscovery of Ancient Skepticism in Modern Times," in Burnyeat, *The Skeptical Tradition*, pp. 225–51.

————. "Towards a Reassessment of Renaissance Aristotelianism." *History of Science* 11 (1973), 159–93.

————. "The University of Pisa in the Renaissance." *History of Education* 3 (1974), 3–17.

SCHOLEM, GERSHOM. *Kabbalah.* Jerusalem: Ketter, 1974.

SCHOTT, GASPAR. *Magia universalis naturae et artis.* 4 vols. Würzburg, 1657–59.

SCHUSTER, JOHN A. "Descartes and the Scientific Revolution, 1618–1634: An Interpretation." Diss., Princeton University, 1977.

SEBEOK, THOMAS A., ed. *Historiography of Linguistics.* Current Trends in Linguistics, vol. 13, pt.1. The Hague: Mouton, 1975.

SEDLEY, DAVID. "The Motivation of Greek Skepticism." In Burnyeat, *The Skeptical Tradition*, pp. 9–29.

SERENE, EILEEN. "Demonstrative Science." In Kretzmann, Kenny, and Pinborg, *The Cambridge History of Later Medieval Philosophy*, pp. 496–517.

SERGESCU, PIERRE. "Mersenne l'animateur." *Revue d'histoire des sciences* 2 (1948), 5–12.

SETTLE, THOMAS B. "Galilean Science: Essays in the Mechanics and Dynamics of the *Discorsi*." Diss., Cornell University, 1966.

SEXTUS EMPIRICUS. *Sextus Empiricus*. Translated by R. G. Bury. Loeb Classical Library. London: Heinemann, 1933–49.

SHAPIRO, ALAN E. "Kinematic Optics: A Study of the Wave Theory of Light in the Seventeenth Century." *Archive for History of Exact Sciences* 11 (1973), 134–266.

SHAPIRO, BARBARA J. *John Wilkins, 1614–1672: An Intellectual Biography*. Berkeley: University of California Press, 1969.

SHARRATT, PETER, ed. *French Renaissance Studies, 1540–70: Humanism and the Encyclopedia*. Edinburgh: Edinburgh University Press, 1976.

———. "Peter Ramus and the Reform of the University: The Divorce of Philosophy and Eloquence?" In Sharratt, *French Renaissance Studies*, pp. 4–20.

SHEA, WILLIAM R. "Marin Mersenne: Galileo's 'traduttore-traditore.'" *Annali dell'Istituto e Museo di Storia della Scienza di Firenze* 2 (1977), fasc. 1, 55–70.

SHIRLEY, JOHN W., AND F. DAVID HOENIGER, eds. *Science and the Arts in the Renaissance*. London: Associated University Presses, 1985.

SIEGEL, JERROLD E. *Rhetoric and Philosophy in Renaissance Humanism: The Union of Eloquence and Wisdom, Petrarch to Valla*. Princeton: Princeton University Press, 1968.

SIEVERT, DONALD. "Frankfurt on Descartes' View of Truth." *New Scholasticism* 51 (1977), 372–83.

SIRVEN, J. *Les années d'apprentissage de Descartes (1596–1628)*. Paris: J. Vrin, 1928.

SLAUGHTER, M. M. *Universal Languages and Scientific Taxonomy in the Seventeenth Century*. Cambridge: Cambridge University Press, 1982.

SNYDERS, GEORGES. *La pédagogie en France aux XVIIᵉ et XVIIIᵉ siècles*. Paris: Presses Universitaires de France, 1965.

SOAREZ, CYPRIAN. *De arte rhetorica libri tres, ex Aristotele, Cicerone & Quintiliano praecipue deprompti*. Rouen: apud Richardum Allemanum, 1605.

SOLOMON, HOWARD M. *Public Welfare, Science and Propaganda in Seventeenth Century France*. Princeton: Princeton University Press, 1972.

SONNINO, LEE A. *A Handbook to Sixteenth-Century Rhetoric*. London: Routledge & Kegan Paul, 1968.

SORTAIS, GASTON. *La philosophie moderne depuis Bacon jusqu'à Leibniz*. 2 vols. Paris: Paul Lethielleux, 1920.

SPENCER, THO. *The Art of Logick, Delivered in the Precepts of Aristotle and Ramus*. London, 1638.

SPINK, J. S. *French Free-Thought from Gassendi to Voltaire*. London: Athlone, 1960.

STEENBERGHEN, FERNAND VAN. *Aristotle in the West*. Louvain: Naeuwelaerts, 1970.

STÉFANINI, JEAN. "Jules César Scaliger et son *De causis linguae Latinae*." In Herman Parret, ed., *History of Linguistic Thought and Contemporary Linguistics*, pp. 317–30. Berlin: Walter de Gruyter, 1976.

STEVIN, SIMON. "Discourse on the Worth of the Dutch Language." In E. J.

Dijksterhuis, ed., *The Principal Works of Simon Stevin*, 1:58–93. Amsterdam: Swets & Zeitlinger, 1955.

STOUGH, CHARLOTTE L. *Greek Scepticism: A Study in Epistemology.* Berkeley: University of California Press, 1969.

SUAREZ, FRANCISCO. *Disputationes metafisicas.* 6 vols. Madrid: Gredos, 1960.

SYLLA, EDITH. "Compounding Ratios: Bradwardine, Oresme, and the First Edition of Newton's *Principia.*" In Everett Mendelsohn, ed., *Transformation and Tradition in the Sciences: Essays in Honor of I. Bernard Cohen,* pp. 11–43. Cambridge: Cambridge University Press, 1984.

———. "The Oxford Calculators." In Kretzmann, Kenny, and Pinborg, *The Cambridge History of Later Medieval Philosophy,* pp. 540–63.

THUILLIER, RENÉ. *Diarium patrum, fratrum et sororum Ordinis Minimorum Provinciae Franciae.* 2 vols. Paris, 1709; rpt., Geneva: Slatkine, 1972.

TIGERSTEDT, E. N. *The Decline and Fall of the Neoplatonic Interpretation of Plato.* Commentationes humanarum litterarum, vol. 52. Helsinki: Societas Scientiarum Fennica, 1974.

TOLETUS, FRANCISCUS. *Introductio in dialecticam Aristotelis, libri quinque.* Rome: apud Dominicum Liliottum, 1601.

TRENTMAN, JOHN A. "Scholasticism in the Seventeenth Century." In Kretzmann, Kenny, and Pinborg, *The Cambridge History of Later Medieval Philosophy,* pp. 818–37.

VASOLI, CESARE. *La dialettica e la retorica dell'Umanesimo.* Milan: Feltrinelli, 1968.

VICKERS, BRIAN. "Analogy versus Identity: The Rejection of Occult Symbolism, 1580–1680." In Vickers, *Occult and Scientific Mentalities,* pp. 95–163.

———, ed. *Occult and Scientific Mentalities in the Renaissance.* Cambridge: Cambridge University Press, 1984.

VIVES, JUAN LUIS. *Vives: On Education.* Translation by Foster Watson of *De tradendis disciplinis.* Cambridge: Cambridge University Press, 1913.

WALKER, D. P. *The Ancient Theology.* London: Duckworth, 1972.

———. "Leibniz and Language." *Journal of the Warburg and Courtauld Institutes* 35 (1972), 294–307. Reprinted in Walker, *Music, Spirit and Language,* chap. 14.

———. *Music, Spirit and Language in the Renaissance.* Edited by Penelope Gouk. London: Variorum Reprints, 1985.

———. "Musical Humanism in the Sixteenth and Early Seventeenth Centuries." *Music Review* 2 (1941), 1–13, 111–21, 220–27, 288–308; 3 (1942), 55–71. Reprinted in Walker, *Music, Spirit and Language,* chap. 1.

———. *Studies in Musical Science in the Late Renaissance.* London: Warburg Institute, 1978.

WALLACE, WILLIAM A. "The Certitude of Science in Late Medieval and Renaissance Thought." *History of Philosophy Quarterly* 3 (1986), 281–91.

———. "The Enigma of Domingo de Soto: *Uniformiter difformis* and Falling Bodies in Late Medieval Physics." *Isis* 59 (1968), 384–401.

———. *Galileo and His Sources: The Heritage of the Collegio Romano in Galileo's Science.* Princeton: Princeton University Press, 1984.

———. "Galileo and the Continuity Thesis." *Philosophy of Science* 51 (1984), 504–10.

———. *Prelude to Galileo: Essays on Medieval and Sixteenth-Century Sources of Galileo's Thought.* Dordrecht: D. Reidel, 1981.

WEBER, JOSEPH G. "Pascal and Music: World Harmony in Early Seventeenth-Century France." *Symposium* 30 (1976), 75–91.

WEINBERG, JULIUS R. *A Short History of Medieval Philosophy.* Princeton: Princeton University Press, 1964.

WELLS, NORMAN J. "Descartes and the Scholastics Briefly Revisited." *New Scholasticism* 35 (1961), 172–90.

———. "Descartes' Uncreated Eternal Truths." *New Scholasticism* 56 (1982), 185–99.

———. "Old Bottles and New Wine: A Rejoinder to J. C. Doig." *New Scholasticism* 53 (1979), 515–23.

———. "Suarez on the Eternal Truths." *Modern Schoolman* 58 (1981), 73–104, 159–74.

WESTFALL, RICHARD S. *Force in Newton's Physics.* London: Macdonald, 1971.

WESTMAN, ROBERT. "Nature, Art, and Psyche: Jung, Pauli, and the Kepler-Fludd Polemic." In Vickers, *Occult and Scientific Mentalities,* pp. 177–229.

WHITMORE, P. J. S. *The Order of Minims in Seventeenth-Century France.* The Hague: Martinus Nijhoff, 1967.

WILLIAMS, ARNOLD. *The Common Expositor: An Account of the Commentaries on Genesis, 1527–1633.* Chapel Hill: University of North Carolina Press, 1948.

WISAN, WINIFRED L. "The New Science of Motion: A Study of Galileo's 'De motu locali.'" *Archive for History of Exact Sciences* 13 (1974), 103–306.

WOODWARD, WILLIAM HARRISON, ed. *Vittorino da Feltre and Other Humanist Educators.* New York: Teachers College Press, 1974.

WOTTON, ANTONY, ed. *The Art of Logick . . . by Peter Ramus.* London, 1626.

YATES, FRANCES A. *The Art of Memory.* Chicago: Chicago University Press, 1966.

———. "The Art of Ramon Lull: An Approach to It through Lull's Theory of the Elements." In Yates, *Collected Essays,* vol. 1, *Lull and Bruno,* pp. 9–77. London: Routledge & Kegan Paul, 1982.

———. *The French Academies of the Sixteenth Century.* London: Warburg Institute, 1947.

———. *Giordano Bruno and the Hermetic Tradition.* Chicago: Chicago University Press, 1964.

———. "The Hermetic Tradition in Renaissance Science." In Yates, *Collected Essays,* vol. 3, *Ideas and Ideals in the North European Renaissance,* pp. 227–46. London: Routledge & Kegan Paul, 1984.

YOLTON, JOHN W. *John Locke and the Way of Ideas.* Oxford: Oxford University Press, 1956.

Index

Library of Congress Cataloging-in-Publication Data

Dear, Peter Robert.
Mersenne and the learning of the schools / Peter Dear.
    p.   cm.—(Cornell history of science series)
Based on the author's thesis (Ph.D.)—Princeton University, 1984.
Bibliography: p.
Includes index.
ISBN 0-8014-1875-5 (alk. paper)
1. Mersenne, Marin. 1588–1648.   2. Religion and science—History—17th
century.   I. Title. II. Series.
BX4705.M53D43 1988   194—dc19   87-23935